PLACES TO VISIT

ENGLISH HERITAGE

WELCOME &
THANK YOU

1 Artist's impression of the new visitor centre at Stonehenge, opening late 2013.

2 Bolsover Castle.

3 Kenilworth Castle and Elizabethan Garden.

We can read about history all we like – but nothing beats standing on the spot where history was made. That's the thrill for me, and what's exceptional about English Heritage is how our interpretations bring the past to life so vividly.

Spending time at one of our properties is to step into history – a chance to discover where prehistoric communities lived and honoured their ancestors, where the Romans dominated life for better or worse, where William the Conqueror triumphed at the Battle of Hastings, where the English Civil War was fought, where the Industrial Revolution drove the British Empire to all corners of the globe and where Hitler's invasion was thwarted.

This year, the big news for us is the transformation of the Neolithic landscape around Stonehenge and the opening of the new visitor centre. I can guarantee that the changes made at our greatest historic monument will alter your perception of the Stones forever and I am anxious to hear your feedback.

You will also see in the handbook that we have included the date when our properties came into our care, something which is appropriate given that we are celebrating the centenary of the 1913 Ancient Monuments Consolidation and Amendment Act, a precursor to the formation of English Heritage.

Today, there are so many ways for our members to get involved, details of which can be found in our exclusive members' magazine. And I would urge you to keep abreast of your favourite properties on Twitter and other social media.

Personally, I can't wait to visit Kenilworth Castle in Warwickshire, a great favourite of mine. For the first time since the 1640s, a series of viewing platforms will give access to the rooms Robert Dudley, Earl of Leicester, built especially for Elizabeth I. We will be able to stand in the room where the 'Virgin Queen' slept – and drove Dudley to distraction!

Likewise, visitors to Kenwood – which has been closed for more than a year while undergoing sweeping improvements – will soon experience four exquisite rooms designed by Robert Adam, and then be invited behind the scenes to learn more about this great house from our gifted and knowledgeable team.

I hope this year's handbook will make our properties even more enticing (note the new symbols indicating sites that have playgrounds for the use of our younger members) as we approach a new season of openings and special events.

Thank you so much for your support.

Simon Thurley
Chief Executive

HIGHLIGHTS FOR 2013

SOUTH WEST **STONEHENGE**

Stonehenge is one of the few structures in the United Kingdom that is instantly recognisable worldwide. Gifted to the nation in 1918 by Cecil Chubb, this ancient monument has been visited by millions over the years, increasing from 38,000 per year in 1922 to over 900,000 today. **Highlights for 2013:** A new exhibition centre opens late in 2013, and work begins to restore the landscape to present this wonderful prehistoric monument in the way it deserves.

LONDON **WELLINGTON ARCH QUADRIGA GALLERY**

Set in the heart of royal London at Hyde Park Corner, Wellington Arch was built in 1825-7 as part of a campaign to improve the royal parks. **Highlights for 2013:** In the Quadriga Gallery within the Arch, we are marking the centenary of the landmark Ancient Monuments Consolidation and Amendment Act (1913) with five special exhibitions highlighting the movement to protect England's heritage – from its early days through to the challenges of tomorrow.

SOUTH EAST **OSBORNE**

Osborne allows you to get extraordinarily close to Queen Victoria, Prince Albert and their children. Not what most people think of as a palace, its scale is domestic, and its decoration fashionable and expensive but not overwhelming. A home from which Queen Victoria ran her empire. **Highlights for 2013:** Recently opened to the public, enjoy the private beach of Queen Victoria – complete with her very own bathing machine!

EAST MIDLANDS **BOLSOVER CASTLE**

Rich interiors and the beautiful Venus Garden help to make this 17th-century castle the stuff of fairytales. Designed for the Cavendish family, it was used as a fantasy house for their parties and pleasure. **Highlights for 2013:** The Horses are back! See riders in 17th-century dress give spectacular performances of 'Haute Ecole' – the highest form of classical dressage, which takes horse and rider years to learn.

WEST MIDLANDS **KENILWORTH CASTLE & ELIZABETHAN GARDEN**

Throughout its illustrious history, Kenilworth Castle has been home to some of the most significant figures in English history, including Robert Dudley, the great love of Queen Elizabeth I. **Highlights for 2013:** New stairs and viewing platforms in Leicester's Building allow a close-up view of the remains of the inner apartments where Queen Elizabeth stayed during her famous 1575 visit.

NORTH EAST **LINDISFARNE PRIORY**

Lindisfarne Priory was the first property brought into the National Collection in the care of English Heritage in 1913. This joined the prehistoric sites gifted to the nation under earlier laws to give a firm foundation to the National Heritage Collection. **Highlights for 2013:** Don't miss the arrival of the Viking Raider stone on its way to Durham to form part of a special exhibition including one of England's great treasures, the Lindisfarne Gospels, returning to the North East after hundreds of years.

NORTH EAST **BELSAY HALL, CASTLE AND GARDENS**

Belsay has something to captivate everyone, with a medieval castle, Regency Hall and both exotic and formal gardens. The Hall is an unfurnished architectural masterpiece inspired by the temples of ancient Greece. **Highlights for 2013:** Belsay will be transported back to the Regency era with a summer full of events celebrating the customs, costumes, romance and finery of this enchanting age.

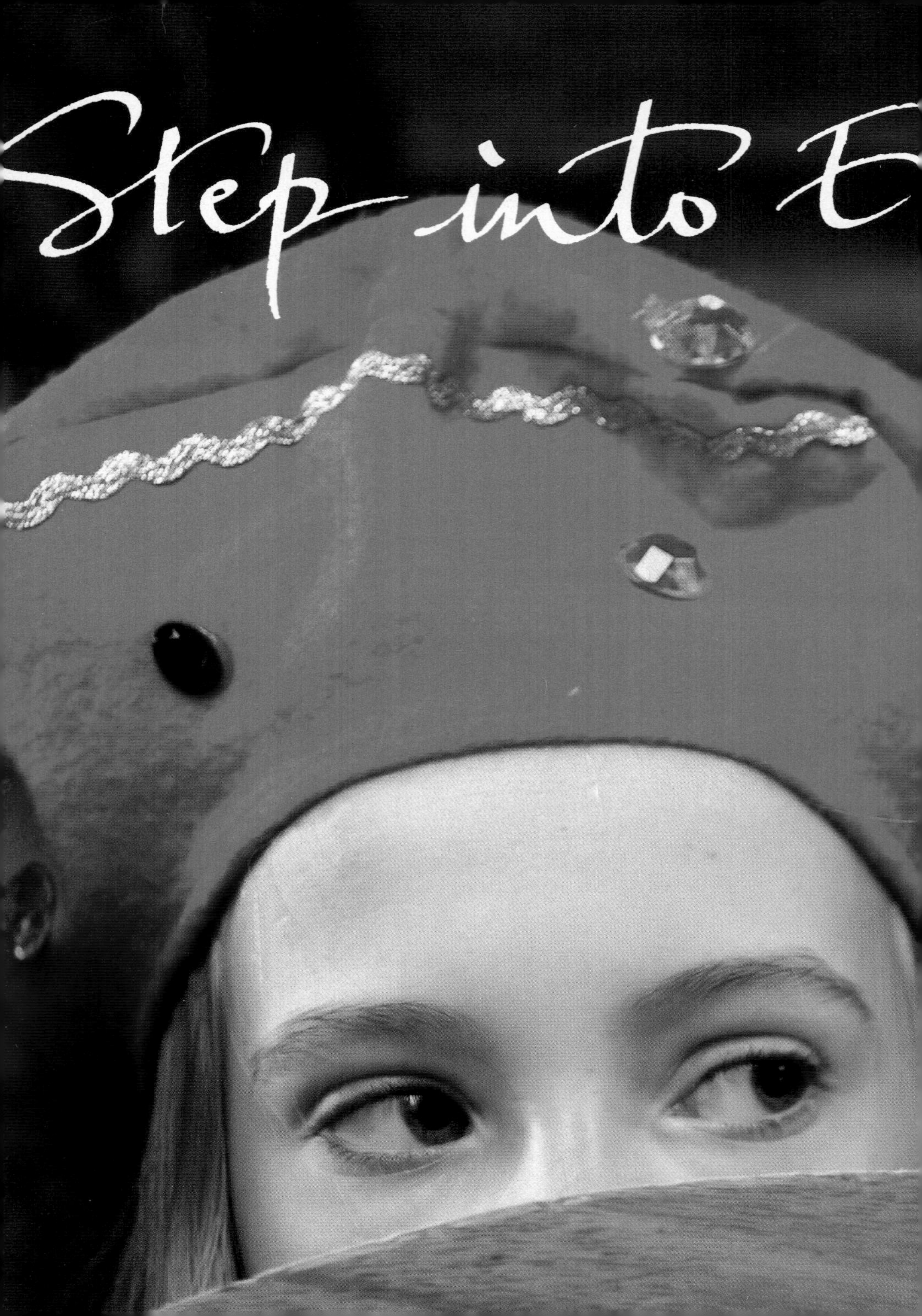
Step into E

England's story

PREHISTORY

BEFORE AD 43

c.500,000 years ago	c.4000–2500 BC	c.2500–750 BC	AD 43
Oldest human remains in England	Neolithic period (First Farmers)	Bronze Age	Roman Conquest begins

c.14,000 years ago	c.3000 BC	from c.750 BC
Continuous human settlement begins	Stonehenge begun	Iron Age

Among the 56 prehistoric sites in English Heritage's care are:

- Avebury Stone Circle
- Castlerigg Stone Circle
- Chysauster Ancient Village
- Grime's Graves
- Maiden Castle
- Silbury Hill
- Stonehenge
- Stanwick Iron Age Fortifications
- West Kennett Long Barrow
- Windmill Hill

The oldest human remains in England – found during the Boxgrove, Sussex excavation supported by English Heritage – are about 500,000 years old. But continuous human occupation began only after the end of the last Ice Age, around 14,000 years ago.

THE FIRST FARMERS

Early 'hunter-gatherer' people left few visible traces: but with the arrival of farming in the Neolithic (New Stone Age), people began constructing monuments. Among the earliest are communal tombs like *West Kennett Long Barrow* and ritual enclosures like *Windmill Hill*.

HENGES, STONE CIRCLES AND RITUAL LANDSCAPES

Circular earthwork 'henges' appear from about 3000 BC, when *Stonehenge* was begun and *Grime's Graves* flint mines were in use. The later Neolithic and early Bronze Ages saw massive stone circles like *Castlerigg Stone Circle* and *Avebury Stone Circle* raised, sometimes as elements of 'ritual landscapes'. The construction of mysterious *Silbury Hill* followed, and individuals were buried in 'round barrows' like *Flowerdown Barrows*. Though monuments like *Hurlers Stone Circles* later attracted legends, their original purpose remains enigmatic.

WEALTH, CONFLICT AND TRADE

Bronze Age sites provide evidence of greater wealth, but also more conflict, apparently worsening in the Iron Age – when pressure on land produced many defensive hill forts like *Maiden Castle*. *Chysauster Ancient Village* reflects locally more peaceful conditions, while *Stanwick Iron Age Fortifications* herald the growth of town-like tribal power centres – a development interrupted by the Roman Conquest.

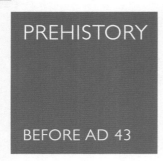

1 Maiden Castle
2 Belas Knap Long Barrow
3 Stonehenge

AD 43	AD 122	c.AD 410–425
Roman Conquest begins	*Hadrian's Wall begun*	*Imperial rule by Rome fades*

AD 84	c.AD 260–360
Furthest extent of Roman rule in Britain	*Saxon Shore defences built*

THE ROMANS

AD 43–C.410

Roman Britain lasted for over three and a half centuries – the span which separates us from the Civil Wars. English Heritage's Roman sites reflect the era from its violent beginning to its obscure end.

CONQUEST

Though Julius Caesar raided Britain in 55 and 54 BC, permanent conquest began when Roman forces landed near *Richborough Roman Fort* in AD 43. Despite resistance by Boudica (Boadicea) and others, Roman armies had reached northern Scotland by

AD 84, before retiring to the permanent frontier of *Hadrian's Wall*. Incomparably the most impressive Roman monument in Britain, the Wall's defensive system includes major forts like *Birdoswald*, *Chesters* and *Housesteads*.

CIVILISATION

Away from the frontiers, Roman Britain was for long periods peaceful and prosperous. 'Country houses' like *Lullingstone Roman Villa* flourished, bath-houses and amphitheatres were built, and many towns were founded – including large *Silchester* and *Wroxeter* and smaller *Aldborough* and *Corbridge* – often at existing British tribal centres. Most were eventually walled against increasing external threats.

THE SAXON SHORE

Towards the end of the 3rd century, attacks by seaborne Germanic raiders prompted the creation of 'Saxon Shore' coastal fortifications like *Burgh Castle*: further trouble saw the system strengthened in the next century, and P*evensey Castle* added. Garrisons were by now mainly British-born, and little distinguished 'Romans' from 'Britons' when imperial rule petered out: there was no clearly definable end of Roman Britain.

Among the 52 Roman sites in English Heritage's care are:

- *Birdoswald Roman Fort*
- *Burgh Castle*
- *Chesters Roman Fort*
- *Corbridge Roman Town*
- *Hadrian's Wall*
- *Housesteads Roman Fort*
- *Lullingstone Roman Villa*
- *Pevensey Castle*
- *Richborough Roman Fort and Amphitheatre*
- *Wroxeter Roman City*

1 Hadrian's Wall
2 Bust from Corbridge
3 Coins from Richborough and Stanwick
4 The winged statue of Victory from Housesteads

BRITONS, ENGLISH & VIKINGS

C.400–1066

c.410–25	597–625	871–900	1066
End of Imperial Roman rule in Britain	*Principal Christian missions*	*Alfred the Great reigns*	*Norman Conquest begins*

c.550–c.620	787–9	927
Anglo-Saxons conquer lowland England	*Viking raids begin*	*Aethelstan becomes first king of all England*

Among the 19 sites within this period in English Heritage's care are:

- 1066 Battle of Hastings, Abbey and Battlefield
- Lindisfarne Priory
- Lydford Castle and Saxon Town
- Offa's Dyke
- St Augustine's Abbey
- St Paul's Monastery, Jarrow
- St Peter's Church, Barton-on-Humber
- Sandbach Crosses
- Tintagel Castle
- Whitby Abbey

1 St Augustine's Abbey
2 St Peter's Church, Barton-upon-Humber
3 Viking stone at Lindisfarne

The centuries between the end of Roman Britain and the Norman Conquest saw the gradual emergence of an English nation, and its narrow escape from Scandinavian domination.

THE ENGLISH CONQUEST

Even before its severance from the Roman Empire, Britain was threatened by seaborne Germanic peoples – Angles, Saxons, Jutes and Frisians. Though long delayed by Romano-British resistance (perhaps inspired by a fabled 'Arthur') these 'Anglo-Saxon' invaders had conquered most of lowland England by the mid-600s, establishing several independent kingdoms. Tantalising hints about this shadowy period have emerged from sites like *Birdoswald Roman Fort, Tintagel Castle* and *Wroxeter Roman City*.

CHRISTIAN CULTURE BLOSSOMS

Increasingly called 'English', the pagan conquerors were converted to Christianity by missionaries from Rome – including *St Augustine* – and Ireland. Christian culture blossomed: *Lindisfarne Priory* produced its illuminated manuscript Gospels, while Bede's writings at *St Paul's Monastery, Jarrow* fostered the concept of an English nation. Through their architecture and craftsmanship, *St Peter's Church, Barton-Upon-Humber* and *Sandbach Crosses* likewise reflect the English Church's vitality.

THE VIKING THREAT

Towards the end of the 3rd century, soon after *Offa's Dyke* defined its western boundary, the development of England was imperilled as Viking raids became invasions. King Alfred of Wessex turned the tide, and his descendants reconquered Viking-held lands: his grandson Aethelstan became the first ruler of a unified English state. But Danish pressure revived – King Cnut subsumed England into his Scandinavian empire – and it was a weakened England which faced the Normans in 1066.

1066	1215	1277–1307
Norman Conquest	Magna Carta	Edward I's wars in Wales and Scotland

1066–1154	1154–1485
Norman Kings	Angevin/Plantagenet Kings

THE MIDDLE AGES

1066–1485

'The Middle Ages', as G. K. Chesterton observed, 'did not all happen at the same time'. The five centuries between the battles of Hastings in 1066 and Bosworth in 1485 witnessed considerable changes in England, including language – from the Anglo-Saxon, Danish and Norman-French spoken here at the beginning of the period to the recognisable ancestor of modern English used by its end. Nearly half of all English Heritage sites date from this era, and their variety mirrors its developing character: but many reflect two constants – the importance of castles and the dominance of the Church.

THE LAND FILLED WITH CASTLES

Earthwork and timber 'motte and bailey' castles were the instruments and symbols of the Norman Conquest: many, like *Clifford's Tower* and *Totnes Castle*, were later refortified in stone. The great stone keeps of the Norman and Angevin kings and their barons formed the core of major early fortresses like *Dover Castle*, *Orford Castle* and *Richmond Castle*, before the focus shifted to many-towered enclosure walls with powerful gatehouses, as at *Framlingham Castle* and *Goodrich Castle*. Equipped with halls, chapels and many domestic buildings, some strongholds like *Beeston Castle* or *Kenilworth Castle* were immense in scale. More compact fortresses – including *Farleigh Hungerford Castle* and *Nunney Castle* – developed towards the end of the era, some (like *Berry Pomeroy* and *Kirby Muxloe* castles) equipped for artillery defence.

MANOR HOUSES, TOWN HOUSES AND BARNS

Only a tiny minority of medieval people lived in castles. English Heritage's collection also includes lightly fortified or undefended manor houses like *Stokesay Castle* or *Old Soar Manor*; and urban houses like Southampton's *Medieval Merchant's House*. Country life is represented by *Wharram Percy Deserted Medieval Village* and farm buildings like imposing *Harmondsworth Great Barn*.

Among the 202 sites within this period in English Heritage's care are:

- Beeston Castle
- Binham Priory
- Carisbrooke Castle
- Carlisle Castle
- Castle Acre Priory
- Clifford's Tower
- Conisbrough Castle
- Dover Castle
- Eleanor Cross, Geddington
- Eltham Palace
- Framlingham Castle
- Goodrich Castle
- Harmondsworth Great Barn
- Kenilworth Castle
- Lanercost Priory
- Old Sarum
- Rievaulx Abbey
- St Mary's Church, Kempley
- Scarborough Castle
- Stokesay Castle

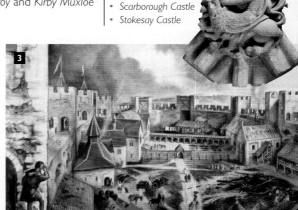

THE MIDDLE AGES
– Continued

1066–1485

1337–1453
Hundred Years War with France

1381
Peasants' Revolt

1476–7
First books printed in England

1349
Black Death

1455–85
Wars of the Roses

OASES OF PEACE

Whether in castle, town or country, medieval life was dominated by the Church: in the 14th century about one in fifteen Englishmen were clergy of some kind. English Heritage cares for parish churches like *St Mary's Kempley* with its wonderful wall-paintings, and bishops' mansions including *Lincoln Medieval Bishops Palace:* and the evocative remains of many monasteries, from big, prosperous *Castle Acre Priory* to tiny *Mattersey Priory*.

Each reflects the characteristics of the monastic order which inhabited it: 'mainstream' Benedictines at *Binham Priory* and *Whitby Abbey;* solitude-seeking Cistercians at *Furness Abbey* and *Rievaulx Abbey;* decoration-loving Cluniacs at *Wenlock Priory;* Augustinian canons at lovely *Lanercost Priory;* hermit-like Carthusians at *Mount Grace Priory* or the urban friars of *Gloucester's Blackfriars* and *Greyfriars*.

MEMORIES OF CONFLICT

Many of English Heritage's medieval sites, by contrast, recall the foreign or internal wars of medieval England. Some – like *Carlisle Castle* – guarded land borders against Scots or Welsh, or like *Carisbrooke Castle* and *Dartmouth Castle* defended coasts against seaborne invasion and raiding. Others, including *Rochester Castle,* endured conflicts between monarchs and barons, or like *Dunstanburgh Castle* or *Warkworth Castle* witnessed the dynastic Wars of the Roses, ended by the Battle of Bosworth which began the Tudor age.

From previous page
1 William the Conqueror from Battle Abbey
2 Roof boss from Hailes Abbey
3 Framlingham Castle (artist's impression)

This page
4 Goodrich Castle (artist's impression)
5 Eleanor Cross, Geddington
6 Castle Acre Priory (artist's impression)

1485	1536–40	1558–1603	1564–1616
Battle of Bosworth	Dissolution of Monasteries	Elizabeth I reigns	Shakespeare living

1509–47	1532–59	1588
Henry VIII reigns	Religious changes	Spanish Armada

THE TUDORS

1485–1603

The crucial pivot of medieval and modern history, the Tudor era saw strong central government established; England transformed from a Catholic to a Protestant nation; and the flowering of a distinctively English culture and the English country house.

THE TRIUMPH OF MONARCHY

Ending the Wars of the Roses, Henry VII curtailed aristocratic power and castle-building, and his successors strengthened the grip of monarchy. Henceforth fortresses would be raised only by the crown, most notably Henry VIII's coastal artillery forts – the first co-ordinated system of national defence – including *Deal Castle* and *Pendennis Castle*.

THE FLOWERING OF ENGLISH CULTURE

Elizabeth's long and glorious reign witnessed the expansion of English sea power (reinforced by her defeat of the Spanish Armada) and the flowering of English culture epitomised by Shakespeare. It also saw the burgeoning of the great English country house – some converted monasteries or adapted medieval fortresses like *Kenilworth Castle and Elizabethan Garden*, but most built from new like *Kirby Hall*. All these developments expressed new-found English self-confidence.

RELIGIOUS UPHEAVALS

Henry's new-style forts defended England against European Catholic reaction to the religious changes he initiated: English Heritage's outstanding collection of monastic ruins bear witness to his Dissolution of the Monasteries. After swinging from Edward VI's radical Protestantism to Mary's revived Catholicism, the nation settled down to religious compromise under Queen Elizabeth.

Among the 50 sites within this period in English Heritage's care are:

- *Blackfriars, Gloucester*
- *Deal Castle*
- *Hailes Abbey*
- *Hardwick Old Hall*
- *Kenilworth Castle and Elizabethan Garden*
- *Kirby Hall*
- *Norham Castle*
- *Pendennis Castle*
- *Rushton Triangular Lodge*
- *Titchfield Abbey*

1 Deal Castle
2 Queen Elizabeth I
3 Rushton Triangular Lodge

THE STUARTS

1603–1714

1

1603–25
James I
(Jacobean period)

1649–60
Commonwealth and Cromwell's Protectorate

1688
William and Mary crowned

1642
Civil Wars

1660–69
Pepys's diary written

1706–7
Acts of Union with Scotland

Among the 39 sites within this period in English Heritage's care are:

- Abingdon County Hall
- Audley End House and Gardens
- Berry Pomeroy Castle
- Bolsover Castle
- Boscobel House and the Royal Oak
- Carisbrooke Castle
- Great Yarmouth Row Houses
- Langley Chapel
- Pendennis Castle
- Tilbury Fort

Following a long period of peace, the intense political and religious conflicts of the Stuart era transformed the government of England. Developments in artistic styles and living standards are also reflected in this era's English Heritage sites.

GRACIOUS LIVING

The earlier ('Jacobean') part of the period saw many lavish mansions like *Audley End House* and *Bolsover Castle* built, and fine interiors created in more modest dwellings like *Bessie Surtees House* and *Great Yarmouth Row Houses*.

CIVIL WARS AND REPUBLIC

The Civil Wars between Charles I and Parliament (1642–51) brought much devastation; epic sieges of *Pendennis Castle* and many other places; and (after his imprisonment at *Carisbrooke Castle*) the king's execution and the creation (1649–60) of the Commonwealth, the only republic in English history. Young Charles II narrowly escaped capture near *Boscobel House*.

RESTORATION AND NEW STYLES

Epitomised by Pepys's diary, the reign of the restored Charles II brought continuing scientific advances, but also plague and fire in London and humiliating Dutch attack, provoking the building of defences like *Tilbury Fort*. The 'English Baroque' style of *Abingdon County Hall* came increasingly into fashion towards the end of the period.

ENGLAND AND BRITAIN

The era's long-simmering religious disputes were addressed in 1689, after the Catholic James II was deposed by the Protestant William and Mary. Under Queen Anne, the Acts of Union with Scotland made England part of 'Great Britain'.

2

3

4

1 Oliver Cromwell
2 Bolsover Castle
3 Audley End
4 Reconstruction of Tilbury Fort

| 1715 & 1745/6 Jacobite Risings | 1779 Industrial Revolution: Iron Bridge completed | 1811–20 Regency period |
| | 1754–63 'Seven Years War' expands British Empire | 1793–1815 Napoleonic Wars | 1825 First public steam railway opens |

THE GEORGIANS

1714–1837

An age of elegant country houses and glittering town mansions, the Georgian era also saw Britain become the world's first industrial nation, at the hub of a rapidly growing empire.

ELEGANT MANSIONS
English Heritage's outstanding collection of Georgian and Regency mansions reflect the period's progression of fashionable styles, from the Palladian of *Chiswick House* via Robert Adam's *Kenwood* to the 'Regency' Greek Revival of *Belsay Hall* and *The Grange at Northington*. Tasteful interiors (as at *Marble Hill House*) were counterpointed by formal or 'landscaped' gardens – an English gift to the world – often adorned (as at *Audley End House* and *Wrest Park*) with charming garden architecture.

INDUSTRIAL REVOLUTION

The wealth which financed these mansions was increasingly founded on England's pioneering Industrial Revolution. Built in the 1730s, *Derwentcote Steel Furnace* produced steel for springs and cutting tools, while the *Iron Bridge* was the world's first of its kind, and the world's first steam trains ran in England in 1825.

WAR AND EMPIRE
International trade boomed alongside an expanding empire, particularly in India and the Americas. Yet as *Dover Castle* and *Dymchurch Martello Tower* demonstrate, Britain's growing military and especially naval power did not go unchallenged, notably during the long wars with Revolutionary and Napoleonic France. Wellington, greatest military hero of these wars, is remembered at *Apsley House*, *Walmer Castle* and *Wellington Arch*.

Among the 42 sites within this period in English Heritage's care are:

- Apsley House
- Belsay Hall, Castle and Gardens
- Chiswick House
- Derwentcote Steel Furnace
- Iron Bridge
- Kenwood House
- Marble Hill House
- The Grange at Northington
- Wellington Arch
- Wrest Park

1 Chiswick House
2 Iron Bridge
3 Barracks in Dover Castle tunnels
4 'Ideal Head' bust by Antonio Canova from Apsley House

THE VICTORIANS & EDWARDIANS

1837–1910

Among the 30 sites within this period in English Heritage's care are:

- Audley End House
- Brodsworth Hall
- The Home of Charles Darwin, Down House
- Fort Brockhurst
- Mount Grace Priory
- Osborne
- St Mary's Church, Studley Royal
- Sibsey Trader Windmill
- Stott Park Bobbin Mill
- Witley Court

The long reign of Queen Victoria, with the Edwardian 'Indian Summer' that followed, saw Britain at the zenith of her international power and status, and the greatest manufacturing nation in the world.

MASTERS AND SERVANTS

The Queen's strong personality is reflected at *Osborne*. Her wealthier subjects also continued to build great mansions like *Brodsworth Hall* and *Witley Court*, operated by armies of servants – as *Audley End*'s service wing and stables demonstrate.

A HIVE OF INDUSTRY

J.W. Evans Silver Factory and *Stott Park Bobbin Mill* reflect Victorian England as a hive of manufacturing industry: rural life was also being transformed by machinery, as seen in English Heritage's collection of windmills.

DOUBT AND CERTAINTY

The publication of Charles Darwin's ideas on evolution (matured and written down at *Down House*) shook Victorian religious certainty, but did not stem the period's flood of chapel and church building – the latter almost always in the ubiquitous 'Gothic Revival' style. *St Mary's Church, Studley Royal* is a flamboyant example.

AN IMPERIAL POWER

Despite the 1860's French invasion scare which produced new fortifications like *Fort Brockhurst* and the updating of older defences like *Dartmouth Castle*, Britannia's fleets continued to rule the waves and her armies to fight far-flung colonial wars. The Boer War of 1899–1902 dented 'Imperial' confidence, but at the death of Edward VII (a very 'un-Victorian' monarch) the British Empire was nearing its greatest extent.

1 Charles Darwin and giroscope
2 Osborne
3 J.W. Evans Silver Factory
4 Perseus and Andromeda Fountain at Witley Court

1914–18	1930	1948	1977 *Personal*
First World War	*First regular TV broadcasting*	*National Health Service established*	*computers and* **1990** *mobile phones widely available*

1922	1939–45	1946–1989
First BBC radio broadcast	*Second World War*	*Cold War*

THE MODERN AGE

1910–PRESENT

The two World Wars which dominate the modern age of British history also acted as catalysts for previously unimaginable changes.

TWO WORLD WARS – AND A THIRD?

The First World War, with its terrible carnage, and the Second World War – whose far greater impact on the civilian population is underlined at *Great Yarmouth Row Houses* – are both reflected in many English Heritage properties. Old fortifications like *Calshot Castle* were updated for new types of warfare, and the *Secret Wartime Tunnels* beneath *Dover Castle* played a crucial role in saving the nation in 1940. The dead of both wars are remembered by the London war memorials cared for by English Heritage, among them the poignant *Royal Artillery Memorial* at Hyde Park Corner. But *York Cold War Bunker* is a chilling reminder that the threat of even greater mass destruction remained ever-present.

SOCIAL TRANSFORMATION

Both World Wars transformed the social structure of England: *Brodsworth Hall* tracks the decline of the country house and its servant-dependent lifestyle – though remodelled *Eltham Palace* glitteringly displays the stylish living still enjoyed by the millionaire few.

AN ONGOING REVOLUTION

The post-World War II creation of the Welfare State made life easier for the many: and the advent of radio and TV and more recently of affordable computer technology have fostered a still greater (and still continuing) revolution in lifestyles.

English Heritage cares for 23 sites with major features of this period – including the following – and several London war memorials

- *Brodsworth Hall and Gardens*
- *Calshot Castle*
- *Dover Castle (Secret Wartime Tunnels)*
- *Eltham Palace*
- *Great Yarmouth Row Houses*
- *J. W. Evans Silver Factory*
- *Richmond Castle*
- *Royal Garrison Church*
- *Tynemouth Priory and Castle*
- *York Cold War Bunker*

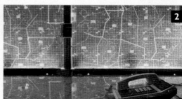

1 Operation Dynamo at Dover Castle
2 Operations Room at York Cold War Bunker
3 Statue of Psyche from the bathroom at Eltham Palace.

MEMBERSHIP AND EVENTS

Thank you for supporting English Heritage – your membership really does make a difference to our work, and helps protect more than 400 historic properties, ranging from castles to grand palaces, inspiring abbeys to lavish gardens. We look forward to welcoming you on your next visit soon.

Don't forget your membership entitles you to:

- Free, unlimited entry to all our sites.
- Free entry for up to six accompanied children (under 19) within your family group per member.
- Free or reduced price admission to over 100 associated attractions.

- Your free handbook (RRP £10.95) to help you get the most out of your visits.
- Our award-winning exclusive members' magazine – packed with ideas, inspiration and news.
- Access to exclusive members' events and behind the scenes tours.

READ ALL ABOUT IT

Our superb magazine is packed with inspiration and ideas for making the most of your membership, including a full list of our events. What's more, it's completely FREE to members and is delivered direct to you, so look out for it. You can also be the first to hear about special events and the latest news by signing up to receive our regular e-newsletter. Go to **english-heritage.org.uk/newsletter**

MORE VALUE, MORE PROPERTIES

Your English Heritage membership card opens doors to many other associated attractions and properties – often at no extra cost. Check details in this handbook or visit **english-heritage.org.uk/members** to see offers and check terms and conditions.

EVENTS

Every year we offer a whole host of fantastic days out. There's something for everyone, from live action spectaculars to ghost tours, arts and crafts fairs, talks, tours, exhibitions and children's quests and trails.

If you have a passion for history, or are just looking for a great day out, we recommend you visit at least one of our unmissable event weekends: St George's Day Festival at Wrest Park (20-22 Apr); World War II Weekend at Dover Castle (25-27 May) and the fantastic History Live! weekend (20-21 Jul) **www.historylive.com**

MEMBERS' EVENTS

There is so much more to our properties than you might think, and as a member you have access to behind the scenes tours guided by our experts, who will share their unique knowledge and insight with you. We have over 100 members-only events throughout the year, across the country.

See page 331 for more information, or visit **english-heritage.org.uk/events**

KEEP IN TOUCH

Tell other members about your visit to one of our properties. Post your message and photos on **flickr.com/groups/englishheritagedaysout** and subscribe to our YouTube channel to check our latest videos **youtube.com/user/englishheritagefilm**

VISITING OUR PROPERTIES

We want you to enjoy every minute of your visit, so please read our section 'Planning Your Visit' on pages 322-3. Each property has a full list of symbols which will help you assess its suitability for your visiting party, and enable you to plan your perfect day. Remember to check the latest opening times and events information on our website www.english-heritage.org.uk or call us on 0870 333 1181. You can also find details of our Access For All policy on page 324, and order a free copy of our detailed *Access Guide* by calling the number above. Detailed access infomation for our properties is also available on our website

LONDON

Wellington Arch

Remember to check opening times before you visit any of our properties **www.english-heritage.org.uk/daysout**

Details of local public transport information in England are available from Traveline **www.traveline.org.uk** or call 0871 200 2233.

Chiswick House and Gardens

Make the most of your membership and keep up to date with upcoming events, the latest news and special offers by subscribing to our e-newsletter. Register online now at **www.english-heritage.org.uk/newsletter**

Eltham Palace

PROPERTIES

HIGHLIGHTS FOR 2013/14 IN **LONDON**

p.32

Eltham Palace & Gardens: immerse yourself in the glamour of the Art Deco period.

p.34

Kenwood: one of the finest of all English Heritage's great houses, will re-open in November 2013.

p.37

Jewel Tower: a fragment of history tucked between the Houses of Parliament and Westminster Abbey.

p.40

Wellington Arch: an unmissable London landmark offering panoramic views.

Apsley House, home of the first Duke of Wellington and his descendants, stands right in the heart of London at Hyde Park Corner. For over 200 years, this great metropolitan mansion has been known colloquially as 'Number 1 London', because it was the first house encountered after passing the tollgates at the top of Knightsbridge.

Don't miss our 15-minute Walk and Talk Gallery Tours which take place twice daily throughout the year.

VISIT US

Address: Apsley House,
149 Piccadilly, Hyde Park Corner,
London W1J 7NT

Direction: 149 Piccadilly, Hyde Park Corner

Train: Victoria ½ mile

Bus: From surrounding areas

Tube: Hyde Park Corner

Tel: 020 7499 5676

NON-MEMBERS

Apsley House

Adult	£6.70
Concession	£6.00
Child	£4.00

Joint ticket with Wellington Arch

Adult	£8.60
Concession	£7.70
Child	£5.20
Family	£22.40

OPENING TIMES

29 Mar-3 Nov, Wed-Sun & Bank Hols	11am-5pm
4 Nov-31 Mar Closed for reburbishment	
24-26 Dec and 1 Jan	Closed

Disabled access very limited.
Please phone property for information.

MAP Page 338 (4E)
OS Map 176, 161/173: TQ284799

Apsley House was originally designed and built by Robert Adam between 1771 and 1778 for Baron Apsley – from whom it takes its name. It passed to the Wellesley family in 1807, being first owned by Richard and then his younger brother Arthur Wellesley – the Duke of Wellington.

Wellington is most famous for defeating Napoleon at the Battle of Waterloo in 1815, but this was only the culmination of a brilliant military career. He was also a major politician, becoming Prime Minister in 1828.

Remodelled by Benjamin Wyatt to reflect the Duke's rising status, Apsley House's dazzling interiors are magnificent examples of the Regency style. They provided the perfect backdrop for entertaining, particularly at the annual Waterloo Banquets which commemorated the great victory.

Inside Apsley House you will see many aspects of the first Duke's life and work, including his outstanding art collection. Paintings by many famous artists are hung throughout the first floor, many of them part of the Spanish Royal Collection, found among abandoned baggage after the Battle of Vitoria in 1813. A colossal nude statue of Napoleon by Canova dominates the stairwell at the centre of the house.

Throughout his military career, the Duke was presented with a vast collection of silver plate and fine porcelain as trophies from grateful nations. Many of these can be seen in the Plate and China Room. Wellington's victories are also celebrated in the fine British craftsmanship of the magnificent Wellington Shield, designed by Thomas Stothard, and the impressive candelabra presented by the Merchants and Bankers of the City of London.

When the seventh Duke of Wellington gave the house to the nation in 1947, the family retained the private rooms, which they still use today. This makes Apsley House not only the last surviving great aristocratic London town house open to the public, but also the only property managed by English Heritage in which the original owner's family still live.

CHANDOS MAUSOLEUM (ST LAWRENCE'S CHURCH)
LITTLE STANMORE
HA8 6RB

© CCT

Chandos Mausoleum was added to early 18th-century St Lawrence's Church (church not part of CCT's estate) in 1736. The Mausoleum contains a magnificent monument by master carver Grinling Gibbons and the walls and ceiling are lavishly decorated. There are also hatchments in the ante-room.

Owned and managed by The Churches Conservation Trust.

OPENING TIMES

Summer, Sun	2pm-5pm
Winter, Sun	2pm-4pm

For other times please call 020 8952 0019 to enquire

VISIT US
Train: Mill Hill Broadway 1¾ miles

Bus: Tfl bus services 79, 186 & 340 all pass the site

Within 1 hour of Apsley House, Wellington Arch, Kenwood, Chapter House and Pyx Chamber and Jewel Tower

MAP Page 338 (3E)
OS Map 176, 173: TQ186913

CHAPTER HOUSE AND PYX CHAMBER
WESTMINSTER ABBEY – SW1P 3PA

Built by the royal masons in 1250, the Chapter House of Westminster Abbey was used from the 13th to the 16th century by Benedictine monks for their daily meetings. It was also sometimes used as a meeting place of the King's Great Council and the Commons, predecessors of today's Parliament.

A beautiful octagonal building with a vaulted ceiling and delicate central column, it offers rarely seen examples of medieval sculpture, an original floor of glazed tiles and spectacular wall paintings. The 11th-century Pyx Chamber also has a medieval tiled floor, and was used as a monastic and royal treasury. It contains a 13th-century stone altar which survived the Reformation.

During 2009/10, English Heritage funded a major programme of conservation repairs to the external fabric of the Chapter House. This included repairs to the roof, gutters, stonework on the elevations and flying buttresses, and repairs to the lead light glazing – thus preserving this highly important building for future generations.

Chapter House free to EH members. Under the care and management of the Dean and Chapter of Westminster.
www.westminster-abbey.org

OPENING TIMES

29 Mar-31 Mar, daily & Bank Hols	10.30am-6pm or dusk (whichever is earlier)
Good Fri, 24-26 Dec & 1 Jan	Closed
May be closed at short notice on state and religious occasions	

VISIT US
Direction: Through the cloister from Dean's Yard if you only want to visit the Chapter House. Turn into Dean's Yard off Broad Sanctuary. Turn left along the square and go through the entrance-way into the cloister

Please show your EH membership card to the Marshal at the gate

Train: Victoria and Charing Cross both ¾ mile, Waterloo 1 mile

Bus: From surrounding areas

Tube: Westminster and St James' Park stations both ¼ mile

Tel: 020 7654 4900

| ACQ 1872 | Chapter House |
| ACQ 1901 | Pyx Chamber |

MAP Page 339 (4F)
OS Map 176/177, 161/173: TQ299795

CHISWICK HOUSE AND GARDENS
SEE FEATURE OPPOSITE

☎ Available for corporate and private hire – contact Chiswick House and Gardens Trust 020 8742 2762

⚱ Licensed for civil wedding ceremonies

VISIT US

Direction: Burlington Lane, W4 2RP

Train: Chiswick ½ mile

Bus: TfL 190, E3

Tube: Turnham Green 1 mile then bus E3

Tel: 020 8995 0508

NON-MEMBERS

Adult	£5.90
Concession	£5.30
Child	£3.50
Family	£15.30

Members may be charged for special events

OPENING TIMES

29 Mar-3 Nov, Sun-Wed & Bank Hols	10am-5pm
1 Feb-31 Mar, Sat-Sun	10am-4pm

⚠ OVP

Disabled access (ground floor; wheelchair stair-climber to first floor, please call to confirm use prior to visit).

Dogs on leads (restricted areas only).

Parking (charged – off westbound A4).

MAP Page 338 (4E)
OS Map 176, 161: TQ210775

Chiswick House is among the most glorious examples of 18th-century British architecture. The third Earl of Burlington, who designed this noble Roman-style Palladian villa, drew inspiration from his 'grand tours' of Italy. The sumptuous interiors, created by William Kent, display a rich collection of Old Master paintings which complement the beautiful painted and gilded ceilings, and show the diversity of Burlington's collections.

Chiswick House Gardens are a site of international importance, both as the birthplace of the English Landscape Movement, and as the setting for one of the most beautiful houses in London. Spreading over 65 acres, they have inspired countless designed landscapes, from Blenheim Palace to Central Park in New York. Highlights of a £12m restoration unveiled in 2010 include the planting of over 1600 trees, including trees propagated from the original 18th-century cedars of Lebanon; the opening up of historic views from the Classic Bridge; and the complete refurbishment of the 19th-century conservatory, housing an internationally important collection of camellias – possibly the oldest collection outside China and Japan.

Complete your day by visiting the acclaimed modern airy café. For more information including events and activities, visit www.chgt.org.uk

Chiswick House Gardens are managed by Chiswick House and Gardens Trust in partnership with English Heritage, which manages and maintains Chiswick House itself.

Don't miss the Camellia Festival, held here in Feb/Mar, where you can discover Chiswick's glorious camellias in the restored conservatory and enjoy spectacular new spring flower displays in the 19th-century Italian Garden. Dates for 2013 can be found on www.chgt.org.uk. Pre-booking is advised.

🎞 *The Golden Compass.*

When millionaires Stephen and Virginia Courtauld built their 1930s Art Deco mansion adjoining the Great Hall of medieval Eltham Palace, they created a masterpiece of 20th-century design.

VISIT US

Address: Court Yard, Eltham, Greenwich, London SE9 5QE

Direction: Off Court Rd SE9, Jct 3 on the M25, then A20 to Eltham

Train: Eltham and Mottingham, both ½ mile

Bus: TfL bus services 124,126, 160 or 161 and then a short walk

Tel: 020 8294 2548

NON-MEMBERS

House and Gardens

Adult	£9.90
Concession	£8.90
Child	£5.90
Family	£25.70

OPENING TIMES

29 Mar-3 Nov, Sun-Wed
& Bank Hols   10am-5pm

4 Nov-31 Mar
Grounds open on Sundays (house closed for conservation repairs)

Events on 11-12 May – Art Deco Fair, 15-16 Jun – Joust, 7-8 Sep – Art Deco Fair. Contact us for more information

The property may close at short notice, please check website in advance for details

Disabled access (and parking via Court Yard entrance).

Parking (signed off Court Rd).

Pushchairs and large rucksacks need to be left at reception.

No photography allowed inside the house.

MAP Page 339 (4F)
OS Map 177, 162: TQ424740

⊤ Available for corporate and private hire

▲ Licensed for civil wedding ceremonies

Completed in 1936, the red brick exterior of the house was built in sympathy with the Great Hall. But the interior remains a glamorous 1930s showpiece, an eclectic mix of Art Deco, ultra-smart ocean-liner style and cutting-edge Swedish design.

The dining room is a tour de force, with pink leather upholstered chairs, bird's-eye maple veneered walls, a shimmering aluminium-leaf ceiling and black-and-silver doors portraying animals and birds.

Even more exotic is Virginia Courtauld's vaulted bathroom, complete with onyx bath and sink and gold-plated bath taps. Luxury also emanates from the centrally-heated sleeping quarters of the Courtaulds' pet ring-tailed lemur, Mah-Jongg. Equipped with all the latest modern conveniences, the house featured underfloor heating, a centralised vacuum cleaner and a built-in audio system.

Upstairs is a display of discoveries from the Courtauld era, including original furniture and family photographs. Visitors can also enjoy a restored original 10-minute Courtauld home movie, giving an intimate glimpse of their family life. A display celebrating the Royal Army Education Corps' (RAEC) post-World War II association with Eltham Palace highlights a further chapter in its fascinating history. It includes a recreation of an officer's bedroom of the 1960s, together with exhibition panels and a photograph album telling the story of the RAEC's time here.

The medieval palace presents a striking contrast to the opulent 1930s house. The Great Hall, with its stunning hammerbeam roof, was built for Edward IV in the 1470s, and Henry VIII spent much of his childhood here.

The palace's 19 acres of beautiful gardens feature both 20th-century and medieval elements. These include a moat, spanned by a medieval bridge, a stunning herbaceous border and plenty of picnic areas. Striking at any time of year, garden highlights include the spring bulbs and the wisteria cascading over the classical pergola in summer.

Eltham Palace hosts a range of events throughout the year, including the popular Art Deco fairs in May and September and the Eltham Joust in June. Look out for details in your exclusive membership magazine or on our website.

📷 *The Gathering Storm; Bright Young Things; Brideshead Revisited; Shanghai; Revolver; Madonna's WE.*

Kenwood, one of the finest of all English Heritage's great houses, will re-open in November 2013 following an extensive programme of repair and enhancement, carried out with the support of funding from the Heritage Lottery Fund.

VISIT US

Address: Kenwood, Hampstead NW3 7JR

Direction: Hampstead Lane, NW3

Train: Gospel Oak or Hampstead Heath

Bus: Tfl 210 (also bus H3 passes within short walk)

Tube: Golders Green or Archway then bus 210

Tel: 020 8348 1286

OPENING TIMES

House	Closed
Re-opening Autumn 2013	
Nov-31 Mar, daily	10am-5pm
Brewhouse Café	
29 Mar-3 Nov, daily	9am-6pm
4 Nov-31 Mar, daily	9am-4pm
24-25 Dec	Closed
Garden Shop	
29 Mar 2013-31 Mar 2014, daily	10am-4pm
24-25 Dec	Closed

Estate open from 8am to dusk (see park entrance for closing time)

Entry to the House and grounds is free; donations welcome. Pre-booked group tours available

New guidebook.

Disabled access (lift to all floors for visitors with a disability or mobility problems; toilets).

Dogs on leads (restricted areas only).

Café open, daily.

Parking (Charge applies. Disabled bays. Mobility service available on request).

MAP Page 338 (3E)
OS Map 176, 173: TQ271874

🅣 Available for corporate and private hire

🅐 Licensed for civil wedding ceremonies

The re-opening of the House in November will reveal a re-presentation of the wonderful Adam interiors; the re-display of the outstanding Iveagh Collection of paintings; imaginative new interpretation for visitors of all ages; and the opening of the restored ornamental Dairy, set in Kenwood's Humphry Repton landscaped parkland.

Crowning Hampstead Heath, Kenwood was remodelled by Robert Adam between 1764 and 1779 into a majestic villa for a great judge, the first Earl of Mansfield, and later extended for his nephew. In recent decades time and weather had taken their toll on the

If you would like to make a donation to the Caring for Kenwood project, please contact the Development Department on 020 7973 3797 or foundation@english-heritage.org.uk. The English Heritage Foundation is a registered charity, no. 1140351.

mansion, necessitating major conservation work to its roof and facades to secure Kenwood and its beautiful interiors and outstanding art collections for generations to come. As a result, the House has been closed since April 2012, but will now re-open in November 2013.

Including paintings by Rembrandt, Vermeer, Turner, Reynolds, Gainsborough and Constable, Kenwood's principal art collection was bequeathed to the nation with the mansion and grounds by brewing magnate Edward Guinness, Earl of Iveagh, in 1927. Now the Iveagh Bequest will be re-displayed and newly interpreted to its best advantage in rooms refurbished – as the donor wished – 'as a fine example of the artistic home of an 18th century gentleman'.

The Suffolk Collection of Tudor and Stuart portraits, including an unrivalled array of full length paintings of extravagantly-dressed Jacobean ladies and gentlemen painted by William Larkin in 1610-19, will meanwhile become more accessible with the installation of a lift to their first floor setting.

Perhaps most striking of all Kenwood's glories, however, is the series of magnificent and internationally important Robert Adam rooms from the Entrance Hall to his masterpiece, the richly decorated Library. These will also be re-presented to show and interpret them as they were originally intended to look and feel.

A new introduction to the house and grounds, and those who lived and worked here, will include an interactive 'dolls-house' model of the mansion and an audio visual display. Dido Belle, Lord Mansfield's mixed-race great-niece, is one of the many people and features of Kenwood which the new interpretation will bring to life. 'Growing Space', an activity base in the Orangery for families, will include areas where they can look at themes connected with Kenwood and select equipment to explore the house together.

Kenwood's 112 acres of leafy parkland, landscaped by Humphry Repton, is beloved by locals and visitors alike for its fine views over London and its meandering woodland paths. The ornamental 18th-century Dairy, which once both supplied the mansion with fresh produce and allowed the ladies of the house to take tea or fashionably play at dairymaids, will re-open to visitors with re-instated decorative interiors.

🎬 *Notting Hill; Mansfield Park; Scenes of a Sexual Nature; Venus*

NEW FOR 2013
Re-opening in November 2013, Kenwood's interiors and exterior will be transformed, and visitors will be able to experience this great house in a much more interactive and engaging way than was possible before.

COOMBE CONDUIT
KINGSTON-UPON-THAMES
KT2 7HE

These two brick-walled chambers, connected by an underground passage, were once part of a system which collected water from nearby springs and channelled it to Hampton Court Palace.

Managed by the Kingston-upon-Thames Society.

OPENING TIMES
1 Apr-30 Sep,
every 2nd Sun   2pm-4pm

VISIT US
Direction: Coombe Lane on the corner of Lord Chancellor's Walk

Train: Norbiton ¾ mile or Raynes Park 1 mile then bus 57

Bus: Tfl 57 Kingston – Streatham

Tube: Wimbledon then bus 57

Tel: 020 8541 3108/020 8942 7387

www.kingstonuponthamessociety.co.uk

ACQ.1978

MAP Page 338 (4E)
OS Map 176, 161: TQ204698

HARMONDSWORTH GREAT BARN
HILLINGDON – UB7 0AQ

Medieval timber-framed barn built in 1426-7 by Winchester College. The Great Barn is one of the largest ever known to have been built in England, and one of the most complete and unaltered pre-Dissolution buildings in Britain.

A free virtual tour and podcast are available on our website **english-heritage.org.uk/harmondsworth-barn**

OPENING TIMES
1 Apr-31 Oct, 2nd and 4th
Sun of each month   10am-5pm
1 Nov-31 Mar   Closed

HARMONDSWORTH GREAT BARN

VISIT US
Direction: Located in HIgh Street, Harmondsworth Village

Train: West Drayton 2 miles, Hayes & Harlington 4¼ miles, Uxbridge 5 miles

Bus: TfL U3 and 350

Tel: 0870 333 1181

ACQ.2012

MAP Page 338 (4E)
OS Map 176, 160: TQ056778

THE HOME OF CHARLES DARWIN, DOWN HOUSE
SEE FEATURE – PAGE 64

ELTHAM PALACE AND GARDENS
SEE FEATURE – PAGE 32

JEWEL TOWER
SEE FEATURE OPPOSITE

KENWOOD
SEE FEATURE – PAGE 34

LONDON WALL
TOWER HILL

This is the best-preserved remnant of the Roman wall which once formed part of the eastern defences of Roman Londinium. Built c. AD 200, the wall defined the shape and size of London for over a millennium.

OPENING TIMES
Any reasonable time

VISIT US
Direction: Located outside Tower Hill Underground station, EC3

Train: Fenchurch Street or London Bridge

Bus: From surrounding areas

Tube: Tower Hill or Tower Gateway

ACQ.1953

MAP Page 339 (3F)
OS Map 176/177, 173: TQ336807

MARBLE HILL HOUSE
SEE FEATURE – PAGE 38

RANGER'S HOUSE – THE WERNHER COLLECTION
SEE FEATURE – PAGE 39

WELLINGTON ARCH
SEE FEATURE – PAGE 40

WINCHESTER PALACE
SOUTHWARK

Part of the great hall of Winchester Palace, built in the early 13th century as the London house of the Bishops of Winchester, including the striking rose window which adorns the west gable. Most of the palace was destroyed by fire in 1814.

OPENING TIMES
Any reasonable time

VISIT US
Direction: Next to Southwark Cathedral and the Golden Hinde replica ship; corner of Clink St and Storey St, SE1

Train/Tube: London Bridge ¼ mile

Bus: From surrounding areas

ACQ.1967

MAP Page 339 (4F)
OS Map 176/177, 173: TQ325803

VISIT US

Direction: Located on Abingdon Street, opposite the southern end of the Houses of Parliament (Victoria Tower)

Train: Victoria and Charing Cross ¾ mile, Waterloo 1 mile

Bus: From surrounding areas

Tube: St James's Park and Westminster ¼ mile

Tel: 020 7222 2219

NON-MEMBERS

Adult	£3.90
Concession	£3.50
Child	£2.30

OPENING TIMES

29 Mar-3 Nov, daily & Bank Hols	10am-5pm
4 Nov-31 Mar, Sat-Sun	10am-4pm
24-26 Dec and 1 Jan	Closed

Last admission ½ hour before closing

ACQ.1938

New guidebook.

Light refreshents available.

Disabled access (limited).

MAP Page 339 (4F)
OS Map 176/177, 161/173: TQ301793

Tucked away between the Houses of Parliament and Westminster Abbey, the Jewel Tower is an easily overlooked but precious fragment of English history, built in c.1365 as the 'King's Privy Wardrobe' to house Edward III's personal treasury. The sole survivor of the private royal quarters within the great medieval Palace of Westminster, it is also the only part of the palace complex which survived the disastrous fire of 1834 and is regularly open to the public. It later housed the House of Lords records and then the national Weights and Measures Office.

NEW FOR 2013
From April 2013, a new exhibition covering all three floors of the tower will highlight its history and changing role over the centuries. Features will include a model of the 'lost' medieval Palace of Westminster, replicas of precious objects and areas of set dressing including an 18th-century clerk's office.

VISIT US

Direction: Richmond Road, Twickenham, London TW1 2NL

Train: St Margaret's or Twickenham

Bus: Tfl 33, 490, H22, R68, R70

Tube: Richmond 1 mile

Tel: 020 8892 5115

NON-MEMBERS

Adult	£5.70
Concession	£5.10
Child	£3.40
Family	£14.80

OPENING TIMES

29 Mar-3 Nov
Entry by guided tours only

Sat	10.30am and 12pm
Sun	10.30am, 12pm, 2.15pm and 3.30pm

Tours last around 1½ hours

Park

All year, daily	7am-dusk

Café

29 Mar-3 Nov, daily	10am-5pm
4 Nov-31 Mar, daily	10am-4pm

ACQ.1986

Café (Coach House Café, open all year).

Disabled access (exterior & ground floor only; toilets).

Parking charge.

MAP Page 338 (4E)
OS Map 176, 161: TQ173736

A lovely Palladian villa still set in 66 acres of riverside parkland, Marble Hill House is the last complete survivor of the elegant villas which bordered the Thames between Richmond and Hampton Court in the 18th-century. It was begun in 1724 for Henrietta Howard, Countess of Suffolk, a remarkable 18th-century woman of letters, who was also the mistress of King George II and friend of some of the cleverest men in England. The house and gardens were planned by a coterie of fashionable connoisseurs, including the poet Alexander Pope.

The interiors of the house have been exquisitely restored and recreated, and there is also a fine collection of early Georgian paintings, including portraits of Mrs Howard and her circle. Marble Hill was intended as an Arcadian retreat from crowded 18th-century London, and there can be few places in England which better recall the atmosphere of Georgian fashionable life.

🎬 *Nanny MacPhee 2: The Big Bang*

T Available for corporate and private hire

▲ Licensed for civil wedding ceremonies

Please note: No photography in the house.

VISIT US

Address: Chesterfield Walk, Blackheath, London SE10 8QX

Direction: Ranger's House is on Chesterfield Walk and overlooks the junction of General Wolfe Road and Shooters Hill Road

DLR: Deptford Bridge then bus 53

Train: Blackheath ¾ mile

Bus: TfL 53, 386

River: Greenwich Pier

Tel: 020 8294 2548

NON-MEMBERS

Adult	£6.70
Concession	£6.00
Child	£4.00

OPENING TIMES

29 Mar-2 Oct, Sun-Wed
Entry by guided tours only at 11am and 2pm. Tours last around 1½ hours

The property may close at short notice, please check the website for details

ACQ.1986

Toilets (including disabled).

MAP Page 339 (4F)
OS Map 177, 161/162: TQ388769

Ranger's House is an elegant Georgian villa built in 1723, which became the official residence of the 'Ranger of Greenwich Park'. From 1815 this post was held by Princess Sophia Matilda, niece of George III. It remained an aristocratic and then royal home until 1902. Today it houses the Wernher Collection – an astounding display of medieval and Renaissance works of art, all purchased by the diamond magnate Sir Julius Wernher (1850-1912).

Arranged within the panelled interiors of this graceful mansion, the Wernher Collection presents a glittering spectacle. Nearly 700 works of art are on display, including early religious paintings and Dutch Old Masters, minute carved Gothic ivories, fine Renaissance bronzes and silver treasures. Together they proclaim the genius of medieval craftsmen, and the unparalleled quality of Renaissance decorative arts.

Entrance is by guided tour only (included in the entrance fee), providing a detailed insight into the history of the Collection.

Available for corporate and private hire

Licensed for civil wedding ceremonies

Set in the heart of the capital at Hyde Park Corner, Wellington Arch is one of London's most famous and striking landmarks. It is crowned by the largest bronze sculpture in Europe, depicting the Angel of Peace descending on the 'Quadriga' – or four-horsed chariot – of War.

VISIT US

Address: Wellington Arch, Apsley Way, Hyde Park Corner, London W1J 7JZ

Direction: Hyde Park Corner, W1J

Train: Victoria ½ mile

Bus: From surrounding areas

Tube: Hyde Park Corner, adjacent

Tel: 020 7930 2726

NON-MEMBERS

Adult	£4.00
Concession	£3.60
Child	£2.40

Joint ticket with Apsley House

Adult	£8.60
Concession	£7.70
Child	£5.20
Family	£22.40

OPENING TIMES

29 Mar-3 Nov, Wed-Sun & Bank Hols	10am-5pm
4 Nov-31 Mar, Wed-Sun	10am-4pm
24-26 Dec and 1 Jan	Closed

Last admission ½ hour before closing

The property may close to install new exhibitions. Please call in advance for details

⚠ OVP

MAP Page 338 (4E)
OS Map 176, 161/173: TQ284798

⊤ Available for corporate and private hire

Despite its air of immovably changeless grandeur, the appearance and the siting of Wellington Arch have altered since it was designed by the architect Decimus Burton and

erected in 1825-7. Intended as a grand outer entrance to Buckingham Palace, it was originally aligned with the Hyde Park Screen, and later took on the role of a victory arch proclaiming Wellington's triumph over Napoleon. In 1846 a colossal equestrian bronze statue of Wellington was added to the top, sparking furious controversy. By 1883, however, the original siting of the Arch was causing serious traffic bottlenecks: so it was moved stone by stone some 20 metres to its current position, the present great bronze sculpture being then substituted for the Wellington statue. Its balconies offer glorious panoramas over the Royal Parks and the Houses of Parliament, as well as unique views of the Household Cavalry, passing beneath to and from the Changing of the Guard at Horse Guards Parade.

The Arch is also now home to the Quadriga Gallery, which hosts changing displays showcasing the best of English Heritage's work.

NEW FOR 2013 AT THE QUADRIGA GALLERY

In 2013, it will be 100 years since the beginnings of the National Heritage Collection, the historic properties and monuments – from Stonehenge to Hadrian's Wall – which today are looked after by English Heritage. To mark this anniversary, five exhibitions in the Quadriga Gallery at Wellington Arch over the course of the year will explore the heritage movement in England – the birth of archaeology; the collecting of the country's historic landmarks for the nation; the planning battles of the 50s and 60s; the sometimes contentious listing of post-war buildings and finally, what London would look like today if there had been no English Heritage and no-one to fight to save the capital's historic buildings.

6 FEB-21 APR: The General, The Scientist & The Banker: The Birth of Archaeology and the Battle for the Past

1 MAY-7 JUL: A Monumental Act: How Britain Saved its Heritage

17 JUL-15 SEP: Pride and Prejudice: The Battle for Betjeman's Britain

25 SEP-24 NOV: Brutal and Beautiful: Saving the Twentieth Century

4 DEC-2 FEB 2014: Almost Lost: London's Buildings Loved & Loathed

Permanent displays also interpret the history of the Arch itself.

Please note that during changeovers of exhibitions Wellington Arch may temporarily close to the public. Please telephone in advance or visit our website for up-to-date information.

An important part of the National Heritage Collection are 47 statues and monuments in Central London, including the Wellington Arch, which you are invited to explore (see p.40).

Statues provide a fascinating insight into the preoccupations of the period. Many of them are associated with wars and military campaigns, such as the Napoleonic Wars, the Boer War and the two World Wars – including the Cenotaph in Whitehall. Others represent Royal figures such as Charles I (1633) and Edward VII (1921).

A leaflet giving more information about the intriguing history of 20th-century war memorials in London is available from Customer Services (tel 0870 333 1181).

The Capital's Monuments

Viscount Alanbrooke Whitehall, SW1	**Duke of Kent** Crescent Gardens (locked), Portland Place, W1
Queen Anne Queen Anne's Gate, SW1	
Belgian War Memorial Victoria Embankment	**Baron Lawrence** Waterloo Place, SW1
Simon Bolivar Belgrave Square, SW1	**Machine Gun Corps** Apsley Way, W1
Duke of Cambridge Whitehall, SW1	
Colin Campbell Waterloo Place, SW1	**Montgomery** Whitehall, SW1
Carabiniers Memorial Chelsea Embankment, SW3	**Lord Napier of Magdala** Queen's Gate, SW7
Edith Cavell St Martin's Place, WC2	**Marble Arch** W1
Cenotaph Whitehall, SW1	**Florence Nightingale** Waterloo Place, SW1
King Charles I Whitehall, SW1	
Queen Charlotte Queen Square, WC1	**Samuel Plimsoll** Victoria Embankment
Clive of India King Charles St, SW1	**Lord Portal** Victoria Embankment
Christopher Columbus Belgrave Square, SW1	**Sir Walter Raleigh** Old Royal Naval College, Greenwich, SE10
Crimea Memorial Waterloo Place, SW1	
Thomas Cubitt St George's Drive, Pimlico, SW1	**Royal Artillery Memorial** Apsley Way, W1
Lord Curzon Carlton House Terrace, SW1	**General de San Martin** Belgrave Square, SW1
Duke of Devonshire Whitehall, SW1	**Captain Scott** Waterloo Place, SW1
Edward VII Waterloo Place, SW1	**Viscount Slim** Whitehall, SW1
General Eisenhower Grosvenor Square, W1	
Sir John Franklin Waterloo Place, SW1	**Lord Trenchard** Victoria Embankment
General de Gaulle Carlton Gardens, SW1	**George Washington** Trafalgar Square, WC2
King George II Golden Square, W1	**Duke of Wellington** Apsley Way, W1
King George III Cockspur St, SW1	
General Gordon Victoria Embankment	**Wellington Arch and Quadriga** Apsley Way, W1
Earl Haig Whitehall, SW1	
Sir Arthur Harris St Clement Danes, WC2	**King William III** St James's Square, SW1
Lord Herbert Waterloo Place, SW1	
King James II National Gallery, Trafalgar Square, WC2	

DISCOUNTED ATTRACTIONS:

Use your membership to get exclusive discounts at these independent attractions in London. Please remember to show your card as proof of membership.

£5 DISCOUNT ON TOUR

⌗ ♦♦ 1

THE ALBERT MEMORIAL
Kensington SW7
A professional Blue Badge guide takes you behind the railings and brings to life the detail of mosaics and marble sculpture on this iconic Victorian monument.
www.tourguides.co.uk
Tel. 020 7936 2568

2 for 1 ENTRY

⌗ OVP ♦♦ 6

BENJAMIN FRANKLIN HOUSE
London WC2N 5NF
The world's only remaining home of US Founding Father Benjamin Franklin, featuring a unique 'Historical Experience'.

www.benjaminfranklinhouse.org
Tel. 020 7925 1405

2 for 1 ADULT ENTRY

⌗

CHURCHILL WAR ROOMS
London SW1A 2AQ
Visit Churchill War Rooms to discover the original Cabinet War Rooms, the underground headquarters that sheltered Churchill and his wartime government during the Blitz.
www.iwm.org.uk
Tel. 020 7930 6961

2 for 1 ENTRY

⌗ OVP ♦♦ 6

CRAVEN COTTAGE (STADIUM)
London SW6
A unique piece of London's heritage – step through the listed turnstiles of our 19th-century Premier League football ground.
www.fulhamfc.com/visit
Tel. 0843 208 1234 (option 4)

50% OFF

⌗ OVP ♦♦ 6

DANSON HOUSE
Kent DA6 8HL
A beautiful Georgian villa with sumptuous interiors built for pleasure and entertaining. Enjoy this superb example of 18th-century architecture with its elegant interiors.
www.dansonhouse.org.uk
Tel. 020 8303 6699

2 for 1 ENTRY

⌗ OVP

DULWICH PICTURE GALLERY
London SE21 7AD
Dulwich Picture Gallery, England's first public gallery, was founded in 1811. A masterpiece of Regency architecture by Sir John Soane.
www.dulwichpicturegallery.org.uk
Tel. 020 8299 8711

LONDON

Discount applies to:

| KEY | ⊞ MEMBERS | OVP OVP HOLDERS | ⁉ NO. OF MEMBER'S CHILDREN |

Terms and conditions may apply, so make sure you check the individual pages on our website or call the individual property for more details.

2 for 1 ADULT ENTRY

2 for 1 ENTRY

2 for 1 ENTRY

⊞ ⁉ 1

HMS BELFAST
London SE1 2JH
HMS *Belfast* tells the stories of life on board this warship during the Second World War and beyond. Explore all nine decks and join in the action in the Gun Turret Experience.
www.iwm.co.uk
Tel. 020 7940 6300

⊞

LONDON CANAL MUSEUM
London N1 9RT
The museum tells the story of London's fascinating canals, their people, horses, and trades, in a former warehouse where ice from Norway was once stored in underground wells.
www.canalmuseum.org.uk
Tel. 020 7713 0836

⊞ ⁉ 3

LONDON TRANSPORT MUSEUM
London WC2E 7BB
Lively and interactive galleries depict the past, present and future of transport in London and how it shaped the culture and lives of its people.
www.ltmuseum.co.uk
Tel. 020 7565 7298

£1 OFF STANDARD ADULT TICKET

⊞ OVP

STRAWBERRY HILL HOUSE
London TW1 4ST
Horace Walpole's 'little gothic castle' is a fairytale castle by the Thames. Now restored to its former glory, visiting Strawberry Hill is a truly theatrical experience.
www.strawberryhillhouse.org.uk
Tel. 020 8744 1241

GIVE THE GIFT OF MEMBERSHIP
Give friends and family the opportunity to enjoy these fantastic discounts too!

- Free entry to over 400 historic properties
- Kids go free (up to six per adult in a family group)
- Free or discounted entry to hundreds of events, activities and other attractions
- Free handbook worth £10.95
- Exclusive members' magazine

SOUTH EAST

Dover Castle

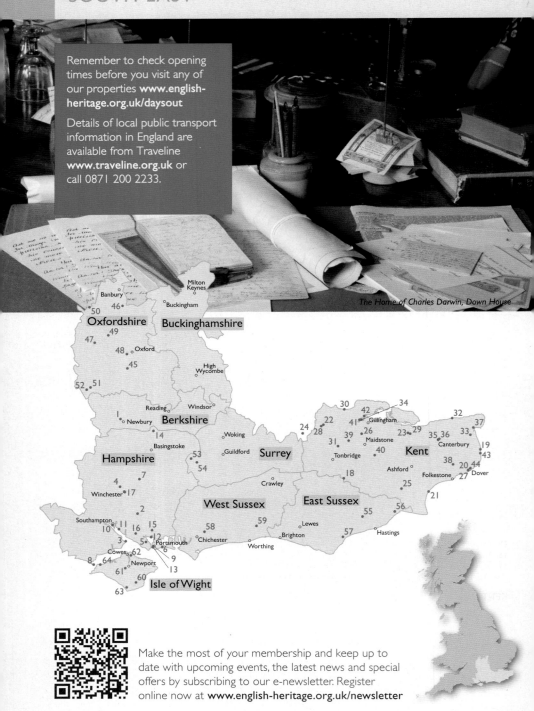

Remember to check opening times before you visit any of our properties **www.english-heritage.org.uk/daysout**

Details of local public transport information in England are available from Traveline **www.traveline.org.uk** or call 0871 200 2233.

The Home of Charles Darwin, Down House

Oxfordshire

Buckinghamshire

Milton Keynes

Banbury

Buckingham

Oxford

High Wycombe

Reading

Windsor

Berkshire

Newbury

Hampshire

Basingstoke

Woking

Surrey

Guildford

Winchester

Southampton

Cowes

Newport

Portsmouth

Isle of Wight

Chichester

West Sussex

Crawley

Worthing

Brighton

Lewes

East Sussex

Hastings

Tonbridge

Maidstone

Gillingham

Kent

Ashford

Canterbury

Folkestone

Dover

Make the most of your membership and keep up to date with upcoming events, the latest news and special offers by subscribing to our e-newsletter. Register online now at **www.english-heritage.org.uk/newsletter**

HIGHLIGHTS FOR 2013/14 IN THE **SOUTH EAST**

Dover Castle: a magnificent day out for all the family, open all year.

Osborne: visit the seaside home of Queen Victoria.

1066 Battle of Hastings, Abbey & Battlefield: scene of the most famous battle in England's history.

PROPERTIES

BERKSHIRE
1 Donnington Castle

HAMPSHIRE
2 Bishop's Waltham Palace
3 Calshot Castle
4 Flowerdown Barrows
5 Fort Brockhurst
6 Fort Cumberland
7 The Grange at Northington
8 Hurst Castle
9 King James's and Landport Gates
10 Medieval Merchant's House
11 Netley Abbey
12 Portchester Castle
13 Royal Garrison Church
14 Silchester Roman City Walls and Amphitheatre
15 Southwick Priory
16 Titchfield Abbey
17 Wolvesey Castle (Old Bishop's Palace)

KENT
18 Bayham Old Abbey
19 Deal Castle
20 Dover Castle
21 Dymchurch Martello Tower
22 Eynsford Castle
23 Faversham Stone Chapel (Our Lady of Elverton)
24 The Home of Charles Darwin, Down House

25 Horne's Place Chapel
26 Kit's Coty House and Little Kit's Coty House
27 Knights Templar Church
28 Lullingstone Roman Villa
29 Maison Dieu
30 Milton Chantry
31 Old Soar Manor
32 Reculver Towers and Roman Fort
33 Richborough Roman Fort and Amphitheatre
34 Rochester Castle
35 St Augustine's Abbey
36 St Augustine's Abbey Conduit House
37 St Augustine's Cross
38 St John's Commandery
39 St Leonard's Tower
40 Sutton Valence Castle
41 Temple Manor
42 Upnor Castle
43 Walmer Castle and Gardens
44 Western Heights, Dover

OXFORDSHIRE
45 Abingdon County Hall Museum
46 Deddington Castle
47 Minster Lovell Hall and Dovecote
48 North Hinksey Conduit House
49 North Leigh Roman Villa
50 Rollright Stones
51 Uffington Castle, White Horse and Dragon Hill
52 Wayland's Smithy

SURREY
53 Farnham Castle Keep
54 Waverley Abbey

EAST SUSSEX
55 1066 Battle of Hastings, Abbey and Battlefield
56 Camber Castle
57 Pevensey Castle

WEST SUSSEX
58 Boxgrove Priory
59 Bramber Castle

ISLE OF WIGHT – see page 84
60 Appuldurcombe House
61 Carisbrooke Castle
62 Osborne
63 St Catherine's Oratory
64 Yarmouth Castle

BERKSHIRE

DONNINGTON CASTLE
WEST BERKSHIRE

The striking, twin-towered, 14th-century gatehouse of this castle, later the focus of a Civil War siege and battle, survives amid impressive earthworks.

OPENING TIMES
Any reasonable time in daylight hours; exterior viewing only

Car park open daily	7am-7pm

VISIT US
Direction: 1 mile N of Newbury, off B4494

Train: Newbury 1¼ miles

Bus: Newbury & District services 6, 6A, 107 & Go-Ride services 5 & 5A

ACQ.1952 P

Disabled access (steep slopes within grounds).

MAP Page 338 (4C)
OS Map 174, 158: SU461692

ST BARTHOLOMEW'S CHURCH, LOWER BASILDON
BERKSHIRE – RG8 9NH

© James Davies

This striking 700-year-old flint and brick church stands in a pretty churchyard near a beautiful stretch of the Thames. Inside it is simple and serene, with ornate roof timbers and memorials to past parishioners. Jethro Tull is buried here.

Owned and managed by The Churches Conservation Trust.

ST BARTHOLOMEW'S CHURCH, LOWER BASILDON

OPENING TIMES
Keyholder nearby

VISIT US
Train: Pangbourne 2 miles

Bus: Thames Travel services 132 & 133

30 mins from Donnington Castle

MAP Page 338 (4C)
OS Map 175, 159/171: SU612793

ST THOMAS' CHURCH, EAST SHEFFORD
BERKSHIRE – RG17 7EF

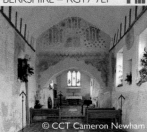
© CCT Cameron Newham

This simple little church stands in an idyllic spot beside a water meadow. Its village has long since vanished, but the spirit of the villagers shines through in the church's simple craftsmanship, glorious medieval wall paintings and fabulous tombs, giving an intriguing glimpse into 15th-century fashion.

Owned and managed by The Churches Conservation Trust.

OPENING TIMES
Open daily during daylight hours

VISIT US
Train: Nearest 🚉 Kintbury 5 miles

Bus: Newbury & District service 4

15 mins from Donnington Castle

MAP Page 338 (4B)
OS Map 174, 158: SU391747

HAMPSHIRE

BISHOP'S WALTHAM PALACE
HAMPSHIRE – SO32 1DH

The ruins of a medieval palace (and its later additions) used by the bishops and senior clergy of Winchester as they travelled through their diocese. Winchester was the richest diocese in England, and its properties were grandiose and extravagantly appointed. Much of what can be seen today is the work of William Wykeham, who was bishop from 1367. The ground floor of the farmhouse adapted from the palace's lodging range is occupied by the Bishop's Waltham Town Museum, which exhibits local artefacts.

Other palaces of the bishops of Winchester include Farnham Castle Keep (p.78) and Wolvesey Castle (Old Bishop's Palace) (p.56).

OPENING TIMES
Grounds

1 May-30 Sep, daily	10am-5pm
Farmhouse Museum	
1 May-30 Sep, Sat-Sun	2pm-4pm

VISIT US
Direction: In Bishop's Waltham

Train: Botley 3½ miles

Bus: Brijan bus 7, 8, 17; Stagecoach bus 69

Tel: 01489 892460

ACQ.1952 P

Disabled access (grounds only).

Dogs on leads (restricted areas only).

MAP Page 338 (6C)
OS Map 185, 119: SU552174

CALSHOT CASTLE
HAMPSHIRE – SO45 1BR

This artillery fort, built by Henry VIII to defend the sea passage to Southampton, later saw service in both World Wars.

Managed by Hampshire County Council.

NON-MEMBERS
Adult	£3.00
Concession	£2.10
Child	£2.10
Family	£7.60

OPENING TIMES
29 Mar-30 Sep,
daily   10.30am-4.30pm
Castle closed 30 minutes during lunchtime period

VISIT US
Direction: On spit, 2 miles SE of Fawley, off B3053

Bus: Solent Blue Line Bluestar 9 & H3 pass within 1 mile

Tel: 02380 892023; when castle is closed, please call 02380 892077

ACQ.1964

Disabled access (Keep: ground floor only; toilets).

MAP Page 338 (6C)
OS Map 196, OL22/OL29/119: SU489025

FLOWERDOWN BARROWS
HAMPSHIRE

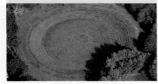

FLOWERDOWN BARROWS

Three Bronze Age burial mounds, including two bowl barrows, and the largest and finest disc barrow in Hampshire.

OPENING TIMES
Any reasonable time in daylight hours

VISIT US
Direction: Off B3049, out of Winchester to Littleton; at crossroads in centre of village

Train: Winchester 2 miles

Bus: Stagecoach in Hampshire 7, 68

ACQ.1972

MAP Page 338 (5C)
OS Map 185, 132: SU459320

FORT BROCKHURST
HAMPSHIRE – PO12 4DS

© Skyscan Balloon Photography

One of a number of forts built in the 1850s and 1860s to protect Portsmouth and its vital harbour against a French invasion. Largely unaltered, the parade ground, gun ramps and moated keep can all be viewed.

FORT BROCKHURST

The fort currently stores a treasure trove of objects from English Heritage's extensive reserve collections. Objects on display have been excavated from sites in the South East and South West. They include stonework, textiles, jewellery and furniture from many periods, as well as rarely-seen treasures on tour from stores in the North and East. The Collections Access Centre offers pre-booked adult and school groups a hands-on experience of English Heritage's rich and varied collections of artefacts, under the guidance of a curator, conservator or trained educator.

Portchester Castle – which acted as a prison during the Napoleonic Wars – is nearby (see p.55).

OPENING TIMES
1 Apr-30 Sep   11am-3pm
on the second Sat of every month

Gosport's Big Day 9 Jun & Heritage Open Days

VISIT US
Direction: Off A32, in Gunner's Way, Elson; on N side of Gosport

Train: Fareham 3 miles

Bus: First E1, E2, 9A,10 & 11 – Gosport Ferry links with (train) Portsmouth & Southsea)

Tel: 02392 581059

ACQ.1963

Disabled access (grounds and ground floor only).

Dogs on leads (restricted areas only).

MAP Page 338 (6C)
OS Map 196, OL29/119: SU596021

FORT CUMBERLAND
HAMPSHIRE – PO4 9LD

Perhaps England's most impressive piece of 18th-century defensive architecture, Fort Cumberland was reconstructed in pentagonal form by the Duke of Richmond between 1785 and 1810, and designed to protect Langstone Harbour. Southsea beach is nearby.

OPENING TIMES
The fort opens for pre-booked group guided tours and Heritage Open Days

Call 023 9285 6700 for opening details

VISIT US
Direction: In Portsmouth's Eastney district on the estuary approach, via Henderson Rd off Eastney Rd, or from the Esplanade

Train: Fratton 2 miles

Bus: First 15 (Mon-Sat), 16 (Sun only)

Tel: 023 9285 6700

ACQ.1975 ⚠

MAP Page 338 (6C)
OS Map 196, 119/120: SZ683993

THE GRANGE AT NORTHINGTON
HAMPSHIRE

Set like a lakeside temple in a landscaped park, the Grange at Northington is the foremost example of the Greek Revival style in England. Created between 1804 and 1809 when William Wilkins encased an earlier house in Classical facades. Most striking is the temple front supported on eight gigantic columns. It provides a stunning backdrop for the opera evenings which

THE GRANGE AT NORTHINGTON

take place here in the summer; call 01962 868600 for details.

🎬 The 1999 film, *Onegin*, with Ralph Fiennes.

OPENING TIMES
Exterior only:

1 Apr-31 May, daily	10am-6pm
1 Jun-31 Jul, daily	9am-12pm
1 Aug-30 Sep, daily	10am-6pm
1 Oct-31 Mar, daily	10am-4pm
Closes early for opera evenings in June and July	
24-26 Dec and 1 Jan	Closed

VISIT US
Direction: Located 4 miles N of New Alresford, off B3046 along a farm track – 450 metres (493 yards)

Train: Winchester 8 miles

Bus: Nearest bus service is Velvet Bus 67 to Itchen Abbas or Mervyns Coaches 95, 96 to Lunways Inn then 3 mile walk

Tel: 0870 333 1181

ACQ.1975 🐕 🛡 P 🏚 ♿ ⚠
Disabled access (with assistance, steep steps to terrace).

MAP Page 338 (5C)
OS Map 185, 132: SU562362

HOLY TRINITY CHURCH, PRIVETT
HAMPSHIRE – GU34 3PE

© Christopher Dalton

HOLY TRINITY CHURCH, PRIVETT

The spire of Holy Trinity is visible for miles around in this idyllic corner of Hampshire. It is extraordinary to find such a lavishly decorated church in a rural location. Magnificent stonework and dazzling stained glass blend beautifully with the colourful marble mosaiced floors.

Owned and managed by The Churches Conservation Trust.

OPENING TIMES
Open daily   10am-3pm

VISIT US
Train: Petersfield 4¾ miles

Bus: Velvet service 67 is closest service. Alight West Meon Hut (c.2½ miles walk)

30 mins from Wolvesey Castle

MAP Page 338 (5C)
OS Map 186, 132: SU677270

HURST CASTLE
HAMPSHIRE – SO41 0TP

One of the most advanced of the artillery fortresses built by Henry VIII: used as a prison for eminent 17th-century captives, including King Charles I, and later strengthened during the 19th and 20th centuries. It commands the narrow entrance to the Solent.

HURST CASTLE

Managed by Hurst Castle Services.

NON-MEMBERS

Adult	£4.50
Concession	£4.00
Child	£2.50

OPENING TIMES

29 Mar-30 Sep, daily	10.30am-5.30pm
1 Oct-3 Nov, daily	10.30am-4pm

Occasional opening winter weekends – please ring 01590 642500 to confirm

VISIT US

Direction: 1½ mile walk on shingle spit from Milford-on-Sea. Best approached by ferry from Keyhaven – call 01590 642500 for ferry details and fares

Train: Lymington Town 6½ miles

Bus: Wilts & Dorset X1 to Milford-On-Sea to within 2½ miles, or 1 mile to ferry

Tel: 01590 642344

ACQ.1933 🐾 ⌷ 🚶 ⬆ 💼 ⚠

New guidebook.

Dogs on leads (restricted areas only).

Tearoom/restaurant (Castle Café, not managed by EH. Open Apr-May weekends only, Jun-Sep daily).

Parking (charge payable, at Milford seafront or Keyhaven).

MAP Page 338 (7B)
OS Map 196, OL22/OL29: SZ318897

KING JAMES'S AND LANDPORT GATES, PORTSMOUTH
HAMPSHIRE – PO1 2EJ

Two ornamental gateways, once part of Portsmouth's defences, King James's Gate

KING JAMES'S AND LANDPORT GATES, PORTSMOUTH

(of 1687) has been moved, but Landport Gate (1760), once the principal entrance to Portsmouth and possibly based on a design by Nicholas Hawksmoor, remains in its original position.

OPENING TIMES

Any reasonable time in daylight hours; exterior viewing only

VISIT US

Direction: King James's Gate forms the entrance to United Services Recreation Ground (officers), Burnaby Rd; Landport Gate as above, men's entrance on St George's Road

Train: Portsmouth Harbour ¼ mile

Bus: First services 1, 8, 15, 16 and Stagecoach service 23 and 700 pass Landport Gate. First services 7, 8, 15, 19 and Stagecoach 23 pass within a short walk of the King James Gate

ACQ.1930 🐾

MAP Page 338 (6C)
OS Map 196, OL29/119
King James's Gate: SZ636999
Landport Gate: SZ634998

MEDIEVAL MERCHANT'S HOUSE, SOUTHAMPTON
HAMPSHIRE – SO1 0AT

John Fortin, a merchant who traded with Bordeaux, started building this house c. 1290.

MEDIEVAL MERCHANT'S HOUSE

A residence and place of business, it stood on one of the busiest streets in medieval Southampton. Now restored to its mid-14th-century appearance by the removal of later additions, it is equipped with replica period furnishings. It stands near the medieval town wall, built to defend Southampton against seaborne attacks. Netley Abbey (p.54), Calshot Castle (p.51) and Hurst Castle (p.52) are all within reasonable travelling distance.

NON-MEMBERS

Adult	£4.00
Concession	£3.60
Child	£2.40

OPENING TIMES

29 Mar-30 Sep, Sun only	12pm-5pm
Easter Sunday	10am-5pm

VISIT US

Direction: 58 French St, ¼ mile S of city centre, just off Castle Way (between High St and Bugle St)

Train: Southampton ¾ mile

Bus: Unilink U1, U6 & First 1, 2, 2A, 3, 6 all stop very close by

Tel: 02380 221503

Local Tourist Information Southampton: 02380 833333

ACQ.1973 ⌷ 🚶 ⬆ 🐾 ♿

Disabled access (two steps). Ground floor only.

MAP Page 338 (6B)
OS Map 196, OL22: SU419112

NETLEY ABBEY
HAMPSHIRE – SO31 5FB

The most complete surviving Cistercian monastery in southern England, with almost all the walls of its 13th-century church still standing, along with many monastic buildings. After the Dissolution, the buildings were converted into the mansion house of Sir William Paulet. Even in ruins, the abbey continued to be influential, inspiring Romantic writers and poets. A free downloadable audio tour is available from the English Heritage website.

OPENING TIMES

29 Mar-30 Sep, daily	10am-6pm
1 Oct-31 Mar, Sat-Sun	10am-4pm
24-26 Dec and 1 Jan	Closed

VISIT US

Direction: In Netley; 4 miles SE of Southampton, facing Southampton Water

Train: Netley 1 mile

Bus: First service 6

Tel: 0870 333 1181

ACQ.1922 🐾 🚶 🚻 P ♿ ⚠

Toilets (nearby, across the road near the estuary).

Gravel car park, limited spaces.

MAP Page 338 (6C)
OS Map 196, OL22: SU453090

PORTCHESTER CASTLE
SEE FEATURE OPPOSITE

ROYAL GARRISON CHURCH, PORTSMOUTH
HAMPSHIRE – PO1 2NJ

Royal Garrison Church was constructed c. 1212 as part of a hospital complex. Although the nave was badly damaged in a 1941 fire-bomb raid on Portsmouth, the chancel remains roofed and furnished.

Managed by the Friends of the Royal Garrison.

OPENING TIMES

29 Mar-30 Sep, Mon-Sat	11am-4pm

Contact EH customer services regarding access at other times

VISIT US

Direction: In Portsmouth; on Grand Parade S of High St

Train: Portsmouth Harbour ¾ mile

Bus: First services 1, 16, 19 and Stagecoach 700 pass within a short walk

Tel: 0870 333 1181

ACQ.1970 P 🐾 ♿

Parking (nearby).

MAP Page 338 (6C)
OS Map 196, OL29/119: SZ633992

SILCHESTER ROMAN CITY WALLS AND AMPHITHEATRE
HAMPSHIRE

Originally a tribal centre of the Iron Age Atrebates, Silchester became the large and important Roman town of Calleva Atrebatum. Unlike most Roman towns, it was never re-occupied or built over after its abandonment in the 5th century, so archaeological investigations give an unusually complete picture of its development. The complete circuit of its 3rd-century walls, among the best-preserved Roman town defences in England and 2½ km (1½ miles) long, can still be traced, although none of

the buildings within them survive above ground. Outside them are the remains of a Roman amphitheatre, which provided seating for over 4500 spectators. A free downloadable audio tour is available from the English Heritage website.

OPENING TIMES
Any reasonable time in daylight hours

VISIT US

Direction: On a minor road, 1 mile E of Silchester

Train: Bramley or Mortimer, both 2¾ miles

Bus: Stagecoach Hampshire 14 to Silchester (within ½ mile). Alternatively Reading Transport service 2/2A to Mortimer then 2 mile walk

ACQ.1965 🐾 P

Parking – prior notice of tall vehicles (coaches and minibuses) wishing to use car park required (car park operated by Hampshire County Council – contact 0118 970 0132 to raise height barrier).

MAP Page 338 (4C)
OS Map 175, 159: SU639624

SOUTHWICK PRIORY
HAMPSHIRE

Remains of a wealthy Augustinian priory, originally founded at Portchester: once a famous place of pilgrimage. Only part of the refectory wall survives.

OPENING TIMES
Any reasonable time in daylight hours

VISIT US

Direction: Fully accessible through Southwick village, signposted. Please park in car park opposite

Bus: The only public transport is the Southwick Taxishare service 38

ACQ.1970

MAP Page 338 (6C)
OS Map 196, 119: SU629084

VISIT US

Direction: On the S side of Portchester off A27; Junction 11 on M27

Train: Portchester 1 mile

Bus: First service 3 to within ¼ mile

Tel: 02392 378291

NON-MEMBERS

Adult	£5.00
Concession	£4.50
Child	£3.00
Family	£13.00

OPENING TIMES

29 Mar-30 Sep, daily	10am-6pm
1 Oct-3 Nov, daily	10am-5pm
4 Nov-16 Feb, Sat-Sun	10am-4pm
17-21 Feb, Mon-Fri	10am-4pm
22 Feb-31 Mar, Sat-Sun	10am-4pm
24-26 Dec and 1 Jan	Closed

Disabled access (grounds and lower levels only).

Dogs on leads (outer grounds only).

Toilets (facilities are in the car park, operated by Fareham District Council).

Portchester Castle's commanding location has made it a major factor in the Solent's defences for hundreds of years.

The most impressive and best-preserved of the Roman 'Saxon Shore' forts, Portchester Castle was originally built in the late 3rd century. Covering an area of nearly ten acres, it is the only Roman stronghold in northern Europe whose walls still mainly stand to their full six metre height, complete with most of their original 20 towers. Subsequently housing a Saxon settlement, the huge waterside fortress became a Norman castle in the 12th century, when a formidable tower-keep was built in one corner.

Portchester Castle was in the front line throughout the Hundred Years War, serving as a staging-post for expeditions to France and repelling cross-Channel raids. Richard II transformed part of the castle into a palace in 1396, and Henry V used it as an embarkation point for the Agincourt campaign in 1415. Thereafter it saw little action, but was used to house troops in the Civil War, and prisoners of war during the Dutch and Napoleonic Wars and the Anglo-American War of 1812-14.

An exhibition in the keep interprets the history of the castle and Portchester village, and displays finds excavated on site. The inclusive audio tour explains life in the castle over the centuries, from the point of view of some of the people who worked or were incarcerated there.

MAP Page 338 (6C)
OS Map 196, OL29/119: SU625046

ST MARY'S CHURCH, ITCHEN STOKE
HAMPSHIRE – SO24 0QU

© CCT

Inspired by the Sainte Chapelle (Paris), this dazzling and colourful Victorian jewel overwhelms the senses. Inside is an exhilarating, kaleidoscopic wonderland of pattern and colour from floor to ceiling, with dazzling stained glass, an unusual floor-tile maze and a richly painted roof.

Owned and managed by The Churches Conservation Trust.

OPENING TIMES

Open daily	10am-4pm

VISIT US

Train: Winchester 5¼ miles

Bus: Velvet bus service 67

10 mins from The Grange at Northington

MAP Page 338 (5C)
OS Map 185, 132: SU559323

TITCHFIELD ABBEY
HAMPSHIRE – PO15 5RA

The ruins of a 13th-century abbey of Premonstratensian canons, later converted into a Tudor mansion. The church was rebuilt as a grand turreted gatehouse. Information panels tell the story of the monastery and its conversion into a mansion. A free downloadable audio tour is available from the English Heritage website.

OPENING TIMES

1 Apr-30 Sep, daily	10am-5pm
1 Oct-31 Mar, daily	10am-4pm
24-26 Dec and 1 Jan	Closed

VISIT US

Direction: Located ½ mile N of Titchfield, off A27

Train: Fareham 2 miles

Bus: First services 4, X4, 26 & 28. Alight Titchfield by-pass and then use public footpath

Tel: 0870 333 1181

ACQ.1923 🚻 **P** ♿

MAP Page 338 (6C)
OS Map 196, 119: SU542067

WOLVESEY CASTLE (OLD BISHOP'S PALACE)
HAMPSHIRE

Wolvesey has been an important residence of the wealthy and powerful Bishops of Winchester since Anglo-Saxon times. Standing next to Winchester Cathedral, the extensive surviving ruins of the palace date largely from the 12th-century work of Bishop Henry of Blois. The last great occasion here was on 25 July 1554, when Queen Mary and Philip of Spain held their wedding breakfast in the East Hall. A free downloadable audio tour is available from the English Heritage website.

OPENING TIMES

29 Mar-3 Nov, daily	10am-5pm
4 Nov-31 Mar	Closed

VISIT US

Direction: ¾ mile SE of Winchester Cathedral, next to the Bishop's Palace; access from College St

Train: Winchester ¾ mile

Bus: From surrounding areas

Tel: 0870 333 1181

ACQ.1962 🚻 🏕 ⚠

MAP Page 338 (5C)
OS Map 185, 132: SU484291

KENT

ALL SAINTS' CHURCH, WALDERSHARE
KENT – CT15 5AT

© CCT Ian Sumner

This pretty church is an ideal resting point for walkers crossing the beautiful North Downs. The south chapel of 1697 contains a touching memorial of life-size marble figures of a husband and wife holding hands. Fantastical monuments, murals and stained glass can be found throughout.

Owned and managed by The Churches Conservation Trust.

OPENING TIMES
Open daily   10.30am-3.30pm

VISIT US
Train: Shepherdswell 3 miles

Bus: Stagecoach services 88, 89 and Regent service 541

10 mins from Dover Castle

MAP Page 339 (5J)
OS Map 179, 138: TR298483

BAYHAM OLD ABBEY
KENT – TN3 8BE

The impressive ruins of an abbey of Premonstratensian 'white canons', on the Kent-Sussex border. They include much of the 13th to 15th-century church, the chapter house and a picturesque 14th-century gatehouse. Now set in a landscape designed by Humphry Repton, the famous landscape gardener, who also planned the grounds of Kenwood House in London. Rooms in the 'Georgian Gothick' dower house are also open to visitors.

NON-MEMBERS
Adult	£4.40
Concession	£4.00
Child	£2.60

OPENING TIMES
29 Mar-30 Sep, daily	10am-5pm
1 Oct-28 Mar	Closed

VISIT US
Direction: 1¾ miles W of Lamberhurst, off B2169

Train: Frant 4 miles then bus 256

Bus: Autocar 256

Tel: 01892 890381

Local Tourist Information
Tunbridge Wells: 01892 515675

ACQ.1961

Disabled access (grounds only over rough ground and lower floor of Dower House via 4 steps).

MAP Page 339 (5G)
OS Map 188, 136: TQ650365

DEAL CASTLE
SEE FEATURE – PAGE 62

DOVER CASTLE
SEE FEATURE – PAGE 58

DOWN HOUSE – SEE THE HOME OF CHARLES DARWIN
SEE FEATURE – PAGE 64

DYMCHURCH MARTELLO TOWER
KENT – TN29 0NL

One of 103 ingeniously-designed artillery towers built from 1805 at vulnerable points around the south and east coasts to resist threatened Napoleonic invasion. Exterior viewing only.

OPENING TIMES
Interior viewing by appointment only – please call 01304 211067

VISIT US
Direction: Access from Dymchurch High Street

Train: Sandling 7 miles; Dymchurch (Romney, Hythe and Dymchurch Railway) ¾ mile

Bus: Stagecoach in East Kent 'The Wave' services 101, 102 & 105

ACQ.1959

MAP Page 339 (5H)
OS Map 189, 138: TR102292

'The Key to England' for over nine centuries, the mighty fortress of Dover Castle displays at its core a dazzling evocation of a medieval royal palace. The Secret Wartime Tunnels in the White Cliffs beneath the castle now host an astonishingly realistic presentation of the 'Miracle of Dunkirk', master-minded here in 1940.

VISIT US

Address: Dover Castle, Castle Hill, Dover, Kent CT16 1HU

Direction: E of Dover town centre

Train: Dover Priory 1½ miles

Bus: Stagecoach in East Kent 15, 15X, 80, 80A; Eastonways 593

Tel: 01304 211067

Local Tourist Information
Dover: 01304 205108

NON-MEMBERS

Adult	£17.00
Concession	£15.30
Child	£10.20
Family	£44.20

Price includes Secret Wartime Tunnels tour. Additional charges for members and non-members may apply on event days

OPENING TIMES

29 Mar-31 Jul, daily	10am-6pm
1-31 Aug, daily	9.30am-6pm
1-30 Sep, daily	10am-6pm
1 Oct-3 Nov, daily	10am-5pm
4 Nov-16 Feb, Sat-Sun	10am-4pm
17-23 Feb, daily	10am-4pm
24 Feb-31 Mar, Sat-Sun	10am-4pm
24-26 Dec and 1 Jan	Closed

Last admission 1 hour before closing

The Great Tower is free-flow and self-guided. Costumed live interpreters welcome you at the Great Tower on selected days and lifelike hologram characters at all other times. The Secret Wartime Tunnels 'Operation Dynamo' tours are part-guided by site staff, and numbers per tour are limited to 30 people, setting off at approximately 10 minute intervals (tour lasts approximately 50 minutes). Due to the immersive nature of these visits, no independent guiding is allowed in these areas. However, tour leaders of groups of younger visitors must stay with their parties at all times. Access to the Underground Hospital (separate access from Operation Dynamo) is by guided tour only (limited to 30 people and lasting approximately 20 minutes). Access to Operation Dynamo and Underground Hospital is included in the admission price. At peak times, there may be queues at the popular new tunnel experiences. Please ask site staff upon arrival for the best time to visit the tunnels on that specific day. Groups of 11+ are asked to call the site in advance.

Please refer to the Dover Castle web page or ring the site directly for information on accessibility. Mobility scooters, wheelchair routes and guides are available on site.

Dogs on leads (restricted areas only).

We advise you to wear comfortable shoes.

MAP Page 339 (5J)
OS Map 179, 138: TR325419

⌂ HOLIDAY COTTAGES
AT **DOVER CASTLE**

Peverell's Tower *(see above)* was
at one time a prison. Today it
sleeps two in liberating comfort.

To stay at the **Sergeant Major's
House** is to be surrounded by
hundreds of years of history. This
elegant and spacious four-storey
Georgian building sleeps six.
Set just inside the Western
Outer Curtain Wall.

Commanding the shortest sea crossing
between England and the continent, Dover
Castle boasts a long and immensely eventful
history. Its spectacular site atop the famous
'White Cliffs' was probably an Iron Age hill
fort, and still houses a Roman lighthouse. The
Anglo-Saxon church beside it was probably
part of a Saxon fortified settlement, converted
soon after 1066 into a Norman earthwork
castle. Thereafter Dover Castle was garrisoned
uninterruptedly until 1958, a record equalled
only by the Tower of London and Windsor
Castle. From 1740 its defences were updated
in response to every European war involving
Britain, and were crucially tested during the
darkest days of World War II.

Operation Dynamo: Rescue from Dunkirk

At the beginning of World War II the network
of chalk-cut tunnels deep beneath the castle –
begun in 1797 to counter the threat of
invasion from Napoleonic France – was

recommissioned and further enlarged. Housing
a hospital, they crucially also became Vice
Admiral Bertram Ramsay's bomb-proof naval
headquarters, where a handful of men and
women planned the activities of a determined
squadron of Royal Navy ships whose task was
to keep the enemy out of the Straits of Dover.

There, at 6:57pm on May 26th 1940, a
teleprinter spluttered into life. The words of
its brief message – 'Operation Dynamo is to
commence' – were meaningless to all but a
few. One of the few was Vice Admiral Ramsay,
and this was the bad news he had been
expecting. The British Army and its French
and Belgian allies were trapped at Dunkirk,
backs to the sea, fighting for their lives in a
shrinking pocket of land. The task of rescuing
them demanded rapid planning and round-the-
clock working to assemble and send a huge
improvised fleet of ships, naval and civilian,
large and small, to Dunkirk, under attack from

air, sea and land. Over 300,000 soldiers were depending on Ramsay, his HQ staff and the sailors in his ships.

Visitors can now make the adventurous journey into the tunnels up to 26 metres beneath the castle, and immerse themselves in the drama of the daring evacuation that followed. Film presentations and displays vividly recreate the outbreak of war in 1939 and the Battle of France in Spring 1940, when allied forces came close to total destruction by the advancing German blitzkrieg. See the pivotal part the Secret Wartime Tunnels played in *Operation Dynamo*. Then, in the very place where it was planned, visitors witness with breathtaking realism the amazing beach rescue operation happening all around them.

They can also take a fascinating guided tour of the (separately accessed) Underground Hospital within the tunnels, and relive the tension as a surgeon battles to save an injured pilot. Find out more about the 'Miracle of Dunkirk', and how it snatched victory from the jaws of defeat, in the *Wartime Tunnels Uncovered* exhibition, featuring the recorded voices of many who actually took part, from rescued soldiers and skippers of 'Little Ships' to those who welcomed the battered forces home. A new guidebook to 'Frontline Fortress Dover' is available in the Secret Wartime Tunnels shop, specialising in 1940s books and material.

The Great Tower

Above ground Dover Castle is essentially the greatest medieval fortress in England, created by King Henry II and his Plantagenet successors. At its heart stands the mighty Great Tower, the grandest and among the last of the keeps raised by the kings of England during the 11th and 12th centuries. Built between 1180 and 1185, this symbol of kingly power was also a palace designed for royal ceremony. Here, Henry could welcome and impress distinguished visitors to England – particularly noble pilgrims travelling to the new shrine in Canterbury Cathedral of St Thomas Becket.

The entire interior of Henry's Great Tower palace has been recreated as it might have appeared when newly completed. Visitors begin their tour in the exhibition near the foot of the towering keep, where imaginative interactive displays tell the dramatic story of Henry II and his turbulent brood – *A Family at War*. A man of superhuman energy and violent rages, Henry ruled an empire stretching from the Scottish Borders to the Pyrenees, but proved unable to master his own quarrelsome and treacherous family. Children can help European pilgrims reach Becket's shrine at Canterbury and visitors can 'Ask the Experts' about the recreated rooms, of which a virtual tour is provided for those unable to tour the Great Tower itself.

Ascending the stairs into the Great Tower, visitors meet the first of the many lifelike projected figures which help to guide them round the six great recreated rooms and several lesser chambers of the palace. Among the most spectacular is the King's Hall, dominated by its canopied throne and decked with wall hangings and recreations of contemporary furniture, all brilliantly coloured. The vibrant colours of the Great Tower's interiors, reflecting medieval reality, are indeed the most striking aspect of the re-creation.

The tour continues via the Royal Chapel to the King's Chamber, focussed on the royal bed. Next come the Guests' Bedchamber and the Guest Hall, shown ready for a feast. The cavernous ground floor is fascinatingly set as the fully-equipped royal Kitchen, Brewery and Bakehouse, while the Armoury displays replicas of the weapons used by Henry's household knights. On selected days, visitors may also encounter costumed live interpreters – including Henry himself – throughout the Great Tower.

A Mighty Fortress

Visitors can then climb to the Great Tower's roof for panoramic views over the castle's immense complex of fortifications, with busy Dover harbour below. Around his impressive keep Henry built a powerful inner curtain wall, and beyond that an outer curtain wall. These three mutually-supporting lines of defence made Dover the very first 'concentric' fortress in western Europe. Its defences were severely tested during the epic sieges of 1216-17, when the castle resisted ten months of attack. Intrepid visitors can still descend into the 'Medieval Tunnels', burrowed beneath the castle during and after the 1216-7 siege.

The cliff-top Admiralty Lookout also played an important role in both World Wars. Inside, a First World War Fire Command Post has been recreated, with displays on the castle's role as a naval signal station.

The Stone Hut, built in 1912 for the Royal Garrison Artillery, is now used as an archaeological store. On the first Friday of every month (or by pre-arranged booking), visitors can view changing exhibitions of treasures from across the region, including artefacts from both World War II and the Cold War.

All this, and very much more, makes Dover Castle well worth a whole day's exploration.

🎬 *The Other Boleyn Girl*, starring Natalie Portman and Scarlett Johanssen; Zeffirelli's *Hamlet*, starring Mel Gibson; and *To Kill a King*, starring Dougray Scott.

DEAL CASTLE KENT – CT14 7BA

EYNSFORD CASTLE
KENT – DA4 0AA

Deal Castle is one of the finest Tudor artillery castles in England. It is among the earliest and most elaborate of a chain of coastal forts, which also includes Calshot, Camber, Walmer and Pendennis Castles. Most were built 'with all speed, and without sparing any cost' between 1539 and 1542 by order of King Henry VIII, who feared an invasion by European Catholic powers. Its squat, rounded bastions were designed to deflect incoming cannon balls, and acted as platforms from which to fire increasingly sophisticated artillery pieces. Deal is also equipped for close-quarter defence, with no less than 145 embrasures for firearms. The fort guarded the sheltered anchorage of 'the Downs' – the stretch of water between the shore and the hazardous Goodwin Sands, a graveyard of ships.

The foreign invasion never materialised, but Deal Castle saw hard fighting during the Civil War (1648). Taken by forces from the rebel Royalist fleet, it was twice besieged by Parliamentarians, and finally surrendered after the bloody repulse of a relief attempt.

Today, it is a fascinating castle to explore, with long, dark passages, battlements and a massive basement in which an absorbing exhibition is housed. A pleasant cycle path links Deal and Walmer Castles along the beachfront.

NON-MEMBERS

Adult	£5.00
Concession	£4.50
Child	£3.00
Family	£13.00

OPENING TIMES

29 Mar-30 Sep, daily	10am-6pm
1 Oct-3 Nov, daily	10am-5pm
4 Nov-31 Mar, Sat-Sun	10am-4pm
24-26 Dec and 1 Jan	Closed

VISIT US

Direction: SW of Deal town centre

Train: Deal ½ mile

Bus: Stagecoach East Kent services 12, 13, 13A, 14, 14A, 15, 15A, 15X, 80, 80A, 82, 82A; Regent Coaches 541, 542, 544 & Eastonways 593

Tel: 01304 372762

ACQ.1904 🎧 🍴 🖼 🚶 🚻 ✕ 📷 ♿
⚠ OVP

Audio tours (also available in Dutch, French and German).

Disabled access (courtyards and ground floor only, parking available).

MAP Page 339 (5J)
OS Map 179, 150: TR378522

The substantial stone walls of a very early Norman 'enclosure castle', begun c. 1085-7 and unusually little altered by later building works. This rare survival stands in an attractive village setting, not far from Lullingstone Roman Villa (p.67).

OPENING TIMES

30 Mar-30 Sep, daily	10am-6pm
1 Oct-31 Mar, daily	10am-4pm
24-26 Dec and 1 Jan	Closed

VISIT US

Direction: In Eynsford, off A225

Train: Eynsford 1 mile

Bus: Arriva bus 478; Go-Coach 421; Nu Venture 405 (Wed)

ACQ.1948 🍴 P ♿

MAP Page 339 (4F)
OS Map 177, 162: TQ542658

FAVERSHAM STONE CHAPEL (OUR LADY OF ELVERTON)
KENT

FAVERSHAM STONE CHAPEL (OUR LADY OF ELVERTON)

The ruins of the small Anglo-Saxon and medieval chapel of Stone-next-Faversham, incorporating within its fabric the remains of a 4th-century Romano-British pagan mausoleum. It lay close to the probable site of the small Roman town of Durolevum and its Roman cemetery at Ospringe, finds from which can be seen at Maison Dieu (see p.68).

Managed by The Faversham Society.

www.faversham.org/society

OPENING TIMES
Any reasonable time in daylight hours

VISIT US
Direction: In field immediately N of A2 just W of Ospringe and opposite Faversham Road

Train: Faversham 1½ miles

Bus: Chalkwell 324, Arriva/ Chalkwell 333

Tel: 01795 534542

E-mail: ticfaversham@btconnect.com

ACQ.1972

MAP Page 339 (4H)
OS Map 178, 149: TQ992613

THE HOME OF CHARLES DARWIN, DOWN HOUSE
SEE FEATURE – PAGE 64

HORNE'S PLACE CHAPEL
KENT

HORNE'S PLACE CHAPEL

A rare survival of a fine domestic chapel, built for William Horne in 1366 and attached to his timber-framed manor house, which was attacked during the Peasants' Revolt of 1381. The house and chapel are privately owned.

OPENING TIMES
By prior arrangement; please call 01304 211067

VISIT US
Direction: 1½ miles N of Appledore

Train: Appledore 2½ miles

Bus: Stagecoach East Kent service 11B (one return weekday journey) & Autocar/Kent Coach Tours service 293 (Mon, Thu, Fri only)

ACQ.1950

Parking (nearby).

MAP Page 339 (5H)
OS Map 189, 125: TQ958309

KIT'S COTY HOUSE AND LITTLE KIT'S COTY HOUSE
KENT

© Kelvin Trundle

The remains of two megalithic burial chambers, impressive Kit's Coty has three uprights and a massive capstone; Little

KIT'S COTY HOUSE AND LITTLE KIT'S COTY HOUSE

Kit's Coty, alias the Countless Stones, is now a jumble of sarsens.

OPENING TIMES
Any reasonable time in daylight hours

VISIT US
Direction: W of A229 2 miles N of Maidstone

Train: Aylesford 2½ miles

Bus: Arriva 101 & 142; Nu Venture 150

ACQ.1883

MAP Page 339 (4G)
OS Map 178/188, 148
Kit's Coty House: TQ745608
Little Kit's Coty House: TQ744604

KNIGHTS TEMPLAR CHURCH, DOVER KENT

The foundations of a small medieval church, traditionally the site of King John's submission to the Papal Legate in 1213.

VISIT US
Direction: On the Western Heights above Dover

Train: Dover Priory ¾ mile

Bus: Eastonways service 593 from Dover town centre

Tel: 01304 211067

OPENING TIMES
Any reasonable time in daylight hours

ACQ.1968

Dogs on leads (restricted areas only).

MAP Page 339 (5J)
OS Map 179, 138: TR313407

LULLINGSTONE ROMAN VILLA
SEE FEATURE – PAGE 67

A delightful place to visit in itself, Down House is also a site of outstanding international significance. Here the famous naturalist Charles Darwin lived with his family for forty years; here he worked on his revolutionary theories; and here he wrote *On the Origin of Species by Means of Natural Selection* – the book which shook the Victorian world and has influenced our thinking ever since.

VISIT US

Address: Down House, Luxted Road, Downe, Kent BR6 7JT

Direction: Luxted Rd, Downe; off A21 or A233

Train: Chelsfield 3¾ miles, Orpington 3¾ miles

Bus: TfL bus R8 from Orpington passes; TfL bus 146 from Bromley North & South terminates in Downe village ½ mile from property

Tel: 01689 859119

NON-MEMBERS

Adult	£10.00
Concession	£9.00
Child	£6.00
Family	£26.00

OPENING TIMES

29 Mar-30 Jun, Wed-Sun & Bank Hols	10am-5pm
1 Jul-31 Aug, daily	10am-5pm
1 Sep-3 Nov, Wed-Sun	10am-5pm
4 Nov-16 Feb, Sat-Sun	10am-4pm
17-23 Feb, Wed-Fri	10am-4pm
24 Feb-31 Mar, Sat-Sun	10am-4pm
24-26 Dec and 1 Jan	Closed

Please note: on open days, gardens can be accessed from 11am in the summer and 10am in the winter

ACQ.1996

Audio tour is the multimedia tour.

Parking (plus space for one coach).

MAP Page 339 (4F)
OS Map 177/187,147: TQ431611

Visitors are guided round Darwin's family rooms by a hand-held multimedia tour, narrated by Sir David Attenborough and Andrew Marr. The tour also includes the extensive gardens – Darwin's 'outdoor laboratory' and the place where he made many of his discoveries.

Stop off at the tearoom, situated in Darwin's kitchen area, for a refreshing break before exploring the grounds.

Darwin's work and personality are vividly reflected throughout the house and gardens. The ground floor rooms have been recreated as they appeared when he lived here with his indefatigably supportive wife Emma – a member of the renowned Wedgwood family – and their many children. They include the 'Old Study' where Darwin wrote his most famous books, following a rigid routine despite chronic illness and frequent good-natured interruptions by his children. It still displays his chair, writing desk and many personal items. The family's Drawing Room – with Emma's grand piano – Billiard Room and Dining Room are also on show, likewise mainly furnished with items original to the house.

The video guide includes commentaries by experts, animations, film footage and games for all the family. It is one of many exciting interactive developments at the Home of Charles Darwin introduced in 2009 to celebrate the 200th anniversary of Darwin's birth and the 150th anniversary of the publication of On the Origin of Species.

'Uncovering Origin' Exhibition

An award-winning exhibition on the house's first floor covers Darwin's life, his scientific work, and the controversy which it provoked. It includes many previously unseen objects, with highlights including manuscript pages from the On the Origin of Species; Darwin's hat, microscope and notebooks; and a copy of Das Kapital inscribed to him by Karl Marx.

Beginning with an introduction to Darwin, his place in Victorian science, and the impact of his theories, the displays continue with his famous five-year voyage aboard the Beagle in 1831-6, including a full-scale recreation of his ship's cabin. The notebooks and journals compiled on this round-the-world voyage have been digitised and annotated, allowing visitors to explore them page by page. Further displays highlight the On the Origin of Species, a book which sold out its first edition immediately and consolidated Darwin's international recognition and notoriety. They also examine how his theories were publicised and defended, principally via letter writing. Visitors can explore some of his key ideas (including his investigations into the expression of emotions in humans and animals) through hands-on interactives and installations. The Darwin children's schoolroom celebrates family life at Down House.

There is also an education room, available for family learning at weekends, and a resources room for those interested in delving deeper.

Experiments in the Gardens

By no means the stereotypically stern Victorian father, Darwin involved his children in his practical experiments in the extensive grounds of Down House. Visitors too can now follow these via the video guide, beginning with Darwin's 'weed garden' illustrating the struggle for existence in nature.

The sundial amid pretty flowerbeds highlights Emma Darwin's role as a gardener; a surviving mulberry tree recalls family traditions; and a 'lawn experiment' investigates proliferation of plant species. Further afield is the 'worm stone', which Darwin used to measure undermining by earthworms.

The nearby hot-house features some of Darwin's most fascinating experiments, involving carnivorous plants, exotic orchids and climbing species. The curiously-shaped tennis court evokes his family and social life, and in the summer there are working beehives in the laboratory. After a tour of the extensive kitchen gardens, visitors finally reach what is for many a place of pilgrimage: the wooded Sandwalk, Darwin's famous 'thinking path', which he paced five times a day while working out his theories.

Virtual Access

Gain virtual access to Darwin's world through the Home of Charles Darwin pages on the English Heritage website. Features include interactive digital highlights from one of the rarest Darwin manuscript collections in the world, including his *Beagle* notebooks and diary, plus a virtual tour of parts of the house and grounds.

Please note: No photography is allowed inside the house.

Unfortunately picnics are not allowed in the grounds, as they are part of a 'Site of Importance for Nature Conservation', nurturing many important protected species, including fungi.

VISIT US

Direction: ½ mile SW of Eynsford; off A225; off junction 3 of M25

Bus: Arriva bus 478; Go-Coach 421; Nu Venture 405 (Wed)

Train: Eynsford 2 miles

Tel: 01322 863467

NON-MEMBERS

Adult	£6.20
Concession	£5.60
Child	£3.70
Family	£16.10

OPENING TIMES

29 Mar-30 Sep, daily	10am-6pm
1 Oct-3 Nov, daily	10am-5pm
4 Nov-16 Feb, Sat-Sun	10am-4pm
17-21 Feb, Mon-Fri	10am-4pm
22 Feb-31 Mar, Sat-Sun	10am-4pm
24-26 Dec and 1 Jan	Closed

ACQ.1958

Parking charge £2.50 to non-members.

Among the most outstanding Roman villa survivals in Britain, Lullingstone Roman Villa has been vividly re-displayed, providing a unique – and all-weather – opportunity to trace Roman domestic life over three centuries.

Set in the attractive surroundings of the Darent Valley, the villa was begun in about AD 100, and developed to suit the tastes and beliefs of successive wealthy owners. These may have included the family of Pertinax, Governor of Britain and later Roman Emperor for just 87 days in AD 193. Additions included a heated bath-suite and a remarkable underground pagan 'cult-room', including a rare painting of three water-nymphs, by far the oldest wall-painting in English Heritage care.

The villa reached its peak of luxury in the mid-4th century, when a big new dining room was added. This still displays spectacular mosaics, including *Europa and the Bull* and *Bellerophon Killing the Chimera*. By now Christians, the owners also created a 'house-church' above the pagan cult-room: the wall-paintings discovered here are among the earliest surviving evidence for Christianity in Britain. Pagan worship may, however, have continued, suggesting a relaxed relationship between the old and new faiths.

All this is appealingly interpreted in the galleries overlooking the fully excavated remains. These display Lullingstone Roman Villa's fascinating and recently-returned collection of Roman artefacts, enlivened by paintings by the award-winning children's illustrator, Jane Ray. Children and other visitors can also play Roman board games, handle original building materials and try on Roman costumes. A specially-commissioned film and light show brings the villa to life, lighting up areas of the remains as the film reveals how they were once used.

MAP Page 339 (4F)
OS Map 177/188, 147/162:
TQ530651

MAISON DIEU
KENT – ME13 8TS

This 13th and 16th-century flint and timber-framed building is virtually all that survives of a much larger complex. It included a 'hospital' for the overnight lodging of pilgrims to Canterbury; a royal suite where many crowned heads stayed on their way to or from the continent; and a school. In layout and appearance it was much like a small monastery. The present building now known as the Maison Dieu is thought to have been a chantry-priest's house. It houses a museum focussing on the Maison Dieu foundation itself and its immediate neighbourhood, and on the extensive finds made during excavations at the main complex and at an important Roman cemetery nearby.

Managed by The Faversham Society.

www.faversham.org/society

NON-MEMBERS
Adult	£2.00
Concession	£1.00

OPENING TIMES
29 Mar-3 Nov, Sat-Sun, & Bank Hols	2pm-5pm

Group visits at other times by appointment

VISIT US
Direction: On main A2 on W corner of Water Lane in village of Ospringe. Public car park 300yds W

Train: Faversham ¾ mile

Bus: Chalkwell 324, Arriva/Chalkwell 333

Tel: 01795 534542

E-mail: ticfaversham@btconnect.com

ACQ.1947 **E** 🚶 🚶 ✂

MAP Page 339 (4H)
OS Map 178, 149: TR003609

MILTON CHANTRY
KENT – DA12 2BH

Mainly encased in brick but still retaining its 14th-century timber roof, this was in turn part of a hospital, a chantry chapel, a public house and a Georgian barracks before its basement became a World War II gas decontamination chamber. The building, in Gravesham's Heritage Quarter, gives a fascinating insight into the borough's heritage.

Managed by Gravesham Borough Council.

OPENING TIMES
6 Apr-29 Sep, Sat-Sun & Bank Hols	12pm-5pm

Admission outside these times by appointment

VISIT US
Direction: In New Tavern Fort Gardens; E of central Gravesend, off A226

Train: Gravesend ¾ mile

Bus: Arriva, Red Route and Nu Venture services pass within a short distance

Tel: 01474 337442

ACQ.1972 🎧 ✂ ⚠

MAP Page 339 (4G)
OS Map 177/178, 162/163: TQ653743

OLD SOAR MANOR
KENT – TN15 0QX

A small but complete portion of a stone manor house built c. 1290. The first floor 'solar' private chamber, with attendant chapel and garderobe, stands over a vaulted undercroft.

Managed by the National Trust on behalf of English Heritage.

OPENING TIMES
1 Apr-30 Sep, Sat-Thu	10am-6pm

OLD SOAR MANOR

VISIT US
Direction: 1 mile E of Plaxtol

Train: Borough Green and Wrotham 2½ miles

Bus: Autocar 222 Tonbridge – Borough Green; New Venture 404 from Sevenoaks. On both alight E end of Plaxtol, then ¾ mile by footpath

Tel: 01732 810378

ACQ.1948 ✂ **P**

Parking (limited).

MAP Page 339 (5G)
OS Map 188, 147/148: TQ619541

RECULVER TOWERS AND ROMAN FORT
KENT – CT6 6SS

An imposing landmark, the twin 12th-century towers of the ruined church stand amid the remains of an important Roman 'Saxon Shore' fort and a Saxon monastery. Richborough Roman Fort is within easy travelling distance. Download the free audio tour from our website.

Managed by Canterbury City Council.

OPENING TIMES
Any reasonable time in daylight hours; external viewing only

Reculver Centre open Sat & Sun 11am-3pm; longer opening hours from Easter and during school holidays – please call 01227 740676 for more information

VISIT US
Direction: At Reculver; 3 miles E of Herne Bay; signed off Thanet Way A299

Train: Herne Bay 4 miles

Bus: Stagecoach in East Kent 7, 7A and Kent Top Travel 36

Tel: 01227 740676

ACQ.1925 ✂ 🖥 🚶 🚻 **P** ♿

Disabled access (grounds only – long slope up from car park).

Please note: parking (pay and display). Not EH.

MAP Page 339 (4J)
OS Map 179, 150: TR228693

VISIT US

Direction: At the A256/A257 roundabout, head for Sandwich then turn left onto Richborough Road and proceed for approx 1 mile

Train: Sandwich 2 miles

Bus: Stagecoach East Kent 87, 88 then walk using Stour Valley Walk/ Saxon Shore Way

Tel: 01304 612013

NON-MEMBERS

Adult	£5.00
Concession	£4.50
Child	£3.00
Family	£13.00

OPENING TIMES

Fort:

29 Mar-30 Sep, daily	10am-6pm
1 Oct-3 Nov, Wed-Sun	10am-5pm
4 Nov-31 Mar, Sat-Sun	10am-4pm
24-26 Dec and 1 Jan	Closed

Amphitheatre: Any reasonable time in daylight hours, access across grazed land from footpath; please call 01304 612013 for details

ACQ.1912

Dogs on leads (restricted areas only).

Evocatively sited amid the East Kent marshes, Richborough Roman Fort is the most symbolically important of all Roman sites in Britain, witnessing both the beginning and almost the end of Roman rule here. Now landlocked, in AD 43 it overlooked a sheltered channel where the invading Roman forces first came ashore. The line of the Roman foreshore, now two miles inland from the sea, was discovered in 2008 by English Heritage archaeologists digging just outside the fort wall.

The landing was commemorated by a mighty triumphal arch, whose foundations still survive: the arch also provided an impressive gateway for arrivals at what became the port of 'Rutupiae', the province's main point of entry.

By the mid-3rd century, however, Roman Britain was threatened by sea-borne raiders. A fort was therefore hastily created within the port. At first defended by the triple ditches still visible, but soon after by stone walls, this became one of the most important of the 'Saxon Shore' forts. It was also among the last to be regularly occupied: there was still a large Roman population here in the early 5th century.

You can choose to reach the fort as the Romans would have done, by boat. Boats sail from Sandwich, but not every day: please telephone the site to obtain details of the contractor.

MAP Page 339 (4J) OS Map 179, 150
Fort: TR324602
Amphitheatre: TR321598

ROCHESTER CASTLE
KENT – ME1 1SW

Strategically placed astride the London Road, guarding an important crossing of the River Medway, this imposing fortress has a complex history of destruction and rebuilding. Its mighty Norman tower-keep of Kentish ragstone was built c. 1127 by William of Corbeil, Archbishop of Canterbury, with the encouragement of Henry I. Consisting of three floors above a basement, it still stands 113 feet high. Attached is a tall protruding forebuilding, with its own set of defences to pass through before the keep itself could be entered at first floor level.

In 1215, garrisoned by rebel barons, the castle endured an epic siege by King John. Having first undermined the outer wall, John used the fat of 40 pigs to fire a mine under the keep, bringing its southern corner crashing down. Even then the defenders held out within the building, until they were eventually starved out after a resistance of nearly two months.

Rebuilt under Henry III and Edward I, the castle remained a viable fortress in the 15th century, but a century later it

ROCHESTER CASTLE

was decaying. Today it stands as a proud reminder of the history of Rochester, along with the nearby cathedral and Dickensian cobbled streets.

Managed by Medway Council.
www.visitmedway.org

NON-MEMBERS
Adult	£5.80
Concession	£3.70
Child	£3.70
Family	£15.30

OPENING TIMES
29 Mar-30 Sep, daily	10am-6pm
1 Oct-31 Mar, daily	10am-4pm
Last admission 45 mins before closing	
24-26 Dec and 1 Jan	Closed

VISIT US
Direction: By Rochester Bridge (A2); junction 1 of M2 and junction 2 of M25

Train: Rochester ½ mile

Bus: Services in Rochester are operated by Arriva and Nu Venture. Alight in Corporation Street within a short distance of the castle

Tel: 01634 332901

ACQ.1965

New guidebook.

Audio tours (small charge).

Toilets (in castle grounds).

MAP Page 339 (4G)
OS Map 178, 148/163: TQ741686

ST AUGUSTINE'S ABBEY
KENT – CT1 1TF

This great abbey, marking the rebirth of Christianity in southern England, was founded shortly after AD 597 by St Augustine. Originally created as a burial place for the Anglo-Saxon kings of Kent, it is part of the Canterbury

ST AUGUSTINE'S ABBEY

World Heritage Site, along with the cathedral and St Martin's Church.

The impressive and historically important abbey is situated outside the city walls, but should not be missed by visitors. You can also enjoy the museum and free audio tour.

NON-MEMBERS
Adult	£5.00
Concession	£4.50
Child	£3.00
Family	£13.00

OPENING TIMES
29 Mar-30 Sep, daily	10am-6pm
1 Oct-3 Nov, Wed-Sun	10am-5pm
4 Nov-31 Mar, Sat-Sun	10am-4pm
24-26 Dec and 1 Jan	Closed

VISIT US
Direction: In Canterbury, ¼ mile E of Cathedral Close

Train: Canterbury East and West, both ¾ mile

Bus: From surrounding areas

Tel: 01227 767345

Local Tourist Information
Canterbury: 01227 378100

ACQ.1938

Audio tours.

Disabled access (all site can be viewed, but some steps).

Parking (nearby).

MAP Page 339 (4J)
OS Map 179, 150: TR155578

ST AUGUSTINE'S ABBEY
CONDUIT HOUSE KENT

The Conduit House is part of the monastic waterworks which supplied nearby St Augustine's Abbey.

OPENING TIMES
Any reasonable time in daylight hours; exterior viewing only

ST AUGUSTINE'S ABBEY CONDUIT HOUSE

VISIT US

Direction: In King's Park. Approx. 5-10 min walk from St Augustine's Abbey. Please call or ask at the abbey for directions

Train: Canterbury East or West, both ¾ mile

Bus: Regent Coaches 649 from George's Street City centre stops to law courts then short walk

ACQ.1977

MAP Page 339 (4J)
OS Map 179, 150: TR159580

ST AUGUSTINE'S CROSS
KENT

This 19th-century cross in Saxon style marks what is traditionally believed to be the site of St Augustine's landing on the shores of England in AD 597. Accompanied by 30 followers, Augustine is said to have held a mass here before moving on.

OPENING TIMES

Any reasonable time in daylight hours

VISIT US

Direction: 2 miles E of Minster off B29048

Train: Minster 2 miles

Bus: Eastonways 42 from Ramsgate

ACQ.1912

MAP Page 339 (4J)
OS Map 179, 150: TR340642

ST JAMES' CHURCH, COOLING
KENT – ME3 8DG

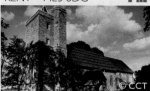

© CCT

Charles Dickens used the churchyard of St James' as his inspiration for the opening chapter of *Great Expectations*. Surrounded by marshes, the site can look desolate, but inside the church is light and spacious. Its vestry walls are lined with thousands of cockle shells, the emblem of St James.

Owned and managed by The Churches Conservation Trust.

OPENING TIMES

Open daily 10am-4pm

VISIT US

Train: Higham 3¼ miles

Bus: Arriva 133 & 193 and Nu Venture 417 to Cliffe then 1½ mile walk

20 mins from Rochester Castle, 40 mins from Eltham Palace and Gardens, 45 mins from The Home of Charles Darwin

MAP Page 339 (4G)
OS Map 178, 163: TQ756759

ST JOHN'S COMMANDERY
KENT

The flint-walled 13th-century chapel and hall of a 'Commandery' of Knights Hospitallers, later converted into a farmhouse. It has a remarkable medieval crown-post roof and 16th-century ceilings with moulded beams.

OPENING TIMES

Any reasonable time in daylight hours for exterior viewing. Internal viewing by appointment only; please call 01304 211067

ST JOHN'S COMMANDERY

VISIT US

Direction: 2 miles NE of Densole, off A260

Train: Kearsney 4 miles

Bus: Stagecoach in East Kent 16/A ➡ Folkestone Central – Canterbury, to within 1 mile

ACQ.1978

MAP Page 339 (5J)
OS Map 179/189, 138: TR232440

ST LEONARD'S TOWER
KENT

An early and well-preserved example of a small free-standing Norman tower keep, surviving almost to its original height. It was probably built c.1080 by Gundulf, Bishop of Rochester, and takes its name from a chapel of St Leonard which once stood nearby.

Managed by West Malling Parish Council.

OPENING TIMES

Any reasonable time in daylight hours for exterior viewing

VISIT US

Direction: Nr West Malling, on unclassified road W of A228

Train: West Malling 1 mile

Bus: New Venture 70, 123, 149, 151; Arriva 72, 77 & 147

ACQ.1937

Disabled access (grounds only).

MAP Page 339 (4G)
OS Map 178/188, 148: TQ676571

ST MARY'S CHURCH, HIGHAM
KENT – ME3 7LS

© CCT Neil Rushton

This remote church stands in the middle of orchards, on the edge of the Thames marshes. It has a great charm and eccentricity, with striped walls of ragstone and flint, and a near-symmetrical arrangement of two naves and two chancels.

Owned and managed by The Churches Conservation Trust.

OPENING TIMES
Open daily   9am-6pm

VISIT US
Train: Higham 1 mile

Bus: Nu Venture bus service 417 to Lower Higham then 1 mile walk

15 mins from Upnor Castle, 40 mins from Eltham Palace and Gardens, 40 mins from The Home of Charles Darwin

MAP Page 339 (4G)
OS Map 178, 163: TQ716742

To discover more about **The Churches Conservation Trust**, visit **www.visitchurches. org.uk**

THE CHURCHES
CONSERVATION TRUST

ST MARY'S CHURCH, SANDWICH
KENT – CT13 9EU

© CCT

Immense, barn-like St Mary's occupies what may be the oldest church site in Sandwich. During its rich history, it has twice survived town sackings by the French in the 13th and 15th centuries; an earthquake in the 16th century; and the collapse of its tower in the 17th century.

Owned and managed by The Churches Conservation Trust.

OPENING TIMES
Open daily   10am-4pm

Occasionally closed for events

VISIT US
Train: Sandwich ½ mile

Bus: Stagecoach services 13, 13A, 14, 14A, 87, 88 & 88A.

15 mins from Deal Castle, 25 mins from Dover Castle

MAP Page 339 (4J)
OS Map 179, 150: TR329584

ST PETER'S CHURCH, SANDWICH
KENT – CT13 9DA

© CCT

This spacious 800-year-old Cinque Port church is a local landmark. The handsome tower has a distinctive onion dome built by Flemish refugees, and the atmospheric crypt was once a charnel house where bones from the graveyard were stored.

Owned and managed by The Churches Conservation Trust.

OPENING TIMES
Open daily but occasionally closed at short notice for events; please telephone 01304 621554 in advance of your visit

VISIT US
Train: Sandwich ¼ mile

Bus: Stagecoach services 13, 13A, 14, 14A, 87, 88 & 88A

5 mins from Richborough Roman Fort and Amphitheatre, 25 mins from Dover Castle

MAP Page 339 (4J)
OS Map 179, 150: TR331580

SUTTON VALENCE CASTLE
KENT

The ruins of a small 12th-century Norman keep, with panoramic views over the Weald.

OPENING TIMES
Any reasonable time in daylight hours

VISIT US
Direction: 5 miles SE of Maidstone; in Sutton Valence village, on A274

Train: Headcorn 4 miles, Hollingbourne 5 miles

Bus: Arriva 12 Maidstone – Tenterden (passes ⇌ Headcorn)

ACQ.1976 ✈

MAP Page 339 (5G)
OS Map 188, 137: TQ815491

TEMPLE MANOR
KENT

Part of a manor house of the Knights Templar, built in about 1240, with a fine first floor hall displaying traces of wall paintings.

Managed by Medway Council.
www.visitmedway.org

OPENING TIMES
30 Mar-3 Nov, Sat-Sun	11am-4pm
4 Nov-31 Mar	Closed

For group visits please call 01634 332901

VISIT US
Direction: Located in Strood (Rochester), off A228

Train: Strood ¾ mile

Bus: Arriva and Nu Venture operate services in Strood. Alight in Knight Road Strood and then short walk

ACQ.1950 ✈ P ♿

Disabled access (grounds only).

MAP Page 339 (4G)
OS Map 178, 148/163: TQ733685

UPNOR CASTLE
KENT – ME2 4XG

Set in tranquil grounds adjoining a riverside village, this rare example of an Elizabethan artillery fort was begun in 1559 and strengthened in 1599-1601 to protect warships moored at Chatham dockyard (p.94). Despite a brave attempt, it entirely failed to do so in 1667, when the Dutch sailed past it to burn or capture the English fleet at anchor.

Managed by Medway Council.
www.visitmedway.org

NON-MEMBERS
Adult	£5.80
Concession	£3.70
Child	£3.70
Family	£15.30

Members also get discounted entry to Chatham Historic Dockyard (p.94)

OPENING TIMES
29 Mar-30 Sept, daily	10am-6pm
1 Oct-3 Nov, daily	10am-4pm
4 Nov-31 Mar	Closed

Last admission 45 mins before closing

May close early on Fri and Sat for weddings. Please call in advance to check

VISIT US
Direction: At Upnor, on unclassified road off A228

Train: Strood 2 miles

Bus: Arriva service 197 from Chatham

UPNOR CASTLE

Tel: 01634 332902 or when castle is closed 01634 332901

ACQ.1961 ∩ E ♦ ✚ ✚ P ♿ ⚠
Audio guide (small charge).

Disabled access (grounds only).

Parking (at a slight distance from castle – park before village).

MAP Page 339 (4G)
OS Map 178, 163: TQ759706

WALMER CASTLE AND GARDENS
SEE FEATURE – PAGE 74

WESTERN HEIGHTS, DOVER
KENT

A huge fortification constructed during the Napoleonic Wars and completed in the 1860s, designed to protect Dover from French invasion.

OPENING TIMES
Any reasonable time in daylight hours

Free to visit the outside and moat. Drop Redoubt fortress open on special occasions and annual open weekends 15-16 Jun & 19-20 Oct, visit www.doverwesternheights.org

VISIT US
Direction: Above Dover town on W side of harbour

Train: Dover Priory ¾ mile

Bus: Eastonways 593 from Dover town centre

Tel: 01304 211067

ACQ.1968 ✈ P ⚠

MAP Page 339 (5J)
OS Map 179, 138: TR312408

Originally built during the reign of Henry VIII as part of a chain of coastal artillery defences against Catholic attack from Europe, Walmer Castle has evolved over time into an elegant residence.

VISIT US

Address: Walmer Castle, Kingsdown Road, Deal, Kent CT14 7LJ

Direction: On coast S of Walmer, on A258; Junction 13 of M20 or from M2 to Deal

Train: Walmer 1 mile

Bus: Stagecoach East Kent service 82/82A

Tel: 01304 364288

Local Tourist Information
Deal: 01304 369576 and
Dover: 01304 205108

NON-MEMBERS

Adult	£7.70
Concession	£6.90
Child	£4.60
Family	£20.00

OPENING TIMES

29 Mar–4 Jul, daily	10am–6pm
8 Jul–30 Sep, daily	10am–6pm
1 Oct–3 Nov, Wed–Sun	10am–4pm
4 Nov–14 Feb, Sat–Sun	10am–4pm
15–23 Feb, daily	10am–4pm
1–31 Mar, Sat–Sun	10am–4pm

Closed 5–7 July when Lord Warden in residence

ACQ.1904

Audio tours (also in Dutch, French and German).

Disabled access (three ground floor display rooms, tea rooms, shop courtyard and garden only; parking available near approach to castle).

MAP Page 339 (5J)
OS Map 179, 138: TR378501

HOLIDAY COTTAGES AT **WALMER CASTLE**

Walmer Castle has two holiday cottages, the Greenhouse Apartment *(see above)* and the Garden Cottage, both offering great views over the traditional kitchen garden to the castle beyond, and only a few minutes walk from a secluded expanse of shingle beach and the sea.

Walmer Castle is the official residence of the Lord Warden of the Cinque Ports. Once an important military command, supervising the five ('Cinque') south-eastern ports which provided ships for medieval England's defence, the Lord Wardenship was later granted as an honorary distinction. It is easy to imagine why the Duke of Wellington, who held the post for 23 years, enjoyed his time here so much.

Wellington's spirit lives on at Walmer Castle, where the armchair in which he died in 1852 can still be seen. His campaign bed also remains on display as a testament to his spartan tastes, along with a pair of original 'Wellington boots' and many personal effects in the fascinating on-site Wellington museum.

Successive Lords Warden have left their mark on Walmer Castle. Thus Lady Hester Stanhope created new landscaping as a surprise for her uncle, Lord Warden William Pitt; while Lord Warden W.H. Smith – member of the famous stationer's family – saved many of the historic and valuable furnishings now on display. Recent Lords Warden have been provided with private apartments above the gatehouse, and both Sir Robert Menzies (former Australian Prime Minister) and Her Majesty Queen Elizabeth the Queen Mother made regular visits to the castle, as does the current title holder, Admiral the Lord Boyce. Some of the rooms used by the Queen Mother are open to visitors, as is her magnificent garden, given to Her Majesty on her 95th birthday.

The beautiful gardens also include the Broad Walk, with formal borders framed by the famous Cloud Yew Hedge; a commemorative lawn; woodland walk; croquet lawn and a working kitchen garden. The gardens include areas carefully managed to encourage wild flowers and insects. These wild garden areas are also a great place to spot birds.

Home-made lunches and teas are available at the Lord Warden's Tearoom and there is a well-stocked gift shop. An audio tour is available and plants are on sale.

OXFORDSHIRE

ABINGDON COUNTY HALL MUSEUM
OXFORDSHIRE – OX14 3HG

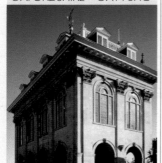

This splendid 17th-century Baroque building housed a courtroom for assizes, raised on arches over a market space. It now houses the Abingdon Museum.

Managed by Abingdon Town Council, maintained by English Heritage.

www.abingdonmuseum.org.uk

OPENING TIMES
29 Mar-23 Dec, Tue-Sun & Bank Hols	10am-4pm
24 Dec-2 Jan	Closed
3 Jan-31 Mar, Tue-Sun	10am-4pm

Roof open Sat-Sun, Easter to Oct & daily in summer, weather permitting (charges apply)

VISIT US
Direction: In Abingdon, 7 miles south of Oxford; in Market Place

Train: Radley 2½ miles

Bus: Oxford Bus Co X2, X3, 4, X13, 35; Stagecoach X15, 31, 34, Thames Travel 32, 32B, 32C, 114, 116; Oxfordshire CC 43; Heyfordian 40, 41, 42, 44

Tel: 01235 523703

ACQ.1952

MAP Page 338 (3C)
OS Map 164, 170: SU498971

DEDDINGTON CASTLE
OXFORDSHIRE

These extensive earthworks are the remains of an 11th-century motte and bailey castle, generally thought to be associated with Odo, Bishop of Bayeux and half-brother of William the Conqueror.

Managed by Deddington Parish Council.

OPENING TIMES
Any reasonable time in daylight hours

VISIT US
Direction: S of B4031 on E side of Deddington; 17 miles N of Oxford

Train: King's Sutton 5 miles

Bus: Heyfordian 81 (Thu, Fri, Sat only) – passes site; Stagecoach in Oxfordshire S4 & Oxfordshire CC 90 to within ½ mile

ACQ.1951

MAP Page 338 (2C)
OS Map 151, 191: SP472316

MINSTER LOVELL HALL AND DOVECOTE
OXFORDSHIRE – OX29 0RR

The extensive and picturesque ruins of a 15th-century riverside manor house, including a fine hall, south-west tower and complete nearby dovecote.

MINSTER LOVELL HALL AND DOVECOTE

The home of Richard III's henchman Lord Lovell.

OPENING TIMES
Any reasonable time in daylight hours. Dovecote – exterior only

VISIT US
Direction: Adjacent to Minster Lovell church; 3 miles W of Witney, off A40

Train: Charlbury 7 miles

Bus: Stagecoach in Oxford S2, 233; Swanbrook 853; also Villager Community Bus then short walk

ACQ.1935 Minster Lovell Hall
ACQ.1957 Dovecote

MAP Page 338 (2B)
OS Map 164, 180: SP325113

NORTH HINKSEY CONDUIT HOUSE
OXFORDSHIRE

Roofed conduit for Oxford's first water mains, constructed during the early 17th century.

A free podcast is available on our website **www.english-heritage.org.uk/northhinksey**

OPENING TIMES
Exterior viewing only
1 Apr-30 Sep, Thu-Sun & Bank Hols	10am-4pm

VISIT US
Direction: In North Hinksey off A34; 1½ miles W of Oxford. Located off track leading from Harcourt Hill; use the footpath from Ferry Hinksey Lane (near railway station)

Train: Oxford 1½ mile

Bus: Heyfordian service 44; also Stagecoach Brookes Bus service U1 passes within ¾ mile

ACQ.1973

MAP Page 338 (3C)
OS Map 164, 180: SP495050

NORTH LEIGH ROMAN VILLA OXFORDSHIRE

The remains of a large, well-built Roman courtyard villa. The most important feature is a nearly complete mosaic tile floor, patterned in reds and browns.

OPENING TIMES

Grounds – any reasonable time in daylight hours. There is a viewing window for the mosaic tile floor

VISIT US

Direction: 2 miles N of North Leigh; 10 miles W of Oxford, off A4095

Train: Hanborough 3½ miles

Bus: Stagecoach in Oxford 11 & 242 to within 1½ miles

ACQ.1952 🐾 P

Pedestrian access only from main road – 550 metres (600 yards).

Parking (lay-by, not in access lane).

MAP Page 338 (2B)
OS Map 164, 180: SP397154

ROLLRIGHT STONES OXFORDSHIRE

Traditionally a monarch and his courtiers petrified by a witch, the Rollright Stones consist of three groups: the King's Men stone circle; the Whispering Knights burial chamber; and the single King Stone. These funerary and ceremonial monuments span nearly 2000 years of Neolithic and Bronze Age development.

ROLLRIGHT STONES

Managed and owned by the Rollright Trust. Refreshments, toilet, guidebook and postcards available at Wyatts Farm Shop: c. 1 mile east towards Great Rollright.

ENTRY

Admission charges applies to EH members and non-members   £1.00

OPENING TIMES

Entry between sunrise and sunset all year by permission of the Rollright Trust

VISIT US

Direction: Off unclassified road between A44 and A3400; 3 miles NW of Chipping Norton, near villages of Little Rollright and Long Compton

Train: Moreton-in-Marsh 6½ miles

Bus: Stagecoach 50 (Chipping Norton – Stratford Upon Avon) passes within ½ mile

Contact: sitemanager@rollright stones.co.uk

ACQ.1883 P 🐾

Parking (in lay-by).

MAP Page 338 (2B)
OS Map 151, OL45/191: SP297309

UFFINGTON CASTLE, WHITE HORSE AND DRAGON HILL OXFORDSHIRE

These atmospheric sites lie along the Ridgeway. Uffington 'Castle' is a large Iron Age hillfort, Dragon Hill a natural mound associated in legend with St George. The famous and enigmatic White Horse is the oldest chalk-cut hill figure in Britain, and is believed to be more than 3000 years old.

Managed by the National Trust on behalf of English Heritage.

UFFINGTON CASTLE, WHITE HORSE AND DRAGON HILL

OPENING TIMES

Any reasonable time in daylight hours

VISIT US

Direction: S of B4507, 7 miles W of Wantage. Ridgeway National Trail runs directly past the site

Bus: Heyfordian service 67 operates to Kingston Lisle approx. 1 mile from the site; Ridgeways Coaches service X47 (Sat only) pass closer to the sites

ACQ.1936 🐾 P

Parking (pay and display). Free to EH members.

MAP Page 338 (3B)
OS Map 174, 170: SU301866

WAYLAND'S SMITHY OXFORDSHIRE

A fine and atmospheric Neolithic chambered long barrow 2km (1¼ miles) along the Ridgeway from the Uffington White Horse: it was once believed to be the habitation of the Saxon smith-god Wayland.

Managed by the National Trust on behalf of English Heritage.

OPENING TIMES

Any reasonable time in daylight hours

VISIT US

Direction: On the Ridgeway; (closed to vehicles) ¾ mile NE of B4000, Ashbury – Lambourn Road

Bus: Thamesdown Transport service 47 then a short walk along the Ridgeway path. Ridgeways Coaches service X47 (Sat only) provide additional facilities

ACQ.1922 🐾

Parking at White Horse (pay and display).

MAP Page 338 (3B)
OS Map 174, 170: SU281854

SURREY

FARNHAM CASTLE KEEP
SURREY – GU9 0JA

The impressive motte and shell keep of a castle founded in 1138 by Bishop Henry of Blois. A residence of the wealthy bishops of Winchester, the accommodation in the keep was updated in the 1520s. The keep was abandoned after Civil War service, but much-altered parts of the medieval bishops' residence remain in use in private hands. A viewing platform and stairway now reveal the buried remains of an earlier tower. Tours of the Bishop's Palace are available on Wednesday afternoons for an additional fee.

Managed by Farnham Castle.

OPENING TIMES

29 Mar-23 Dec, Mon-Fri	9am-5pm
(or dusk, whichever is earlier)	
Sat-Sun & Bank Hols	10am-4pm
24 Dec-31 Jan	Closed
1 Feb-31 Mar, Mon-Fri	9am-5pm
(or dusk, whichever is earlier)	
Sat-Sun & Bank Hols	10am-4pm

Last admission 30 minutes before closing time

VISIT US
Direction: ½ mile N of Farnham

Train: Farnham ¾ mile

Bus: Fleet Buzz services 71 & 79 pass the castle; Stagecoach services 4, 5, 16, 17, 18, 19, 46 and 65 stop in the town centre which is a ¾ walk uphill

Tel: 01252 721194

MAP Page 338 (5D)
OS Map 186, 145: SU837473

WAVERLEY ABBEY
SURREY

Ruins of the church and monastic buildings of the first Cistercian abbey in England, founded in 1128. A free downloadable audio tour is available from the English Heritage website.

Elizabeth.

OPENING TIMES
Any reasonable time in daylight hours

VISIT US
Direction: 2 miles SE of Farnham, off B3001; off Junction 10 of M25

Train: Farnham 2 miles

Bus: Stagecoach in Hants & Surrey 46 Guildford – Aldershot (passing ≋ Farnham)

ACQ.1961   P
Parking (limited).

MAP Page 338 (5D)
OS Map 186, 145: SU868453

ENGLISH HERITAGE PROPERTY GUIDEBOOKS

Want to know more about a property near you?

Visit www.english-heritageshop.org.uk

SUSSEX (EAST)

1066 BATTLE OF HASTINGS, ABBEY AND BATTLEFIELD
SEE FEATURE – PAGE 80

CAMBER CASTLE
EAST SUSSEX

The ruins of an unusually unaltered artillery fort, built by Henry VIII to guard the port of Rye. There are limited opening times, but regular guided walks around Rye Harbour Nature Reserve include the castle.

Contact the Reserve Manager for further details.

Managed by Rye Harbour Nature Reserve.

www.wildrye.info/reserve/cambercastle

NON-MEMBERS

Adult	£3.00
Concession	£1.50
Child	Free
when accompanied by an adult	

OPENING TIMES
Jul-Sep open on the first Sat of the month at 2pm for guided tour. Regular guided walks around the Rye Harbour Nature Reserve include the castle.

Please check website or visit wildrye.info/dates

VISIT US
Direction: 1 mile walk across fields, off the A259; 1 mile S of Rye, off Harbour Road. No vehicle access. Follow the public footpath from Brede Lock

Train: Rye 1¼ miles

Bus: From surrounding areas to Winchelsea or Rye, then 1½ mile walk; or Stagecoach 344 Hastings – Northiam then ¾ mile walk

Tel: Nature reserve office number 01797 227784 (Mon-Fri, 9am-5pm only, please call customer services outside office hours)

ACQ.1967

MAP Page 339 (6H)
OS Map 189, 125: TQ922185

PEVENSEY CASTLE EAST SUSSEX – BN24 5LE

With a history stretching back over 16 centuries, Pevensey Castle chronicles more graphically than any other fortress the story of Britain's south coast defences.

Beginning in the late 3rd century as one of the last and strongest of the Roman 'Saxon Shore' forts – two-thirds of whose towered walls still stand – Pevensey was the landing place of William the Conqueror's army in 1066.

During the century after the Conquest a full-scale Norman castle, with a great square keep and a powerful gatehouse, was built within one corner of the fort. In the 1250s the towered bailey wall was constructed, and soon put to the test during the great siege of 1264. Later still the castle was strengthened to face the threat of the Spanish Armada in 1588. This was not Pevensey's last military service: during World War II, pillboxes and machine-gun posts were cunningly camouflaged among its ancient walls.

An exhibition with artefacts found on-site and an audio tour tell the story of the castle.

OPENING TIMES

29 Mar-30 Sep, daily	10am-6pm
1 Oct-3 Nov, daily	10am-4pm
4 Nov-31 Mar, Sat-Sun	10am-4pm
24-26 Dec and 1 Jan	Closed

VISIT US

Direction: In Pevensey off A259

Train: Pevensey & Westham or Pevensey Bay, both ½ mile

Bus: Stagecoach 55 passes the site; Cuckmere Community Bus service 46 (Sat) terminates adjacent to the castle; Frequent Stagecoach service 99 also runs within ½ mile – alight at Pevensey, Church Lane

Tel: 01323 762604

NON-MEMBERS

Adult	£5.00
Concession	£4.50
Child	£3.00
Family	£13.00

ACQ.1925

Dogs on leads (restricted areas only).

Parking (charge payable). Car park managed by Pevensey Town Trust.

Toilets (nearby).

MAP Page 339 (6G)
OS Map 199, 123/124: TQ645048

ST PETER'S CHURCH, PRESTON PARK
EAST SUSSEX – BN1 6SD

©CCT

This simple, 800-year-old church stands in the beautiful landscaped park of Preston Manor. The church nearly lost its greatest treasures – its magnificent 14th-century wall paintings – in a fire in 1906; but today the interior glows with a gorgeous mix of pattern and colour.

Owned and managed by The Churches Conservation Trust.

OPENING TIMES

Open daily	11am-3pm
Sometimes longer in the summer	

VISIT US

Train: Preston Park less than ½ mile

Bus: From surrounding areas

20 mins from Bramber Castle

MAP Page 339 (6F)
OS Map 198, 122: TQ304064

For information on events taking place at Battle Abbey, visit **www.english-heritage.org.uk/events**

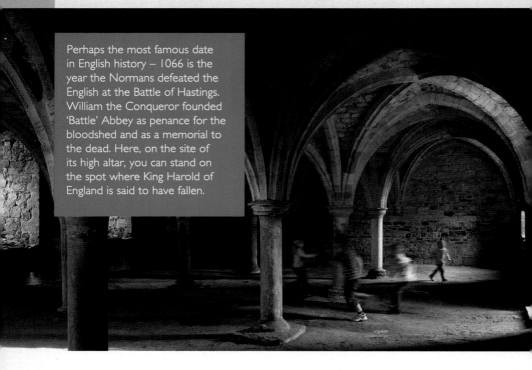

Perhaps the most famous date in English history – 1066 is the year the Normans defeated the English at the Battle of Hastings. William the Conqueror founded 'Battle' Abbey as penance for the bloodshed and as a memorial to the dead. Here, on the site of its high altar, you can stand on the spot where King Harold of England is said to have fallen.

VISIT US

Address: Battle Abbey, High Street, Battle, East Sussex TN33 0AD

Direction: In Battle, at south end of High St. Take the A2100 off the A21

Train: Battle ½ mile

Bus: Renown Coaches 5, 95, 355; Stagecoach 254, 304, 305 & 384; Battle Community Transport B67, B73, B75, B79

Tel: 01424 775705/776787 (shop)

Local Tourist Information
Battle and Bexhill Tourist information: 01424 776789/776790

NON-MEMBERS

Adult	£7.80
Concession	£7.00
Child	£4.70
Family	£20.30

OPENING TIMES

29 Mar-30 Sep, daily	10am-6pm
1 Oct-3 Nov, daily	10am-5pm
4 Nov-16 Feb, Sat-Sun	10am-4pm
17-21 Feb, Mon-Fri	10am-4pm
22 Feb-31 Mar, Sat-Sun	10am-4pm
24-26 Dec and 1 Jan	Closed

Audio tours (suitable for families, the visually impaired and for those in wheelchairs or with learning difficulties. Also available in Dutch, French, German, Japanese and Spanish; braille guides in English only). Audio tours are complimentary but will not be issued on special events days.

Café – winter opening may be limited. Please call for details.

Disabled access (grounds and visitor centre).

Dogs on leads (restricted areas only).

Parking – Charge payable for members and non-members. Members parking concessionary rate available during open hours only.

MAP Page 339 (6G)
OS Map 199, 124: TQ749157

From Battle you can take the 1066 Walk to Pevensey Castle (one of Britain's oldest strongholds) where William first landed before moving to Hastings (see p.79).

An imaginative exhibition, *1066: The Battle for England*, brings the background and impact of this renowned conflict vividly to life. Up-to-date technology and interactive displays draw a striking picture, from both English and Norman viewpoints, of the years which led up to the conflict. They also illustrate how this pivotal battle shaped English history. Listening points, graphic presentations, handsome exhibits and touch-screen displays explore how life was for the opposing sides. Central to the exhibition is a short film, narrated by Dr David Starkey, which dramatically recounts the events preceding the bloody struggle, culminating on 14 October 1066 when 'the fields were covered in corpses, and all around the only colour to meet the gaze was blood-red'. [*The Chronicle of Battle Abbey*].

The audio tour vividly describes and re-creates the sounds of the battle on the very site where it took place. From their ridge-top 'shield wall' the English watched the Normans advancing towards them. Early in the battle, part of the Norman army panicked and retreated, but William rallied his soldiers and successfully counterattacked. Several 'pretended retreats' followed, in which the English were lured into breaking ranks in pursuit, only to be cut down. After some ten hours of fighting, the Normans launched an assault which finally broke the fatally weakened English shield wall.

At this stage King Harold was killed, perhaps struck in the eye by an arrow as depicted in the famous Bayeux Tapestry. By nightfall the Norman victory was complete. The audio tour uses 'interviews' with soldiers, monks and key figures of the time to retell the story of this fateful event, and there also is a version especially created for children.

Battle Abbey enjoyed great wealth and special privileges as the symbol of Norman triumph. Though little of its original Norman structure survives, you can still see many later monastic buildings, including the dormitory range with its fine vaulted novices' chamber. The west range, incorporating the abbots' Great Hall, was converted into a mansion after Henry VIII's Dissolution of the Monasteries, and is now a school.

⌂ HOLIDAY COTTAGE AT BATTLE ABBEY

South Lodge is the former gatehouse, which sleeps four and comes with its own fully enclosed garden. There is so much to see and experience here but nothing beats soaking up the atmosphere as the evening sun lights up the Great Gatehouse – one of the finest in England.

Best preserved and most impressive of all is the Great Gatehouse, rebuilt in about 1338 and among the finest surviving monastic entrances in Britain. The battlefield – later part of the abbey's Great Park – and abbey were purchased for the nation in 1976.

Visit the Abbey Museum, which explores the history of the abbey and includes artefacts found on-site during excavations. Children will also enjoy the Discovery Centre which is open every weekend and throughout the school holidays. Look out, too, for our programme of family friendly events, including Halloween ghost tours and daily children's activities in August.

Take a break in the stylish café, serving light lunches and all-day refreshments. Contemporary in design, it has both indoor and outdoor seating and wonderful views of the historic gatehouse.

Following your visit, why not spend a pleasant afternoon in Battle town: it has a Town Trail, museum, and interesting shops, and hosts events and farmers' markets. From Battle you can take the '1066 Walk' to Pevensey Castle (one of Britain's oldest strongholds) where William first landed before moving to Hastings.

NEW FOR 2013

Within the ancient walls of the south east corner of the monastic precinct, the Walled Garden has existed since at least the early 19th century: there may have been gardens here during the medieval period. We are replanting the Victorian orchard, inspired by the historic plans from its use as a private garden for the Duchess of Cleveland. Old varieties of fruit trees local to the area are being introduced, together with wild flowers and beehives to add year-round interest. Visitors will be able to relax and enjoy the views and wildlife in this tranquil space. Opens for the first time in early summer.

BOXGROVE PRIORY WEST SUSSEX

BRAMBER CASTLE
WEST SUSSEX

The remains of a Norman motte-and-bailey castle on the banks of the River Adur, founded by William de Braose c. 1073. The earthworks are dominated by a towering wall of the keep-gatehouse.

OPENING TIMES
Any reasonable time in daylight hours

VISIT US
Direction: On W side of Bramber village, off A283

Train: Shoreham-by-Sea 4½ miles

Bus: Brighton & Hove 2A, 20 & Compass Bus 100 & 106

ACQ.1975 ⚓ **P**
Parking (limited).

MAP Page 338 (6E)
OS Map 198, 122: TQ185107

In a beautiful setting at the foot of the South Downs, the small Benedictine priory of Boxgrove was founded in about 1117 – originally for just three monks – by Robert de la Haye, as a 'cell' or dependency of Lessay Abbey in Normandy. Like most such 'alien priories', it was 'nationalised' at the outset of the Hundred Years War in 1339, becoming independent of its French mother-house.

The principal survivor of the monastic buildings is the two-storey lodging house for guests and travellers, roofless but standing to full height at the gable ends. One arcaded wall of the chapter house also remains, attached to the north transept of the priory church. This lovely building (not in the guardianship of English Heritage) became Boxgrove's parish church at the Dissolution of the Monasteries.

Though much of its west end was demolished in the 18th century, the church's splendid 12th-century chancel, central tower and unusual transepts still survive complete, along with the Early Tudor de la Warr chantry chapel with its fine Renaissance carvings. There is a model of the monastic buildings in the church.

Nearby, in Boxgrove gravel pit, archaeological excavation (funded by English Heritage) has produced much the oldest human remains yet discovered in England: a shinbone and two teeth dating from around 500,000 years ago.

OPENING TIMES
Priory open for viewing at any reasonable time (daylight hours)

VISIT US
Direction: N of Boxgrove; 4 miles E of Chichester, on minor road off A27

Train: Chichester 4 miles

Bus: Stagecoach bus 55/55a (Sun only); Compass bus 99

ACQ.1977 ⚓ **P**

MAP Page 338 (6D)
OS Map 197, 121: SU908076

Don't forget to check opening times online before you visit.

www.english-heritage. org.uk/daysout/ properties

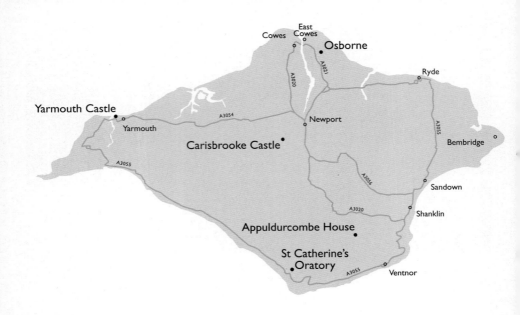

APPULDURCOMBE HOUSE

APPULDURCOMBE HOUSE
ISLE OF WIGHT – PO38 3EW

The shell of Appuldurcombe, once the grandest house on the Isle of Wight and still an important example of English Baroque architecture, standing in 'Capability' Brown-designed grounds. The 1701 east wing has been re-roofed. An exhibition of photographs and prints depicts the house and its history. You can also visit the Freemantle Gate (part of the 1770s neo-Classical addition to the estate) on the nearby public footpath, and the adjacent Falconry Centre (not under the care of English Heritage – extra charge applies).

Managed by Mr and Mrs Owen.

APPULDURCOMBE HOUSE

NON-MEMBERS

Adult	£4.00
Concession	£3.50
Child	£2.75
Family	£13.00

OPENING TIMES
27 Mar-20 Oct, Sun-Fri   10am-4pm

VISIT US
Direction: Wroxall ½ mile, off B3327

Train: Shanklin 3½ miles then bus

Bus: Southern Vectis 3

Ferry: Ryde 11 miles (Wightlink 0870 582 7744; Hovercraft 01983 811000); West Cowes 12 miles, East Cowes 12 miles (both Red Funnel – 0844 844 9988)

Tel: 01983 852484

ACQ.1952

MAP Page 338 (7C)
OS Map 196, OL29: SZ543800

A fascinatingly varied site to visit, Carisbrooke Castle has been the key to the Isle of Wight's security for more than nine centuries. This great hilltop-crowning fortress has a keep to climb for panoramic views, a colourful history, and of course the famous Carisbrooke donkeys.

VISIT US

Address: Carisbrooke Castle, Castle Hill, Newport, Isle of Wight PO30 1XY

Direction: 1¼ miles SW of Newport. Follow signs to Carisbrooke village, then castle

Bus: Southern Vectis 6, 7, 12, 38 pass nearby to within ¼ mile

Ferry: West Cowes 5 miles, East Cowes 6 miles (Red Funnel – 0844 844 9988); Fishbourne 6 miles, Ryde 8 miles, Yarmouth 9 miles (Wightlink 0870 5827744)

Tel: 01983 522107

Local Tourist Information 01983 813813

NON-MEMBERS

Adult	£7.70
Concession	£6.90
Child	£4.60
Family	£20.00

OPENING TIMES

29 Mar-30 Sep, daily	10am-6pm
1 Oct-3 Nov, daily	10am-4pm
4 Nov-16 Feb, Sat-Sun	10am-4pm
17-21 Feb, Mon-Fri	10am-4pm
24-26 Dec and 1 Jan	Closed
22 Feb-31 Mar, Sat-Sun	10am-4pm

Disabled access (grounds and lower levels only).

Tearoom (open Apr-Oct). Closed in winter.

MAP Page 338 (7C)
OS Map 196, OL29: SZ486878

⌂ HOLIDAY COTTAGE AT CARISBROOKE CASTLE

The secluded location of the holiday cottage within the castle walls and the romance of its unique history make this the ideal hideaway for a peaceful break. Enjoy the grounds of the castle in private once the gates close to the public.

After the Spanish Armada passed alarmingly close in 1588, Carisbrooke was updated as an artillery fortification by surrounding it with 'bastioned' outer earthworks, still impressively visible.

There has been a fortress here since Saxon times, but the present castle was begun in c. 1100, when the Isle of Wight was granted to the de Redvers family. They raised the great stone shell-keep on its towering mound and after 1262 the formidable Countess Isabella de Redvers extensively rebuilt the whole stronghold. Following the addition of its double-towered 14th-century gatehouse, Carisbrooke Castle experienced its only siege in 1377, beating off a French raiding force. After the Spanish Armada passed alarmingly close in 1588, the castle was updated as an artillery fortification by surrounding it with 'bastioned' outer earthworks, still impressively visible.

Most famous among the castle's extensive cast of past

residents was Charles I, imprisoned here in 1647-8 after his defeat in the Civil War. At first comfortably accommodated in the Constable's Lodging, he later became a closely guarded captive: an attempt to escape was foiled only when he became wedged in the window bars.

Much later, Princess Beatrice, Queen Victoria's youngest daughter and Governor of the Isle of Wight between 1896-1944, made Carisbrooke Castle her summer home. Princess Beatrice also commissioned the altar painting in the tranquil castle chapel in memory of a son killed in action in 1914. The Edwardian-style Princess Beatrice garden, designed by TV and radio gardening presenter Chris Beardshaw, was inspired

Family Events at Carisbrooke Castle include Castle Quest, Clash of the Knights, the Grand Medieval Joust – all in August – and Spooky Castle in October.

by the Princess, and includes a fountain and plantings in the rich colours of the royal arms. We are grateful to the late Mrs Dorothy Frazer, whose generous bequest and devotion to the island has made the creation of this garden possible.

The castle's most beloved modern residents are undoubtedly the renowned Carisbrooke donkeys. These happy, hard-working animals still operate the tread wheel in the Elizabethan wheelhouse, which raises water 49 metres (161 feet) from the castle well. They give daily demonstrations,

and their story is told in a film hosted by Jupiter the cartoon donkey, voiced by locally-raised comedian Phill Jupitus.

The on-site Carisbrooke Museum (managed by the Carisbrooke Museum Trust) provides more historical information about the castle, as well as Charles I memorabilia.

An extensive presentation – including film, hands-on weapons and family interactives and a virtual tour – highlights Carisbrooke Castle's long and often tumultuous history.

After her marriage to Prince Albert in 1840, Queen Victoria felt the need for a family residence in the country. To use her own words, 'a place of one's own – quiet and retired'. With the recent opening for the very first time of the Queen's private bathing beach, visitors can now share even more of the Victorian royal family's holiday life here.

VISIT US

Address: York Avenue, East Cowes, Isle of Wight PO32 6JX

Direction: 1 mile SE of East Cowes. For sat nav use postcode PO32 6JT

Train: Ryde Esplanade 7 miles

Bus: Southern Vectis services 4 & 5

Ferry: East Cowes 1½ miles (Red Funnel. Tel: 0844 844 9988); Fishbourne 4 miles; Ryde 7 miles (Wightlink. Tel: 0870 5827744)

Hovertravel: 08434 878887

Tel: 01983 200022

Local Tourist Information
Cowes and Newport: 01983 813818

NON-MEMBERS

House and Grounds

Adult	£13.40
Concession	£12.10
Child	£8.00
Family	£34.80

Winter Opening: House Ground Floor only and Grounds
(excluding Swiss Cottage Quarter)

Adult	£10.00
Concession	£9.00
Child	£6.00
Family	£26.00

OPENING TIMES

House and Grounds

29 Mar–30 Sep, daily (house closes 5pm)	10am–6pm
1 Oct–3 Nov, daily	10am–5pm
1–30 Mar, Sat–Sun	10am–4pm
24–26 Dec and 1 Jan	Closed

House guided tours and grounds

4 Nov–16 Feb, Sat–Sun	10am–4pm
17–21 Feb, daily	10am–4pm
22–28 Feb, Sat–Sun	10am–4pm

Pre-booked guided tours of selected ground floor rooms

Last tour starts 2.30pm

Victorian Christmas Event
7-8 Dec, Sat-Sun

Festive guided tours Dec weekends
Ground floor of house open for pre-booked guided visits

Baby carriers are available at the house entrance as pushchairs are not permitted within the house, but are welcome in the garden.

Disabled access – access for wheelchairs to the first floor is by an existing lift. Manual wheelchairs are available to borrow on a first come, first served basis. Mobility scooters are not permitted inside the house, but they can be used in the gardens.

MAP Page 338 (7C)
OS Map 196, OL29: SZ516948

⊞ Available for corporate and private hire

Queen Victoria knew and liked the Isle of Wight after visiting as a child, and she and the future Prince Consort were both determined to buy a property there. 'It is impossible to imagine a prettier spot,' wrote the Queen after a visit to Osborne. In 1845 the royal couple purchased the property with an estate of 342 acres. Before the deeds had even changed hands, master builder Thomas Cubitt had been approached – firstly to build a pavilion to house private apartments and then to demolish the old house and add further wings for the royal household. Once all the work was complete, an exquisite pair of Italianate towers dominated the landscape and looked out over passing ships on the nearby Solent.

The interiors of Osborne House abound with opulence in both architectural design and decoration. Marble sculptures, purchased by Victoria and Albert, line the Grand Corridor of the house and recall the royal couple's love of the arts. Portraits and frescos adorn the walls, serving as a reminder of the family's links to the crowned heads of Europe, and of the unrivalled supremacy of the British Empire. Queen Victoria's role as Empress of India is celebrated in the Durbar Room. Constructed from 1890-91, the room served as an elaborate banqueting hall and every surface, from floor to ceiling, is ornately embellished. The walls are decorated with symbols from India, including Ganesh – the elephant god of good fortune – and the deeply coffered ceiling is composed of fibrous plaster. The completion

of the room coincided with the introduction of electricity, so the Indian-influenced lamp stands were designed to take full advantage of this emerging technology Prince Albert worked with Cubitt on the Italianate designs for the terraced formal gardens which complement the house. Visitors can now enjoy the Walled Garden with cut flowers and fruit displays since it was restored by English Heritage.

Prince Albert was responsible for the layout of the Terrace overlooking the Solent – the view is said to have reminded him of the Bay of Naples – and for the introduction of many fine trees onto the estate. An original palm on the terrace was a gift to the royal couple from King Ferdinand of Portugal, and was one of the first ever to be planted in this country. It died in 2003 and the current tree – its direct descendent – was planted in 2004 by Queen Elizabeth II. The Terraces are planted to recreate their Victorian appearance.

Please note: that the Swiss Cottage will be closed for a major restoration and re-interpretation project from September 2013-April 2014. If you would like to find out more or make a donation please contact the Development Department on 020 7973 3797 or foundation@english-heritage.org.uk (The English Heritage Foundation is a registered charity, no. 1140351).

'It is impossible to imagine a prettier spot,' wrote Queen Victoria after a visit to Osborne.

On Saturday 7 and Sunday 8 December, Osborne celebrates the festive season with its popular annual Victorian Christmas event. The ground floor of the house, dressed festively for the season, is open for guided tours on December weekends. Find out how the Victorian Royal Family celebrated Christmas with these fascinating tours led by our expert guides.

Visitors shouldn't miss the Swiss Cottage and its surrounding gardens. This charming building was constructed and furnished as an educational tool, where the royal children could learn domestic skills. The surrounding grounds contain a museum, housing fascinating artefacts collected by the royal children and given to Queen Victoria, as well as a child-size fort and barracks, and the vegetable gardens where the royal children grew their own produce. A beautiful wild flower meadow is nearby, and rare red squirrels can sometimes be seen. Queen Victoria loved to stroll through the gardens, and the primroses in the woods were her particular favourites. Most of the gardens are accessible on tarmac and compacted gravel paths. There is a courtesy minibus, with wheelchair access, to the Swiss Cottage.

One of the many joys of royal family holidays at Osborne was sea bathing – for which, of course, 'we have quite a charming beach to ourselves', where no passing boats were permitted to land. The Queen's once strictly

⌂ HOLIDAY COTTAGE AT **OSBORNE**

The early 1900s holiday cottage brims with period character and once served as a cricket pavilion. Enjoy tranquil views and explore the grounds in private after the gates close to the public.

private beach is now open to visitors. Its attractions include the original royal bathing machine, later converted into a chicken shed but now fully restored: designed to protect the Queen's modesty, it includes a plumbed-in toilet as well as a changing room and curtained verandah. Here too is the Queen's refurbished reading and sketching 'Alcove', a pretty little shelter bedecked with vibrant blue and pink Minton tiles and equipped with a seat supported by cast iron dolphins on a mosaic floor.

Modern visitors can also recreate traditional 'beach holidays' by relaxing in deckchairs and enjoying the Solent views, or enjoy traditional seaside refreshments from the beach café. In summer there are also beach games, Punch and Judy shows, and other events. The beach is a 1.2km (¾ mile) walk from the house and minibus transfers are available in the summer.

The exhibition in the Petty Officers Quarters is the best place to start any visit. It covers various aspects of the sumptuously furnished house and magnificent grounds, as well as the lives and personalities of the Victorian royal family and the servants who cared for them. A play area for children and picnic tables are located off the visitors' car park.

Visitors can choose to bring a picnic to enjoy in the glorious grounds, or enjoy a light lunch in the stylish café, which is located near the shop in the visitor entrance building. You can also enjoy a delicious served lunch or afternoon tea in the elegant Terrace Restaurant, which is nearer the house and offers wonderful views across the Terrace Gardens towards the Solent. Please note, non-members will need to purchase an admission ticket to the house to gain access to the restaurant.

ST CATHERINE'S ORATORY
ISLE OF WIGHT

The tall, medieval, octagonal tower, allegedly a lighthouse, was built here in 1328 as penance for stealing church property from a wrecked ship. Affectionately known as the Pepperpot, it stands on one of the highest parts of the Isle of Wight. It is part of the Tennyson Heritage Coast, a series of linked cliff-top monuments. A later lighthouse can be seen nearby.

Managed by the National Trust on behalf of English Heritage.

OPENING TIMES
Any reasonable time in daylight hours

VISIT US
Direction: E of Blackgang roundabout, off A3055. Approx ¼ mile ascent across fields

Train: Shanklin 9 miles

Bus: Southern Vectis service 6 or Island Coaster (Summer) to Blackgang Chine and then ½ mile walk

Ferry: West Cowes 14 miles, East Cowes 14 miles (both Red Funnel – Tel: 0870 444 8898); Yarmouth 15 miles (Wightlink – Tel: 0844 844 9988)

ACQ.1952 ⚔ P

MAP Page 338 (7C)
OS Map 196, OL29: SZ494773

OSBORNE
SEE FEATURE – PAGE 88

YARMOUTH CASTLE ISLE OF WIGHT – PO41 0PB

Built to protect strategic Yarmouth harbour and (in conjunction with Hurst Castle on the mainland) to defend the western end of the Solent against invasion fleets, this last and most sophisticated addition to Henry VIII's chain of coastal forts was completed after his death in 1547. Unlike Henry's earlier circular forts – such as Deal, Portland and Pendennis Castles – Yarmouth Castle is a square blockhouse, with a battery to the front and the first new-style 'arrowhead' bastion built in England protecting its most exposed angle. In the 1560s the castle's central square was filled in to provide a solid gun platform.

Displays inside the castle include atmospheric recreations of how the rooms were used in the 16th century, and an exhibition about the many wrecks which occurred in 'Yarmouth Roads', the treacherous stretch of sea which the castle overlooks. Also a magnificent picnic site, with views over the Solent.

NON-MEMBERS
Adult	£4.00
Concession	£3.60
Child	£2.40

OPENING TIMES
29 Mar-30 Sep, Wed-Sun & Bank Hols	10am-4pm
1-31 Oct, Wed-Sun	10am-4pm
1 Nov-28 Mar	Closed

VISIT US
Direction: In Yarmouth town centre, adjacent to car ferry terminal. Located just off Quay Street, up the short walkway and through the main gates into the Castle

Train: Lymington Pier 🚆 adjoins the ferry berth for the Wightlink service to Yarmouth

Bus: Southern Vectis 7 & Needles Tour & Island Coaster (summer only)

Ferry: Yarmouth, adjacent (Wightlink – Tel: 0870 5827744)

Tel: 01983 760678

ACQ.1913 ⚔ 🏛 P 🏠 ♿ ⚠ OVP

Disabled access (ground floor only).

Parking (coaches and cars 200 metres (220 yards). Charges payable).

MAP Page 338 (7B)
OS Map 196, OL29: SZ354898

DISCOUNTED ATTRACTIONS: **SOUTH EAST**

Use your membership to get exclusive discounts at these independent attractions in the South East. Please remember to show your card as proof of membership.

Discount applies to:

KEY ⊞ MEMBERS | OVP OVP HOLDERS | 👥? NO. OF MEMBER'S CHILDREN

Terms and conditions may apply, so make sure you check the individual pages on our website or call the individual property for more details.

⊞
ANNE OF CLEVES HOUSE
East Sussex BN7 1JA
Impressive 15th-century timber framed Wealden hall-house, given to Anne as part of her divorce settlement from Henry VIII.

www.sussexpast.co.uk/anneofcleves
Tel. 01273 474610

⊞ 👥3
ARUNDEL CASTLE
West Sussex BN18 9AB
Ancient Castle & Stately Home of The Duke of Norfolk with outstanding gardens, including the new Collector Earl's Garden based on early 17th-century classical designs.

www.arundelcastle.org
Tel. 01903 882173

⊞ OVP 👥6
BLETCHLEY PARK
Buckinghamshire MK3 6EB
Bletchley Park was home to the WWII Codebreakers whose breathtaking achievements helped shorten the war by two years, saving countless lives.

www.bletchleypark.org.uk
Tel. 01908 640404

⊞
DOVER MUSEUM AND BRONZE AGE BOAT GALLERY – Kent CT16 1PB
This modern museum tells the story of Dover's history and is home to the Dover Bronze Age Boat. Managed by Dover District Council.

www.dovermuseum.co.uk
Tel. 01304 201066

⊞
FISHBOURNE ROMAN PALACE
West Sussex PO19 3QR
Remains of a 1st-century palatial building with the largest collection of early Roman mosaic floors in Britain.

www.sussexpast.co.uk/fishbourne
Tel. 01243 785859

⊞ 👥6
FORT AMHERST
Kent, ME4 4UB
Fort Amherst is a Napoleonic fortress. Visit the 2500ft tunnel system, gun batteries and WWII Civil Defence Centre. Café and children's play area on site.

www.fortamherst.com
Tel. 01634 847747

DISCOUNTED ATTRACTIONS:

Use your membership to get exclusive discounts at these independent attractions in the South East. Please remember to show your card as proof of membership.

50% DISCOUNT ON ENTRY

GOODWOOD HOUSE
West Sussex PO18 0PX
The family seat of the Dukes of Richmond, set in the heart of the Sussex Downs, houses astonishing treasures, including celebrated paintings by George Stubbs and Canaletto.
www.goodwood.com
Tel. 01243 755040

15% DISCOUNT ON ENTRY

THE HISTORIC DOCKYARD, CHATHAM
Kent ME4 4TZ
This award-winning dockyard has a remarkable range of galleries, buildings and warships to explore and programme of events, activities and exhibitions.
www.thedockyard.co.uk
Tel. 01634 823800

50% DISCOUNT ON ENTRY

LEWES CASTLE & BARBICAN HOUSE MUSEUM
East Sussex BN7 1YE
This imposing Norman castle offers magnificent views across the town of Lewes and surrounding Downland.
www.sussexpast.co.uk/lewescastle
Tel. 01273 486290

2 for 1 ENTRY

LULLINGSTONE CASTLE AND THE WORLD GARDEN Kent DA9 0JA
Lullingstone Castle is one of England's oldest family estates. Visit the World Garden, containing nearly 8000 different plant species.
www.lullingstonecastle.co.uk
Tel. 01322 862114

50% DISCOUNT ON ENTRY

MARLIPINS MUSEUM
West Sussex BN43 5DA
Once a medieval customs house, Marlipins now holds artefacts and archaeological material from the Shoreham area and its maritime past.

www.sussexpast.co.uk/marlipins
Tel. 01273 462994

50% DISCOUNT ON ENTRY

MICHELHAM PRIORY
East Sussex BN27 3QS
Explore the beautiful gardens or historic house. Visit the watermill, working forge, rope museum and Elizabethan Great Barn.

www.sussexpast.co.uk/michelham
Tel. 01323 844224

SOUTH EAST CONTINUED

Discount applies to:

KEY | ⊞ MEMBERS | OVP OVP HOLDERS | 👫? NO. OF MEMBER'S CHILDREN

Terms and conditions may apply, so make sure you check the individual pages on our website or call the individual property for more details.

40% DISCOUNT ON ENTRY

⊞ OVP 👫6

NEWPORT ROMAN VILLA
Isle of Wight PO30 1HA
Discover this Romano-British farmhouse with its fine bath suite. Hands-on activities, weaving, herb garden and museum display. Open 28th March-2nd November.
www.iwight.com/museums
Tel. 01983 529720

FREE ADMISSION TO HOUSE, IF GROUNDS TICKET PURCHASED

⊞ 👫6

PENSHURST PLACE & GARDENS
Kent TN11 8DG
Stunning family-owned stately home with a place in history – unique medieval Baron's Hall and historic gardens. Adventure playground for children.
www.penshurstplace.com
Tel. 01892 870307

50% DISCOUNT ON ENTRY

⊞ 👫3

THE PRIEST HOUSE
West Sussex RH19 4PP
Standing on the edge of Ashdown Forest, the Priest House is an early 15th-century timber-framed hall-house.
www.sussexpast.co.uk/priesthouse
Tel. 01342 810479

20% OFF ADULT TICKET

⊞ 👫2

THE ROYAL PAVILION
Brighton BN1 1EE
Discover the magnificent seaside residence of King George IV. The Indian architecture contrasts with interiors inspired by China. Regency gardens, tearoom and gift shop.
www.brighton-hove-pavilion.org.uk
Tel. 03000 290900

CONCESSIONARY RATE APPLIES

⊞

RYCOTE CHAPEL
Oxfordshire OX9 2PE
The 15th-century chapel has original furniture, including exquisitely carved and painted woodwork. Managed by the Rycote Buildings Charitable Foundation.
www.visitsouthoxfordshire.co.uk
Tel. 01844 210210

GIVE THE GIFT OF MEMBERSHIP

Give friends and family the opportunity to enjoy these fantastic discounts too!

- Free entry to over 400 historic properties
- Kids go free (up to six per adult in a family group)
- Free or discounted entry to hundreds of events, activities and other attractions
- Free handbook worth £10.95
- Exclusive members' magazine

SOUTH WEST

Pendennis Castle

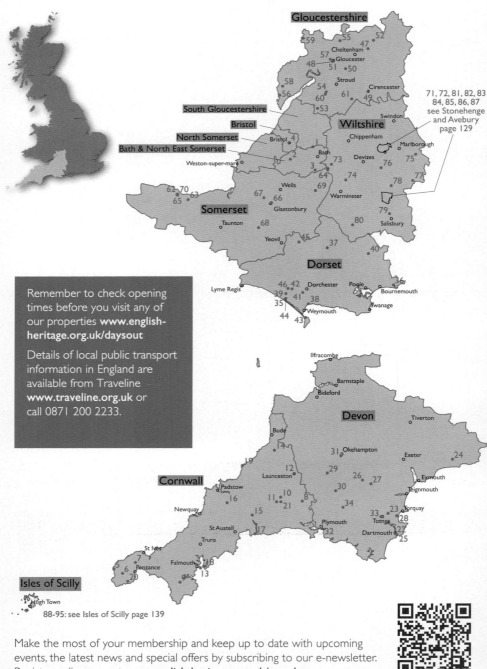

Gloucestershire

59 55 47 52
Cheltenham
57
48 Gloucester
51 50
58 54 Stroud Cirencester
56 60 61 49
53

South Gloucestershire
Bristol
North Somerset
Bath & North East Somerset
Weston-super-mare

71, 72, 81, 82, 83
84, 85, 86, 87
see Stonehenge
and Avebury
page 129

Swindon
Wiltshire
Chippenham
Bristol 4
2 Bath Marlborough
3 73 Devizes 76 75
64 74 78 77
62 70 69
65 63 67 66 Warminster
Somerset Wells 79
Glastonbury 80
Taunton 68 Salisbury
Yeovil 75
37 40
Dorset
46 42 Dorchester Poole
39 41 38 Bournemouth
Lyme Regis 35 Swanage
44 43 Weymouth

Ilfracombe
Barnstaple
Bideford

Devon Tiverton

Bude 31 Okehampton
4 29 Exeter 24
19 12 26 Exmouth
Launceston 30 27 Teignmouth
Cornwall 11 10 34 23 Torquay
Padstow 16 21 8 33 28
Newquay 15 Plymouth Totnes
St Austell 17 32 Dartmouth 25
Truro
St Ives
6 7 Falmouth 18
Penzance 13
20

Isles of Scilly
Hugh Town
88-95: see Isles of Scilly page 139

Remember to check opening
times before you visit any of
our properties www.english-
heritage.org.uk/daysout

Details of local public transport
information in England are
available from Traveline
www.traveline.org.uk or
call 0871 200 2233.

Make the most of your membership and keep up to date with upcoming
events, the latest news and special offers by subscribing to our e-newsletter.
Register online now at www.english-heritage.org.uk/newsletter

PROPERTIES

HIGHLIGHTS FOR 2013/14 IN THE SOUTH WEST

p.104

p.107

p.134

Pendennis Castle: fantastic views & family fun at Cornwall's greatest fortress.

Tintagel Castle: dramatic coastal stronghold of Arthurian legend.

Stonehenge: a fabulous new visitor centre to open at the end of 2013.

BRISTOL & BATH

CHURCH OF ST THOMAS THE MARTYR, BRISTOL
BRISTOL – BS1 6QR

© David Martyn

Located in Bristol city centre, this handsome Georgian building replaced a medieval church deemed unsafe for use. The light-filled Classical interior is elegantly presented and there is a fine ring of eight bells, all cast by local founders.

Owned and managed by The Churches Conservation Trust.

OPENING TIMES
Wed	10.30am-2.30pm

Other days by appointment, please call 0117 929 1766 before your visit

VISIT US
Train: Bristol Temple Meads ¼ mile

Bus: Close to bus routes to city centre and bus station, operated mainly by First, Wessex and ABus. Bus and coach terminus 1 mile.

2 mins walk from Temple Church

MAP Page 337 (3H)
OS Map 172, 154/155: ST591727

SIR BEVIL GRENVILLE'S MONUMENT
BATH & NE SOMERSET

Erected to commemorate the heroism of a Royalist commander and his Cornish pikemen at the Battle of Lansdown, 1643.

SIR BEVIL GRENVILLE'S MONUMENT

OPENING TIMES
Any reasonable time

VISIT US
Direction: Located 4 miles NW of Bath on the N edge of Lansdown Hill, near the road to Wick

Train: Bath Spa 4½ miles

Bus: Wessex service 620 Bath Spa – Tetbury

ACQ.1953 Parking (in lay-by).

MAP Page 337 (3H)
OS Map 172, 155: ST722703

STANTON DREW CIRCLES AND COVE
BATH & NE SOMERSET

The third largest complex of prehistoric standing stones in England, although the three circles and three-stone 'cove' of Stanton Drew are surprisingly little-known. Recent surveys have revealed that they were only part of a much more elaborate ritual site.

OPENING TIMES
Cove: any reasonable time.
Two main stone circles: access at the discretion of the landowner, who may levy a charge

VISIT US
Direction: Cove: in the garden of the Druid's Arms public house. Circles: E of Stanton Drew village

Train: Bristol Temple Meads 7 miles

Bus: Abus service 67; Somerbus 640 (Fri only) & 754 (Mon only); Bugler Coaches service 683 (Tue only), BANES 752 (Wed only); CT Coaches 834 (Tue only); Eurotaxis/CT Coaches 672 all serve the village of Stanton Drew

ACQ.1883

Cove: parking, Stones: limited parking at entrance to Stones field.

MAP Page 337 (3H)
OS Map 172/182, 154/155
Cove: ST597631
Circles: ST601633

STONEY LITTLETON LONG BARROW
BATH & NE SOMERSET

One of the finest accessible examples of a Neolithic chambered tomb, with its multiple burial chambers open to view.

OPENING TIMES
Any reasonable time

VISIT US
Direction: 1 mile S of Wellow off A367. Narrow lane west of village leads to small parking area (1 mile)

Train: Bath Spa 6 miles

Bus: Somerbus service 757 (Wed only) to Wellow then 1 mile walk from village. Otherwise use First 173, 178 or 184 to Peasedown St John and walk 2½ miles

ACQ.1884

Parking (limited). Sheep grazing.
Note: visitors are advised to bring a torch.

MAP Page 337 (3H)
OS Map 172, 142: ST735572

TEMPLE CHURCH
BRISTOL

Originally built by the Knights Templar, the 'leaning tower' and walls of this large, late medieval church survived bombing during World War II. The graveyard is now a public garden.

OPENING TIMES
Exterior only: any reasonable time

VISIT US
Direction: Located in Temple St, off Victoria St

Train: Bristol Temple Meads ¼ mile

Bus: From surrounding areas

ACQ.1958

MAP Page 337 (3H)
OS Map 172, 154/155: ST593727

CORNWALL

BALLOWALL BARROW
CORNWALL

In a spectacular cliff-edge position, this unique Bronze Age cairn has a long and complex history as a burial site. Seen as excavated in 1878 by Cornish antiquarian William Borlase.

Managed by the National Trust.

OPENING TIMES
Any reasonable time

VISIT US
Direction: 1 mile W of St Just, near Carn Gloose

Train: Penzance 8 miles

Bus: First 10, 300 (summer only); Western Greyhound 504, 507, 509

MAP Page 336 (7A)
OS Map 203, 102: SW355312

CARN EUNY ANCIENT VILLAGE CORNWALL

Among the best preserved ancient villages in the South West, occupied from the Iron Age until late Roman times. It includes the foundations of stone houses and an intriguing 'fogou' underground passage.

Managed by the Cornwall Heritage Trust.

OPENING TIMES
Any reasonable time

VISIT US
Direction: 1½ miles W of Sancreed along narrow but signed lanes

Train: Penzance 6 miles

Bus: Western Greyhound service 509 to Grumbla

Parking 600 metres (660 yards) away in Brane.

MAP Page 336 (7A)
OS Map 203, 102: SW402288

CHYSAUSTER ANCIENT VILLAGE
CORNWALL – TR20 8XA

This Romano-British settlement was originally occupied 2000 years ago. The village consisted of stone-walled homesteads known as 'courtyard houses', found only on the Land's End peninsula and the Isles of Scilly. The houses line a 'village street', and each had an open central courtyard surrounded by a number of thatched rooms. There are also the remains of an enigmatic 'fogou' underground passage.

NON-MEMBERS
Adult	£3.60
Concession	£3.20
Child	£2.20

OPENING TIMES
29 Mar-30 Jun, daily	10am-5pm
1 Jul-31 Aug, daily	10am-6pm
1-30 Sep, daily	10am-5pm
1 Oct-3 Nov, daily	10am-4pm
4 Nov-31 Mar	Closed

VISIT US
Direction: Located 2½ miles NW of Gulval, off B3311

Train: Penzance 3½ miles

Bus: Western Greyhound 508 alight New Mill, then 1½ miles walk. Alternatively First 16 to Castle Gate and then about 1¾ miles walk

Tel: 07831 757934

Local Tourist Information
Penzance: 01736 335530

MAP Page 336 (7B)
OS Map 203, 102: SW472350

DUPATH WELL CORNWALL

This charming well-house of c. 1500 stands over an ancient spring believed to cure whooping cough. Built by the Augustinian canons of nearby St Germans priory, it houses the remains of an immersion pool for cure-seekers.

Managed by the Cornwall Heritage Trust.

OPENING TIMES
Any reasonable time

VISIT US
Direction: 1 mile E of Callington off A388

Train: Gunnislake 4½ miles

Bus: DAC 283 and Western Greyhound 573 pass the site. Main services to Callington are First 76 or Western Greyhound 576 then ½ mile

ACQ.1937 [icons] Parking off the farmyard.

MAP Page 336 (6D)
OS Map 201, 108: SX375692

HALLIGGYE FOGOU
CORNWALL

Roofed and walled in stone, this complex of passages is the largest and best-preserved of several mysterious underground tunnels associated with Cornish Iron Age settlements. The purpose of such 'fogous' – a Cornish-language word meaning 'cave' – is unknown. Refuges, storage chambers or ritual shrines have all been suggested.

Free entry to the fogou. Entry to the rest of the Trelowarren Estate is charged.

Managed by the Trelowarren Estate.

OPENING TIMES
Reasonable daylight hours May-Sep, but completely blocked Oct-Apr inclusive

HALLIGGYE FOGOU

VISIT US

Direction: 5 miles SE of Helston off B3293. E of Garras on Trelowarren Estate. There is a lay-by at the side of the lane through the Trelowarren Estate. Walk up hill and the entrance to the fogou is signposted through a gate

Train: Penryn 6 miles

Bus: First 36 to Garras and then c. 1 mile walk

Parking (free to members).

Steps down into the fogou can be slippery: take care when descending.

Visitors are strongly advised to bring a torch.

MAP Page 336 (7B)
OS Map 203, 103: SW713239

HURLERS STONE CIRCLES
CORNWALL

Three fine late Neolithic or early Bronze Age stone circles arranged in a line, a grouping unique in England. Probably the best examples of ceremonial circles in the South West, they are traditionally reputed to be the remains of men petrified for playing 'hurling' on a Sunday.

Managed by the Cornwall Heritage Trust.

OPENING TIMES
Any reasonable time

VISIT US

Direction: Located ½ mile NW of Minions, off B3254

Train: Liskeard 7 miles

Bus: Western Greyhound service 573 to Darite and walk (1 mile). Also DAC occasional services 236 & 261 to Upton Cross (1¼ miles walk)

Parking ¼ mile walk.

MAP Page 336 (6D)
OS Map 201, 109: SX258714

KING DONIERT'S STONE
CORNWALL

Two richly carved pieces of a 9th-century 'Celtic' cross, with an inscription commemorating Dumgarth, British King of Dumnonia, who drowned in c. AD 875.

Managed by the Cornwall Heritage Trust.

OPENING TIMES
Any reasonable time

VISIT US

Direction: 1 mile NW of St Cleer, off B3254

Train: Liskeard 7 miles

Bus: Western Greyhound service 573

ACQ.1933

Parking (in lay-by).

MAP Page 336 (6D)
OS Map 201, 109: SX236688

LAUNCESTON CASTLE
CORNWALL – PL15 7DR

Set on a large natural mound, Launceston Castle dominates the surrounding landscape. Begun soon after the Norman Conquest, its focus is an unusual keep consisting of a 13th-century round tower built by Richard, Earl of Cornwall, inside an earlier circular shell-keep. The tower top is now reached via an internal staircase.

The castle long remained a prison and George Fox, founder of the Quakers, suffered harsh confinement here in 1656. An exhibition traces 1000 years of history, with finds from site excavations.

LAUNCESTON CASTLE

NON-MEMBERS

Adult	£3.60
Concession	£3.20
Child	£2.20

OPENING TIMES

29 Mar-30 Sep, daily	10am-6pm
1 Oct-3 Nov, daily	10am-5pm
4 Nov-31 Mar	Closed

VISIT US

Direction: In Launceston

Bus: First 76; Jackets X85 (Sat only); Western Greyhound 510, 576 & 577; Group Travel 220, 223, 225 & DAC 236

Tel: 01566 772365

Local Tourist Information
Launceston: 01566 772321

ACQ.1952

Disabled access (outer bailey, exhibition and shop).

MAP Page 336 (5D)
OS Map 201, 112: SX331846

PENDENNIS CASTLE
SEE FEATURE – PAGE 104

PENHALLAM MANOR
CORNWALL

The low and grass-covered but complete ground-plan of a moated 13th-century manor house, in a delightful woodland setting.

OPENING TIMES
Any reasonable time

VISIT US

Direction: Signposted from Week St Mary, off a minor road. From A39 heading north turn right at Treskinnick Cross. (10 minute walk from the car park along a forest track)

Bus: Western Greyhound service 595 stops at Treskinnick Cross (2 miles); Group Travel service 208 (Mon, Wed, Thu, Fri only) and 220 (Tue only) to the nearby village of Week St Mary (c. 1 mile walk)

ACQ.1981   Parking (5 spaces).

MAP Page 336 (5D)
OS Map 190, 111: SX224974

RESTORMEL CASTLE
CORNWALL – PL22 0EE

The great 13th-century circular shell-keep of Restormel still encloses the principal rooms of the castle in remarkably good condition. It stands on an earlier Norman mound surrounded by a deep dry ditch, atop a high spur beside the River Fowey. Twice visited by the Black Prince, son of Edward III, it finally saw action during the Civil War in 1644. It commands fantastic views and is a favourite picnic spot.

NON-MEMBERS

Adult	£3.60
Concession	£3.20
Child	£2.20

OPENING TIMES

29 Mar-30 Jun, daily	10am-5pm
1 Jul-31 Aug, daily	10am-6pm
1 Sep-3 Nov, daily	10am-5pm
4 Nov-31 Mar	Closed

VISIT US

Direction: Located 1½ miles N of Lostwithiel, off A390

Train: Lostwithiel 1½ miles

Bus: Travel Cornwall 423 or 482 (Wed only); Roselyn 296 (Tue only); Gorran & District Community Bus G4 to Lostwithiel then 1½ mile walk

Tel: 01208 872687

Local Tourist Information
Lostwithiel: 01208 872207

ACQ.1925

OVP

Access via a stock grazing area, appropriate footwear is advisable. There are steps on the entrance path. Disabled visitors may wish to call the site in advance to arrange alternative access.

MAP Page 336 (6C)
OS Map 200, 107: SX104614

ST BREOCK DOWNS
MONOLITH CORNWALL

Originally 5 metres (16 feet) high and weighing some 16.75 tonnes, this is Cornwall's largest and heaviest prehistoric standing stone. It stands on the summit of St Breock Downs, offering wonderful views.

Managed by the Cornwall Heritage Trust.

OPENING TIMES
Any reasonable time

VISIT US

Direction: Located on St Breock Downs; 3½ miles SW of Wadebridge off unclassified road to Rosenannon

Train: Roche 5½ miles

Bus: Closest bus service is the Western Greyhound services 594 to St Jidgey from there you should walk along the Saints Way (2½ mile)

ACQ.1965

MAP Page 336 (6C)
OS Map 200, 106: SW968683

ST CATHERINE'S CASTLE
CORNWALL

One of a pair of small artillery forts built by Henry VIII in the 1530s to defend Fowey Harbour, consisting of two storeys with gun ports at ground level.

OPENING TIMES
Any reasonable time

VISIT US

Direction: 1½ miles SW of Fowey, along a woodland footpath off A3082

Train: Par 4 miles

Bus: Western Greyhound 524, 525 & 526 to within ¾ mile walk of the castle

ACQ.1909

Parking (Ready Money Cove Car Park, Fowey, ¾ mile walk).

Steep drops within castle; keep children under close control.

MAP Page 336 (6C)
OS Map 200/204, 107: SX119509

TINTAGEL CASTLE
SEE FEATURE – PAGE 107

TREGIFFIAN BURIAL
CHAMBER CORNWALL

The remains of a Neolithic or early Bronze Age chambered tomb with an entrance passage, walled and roofed with stone slabs, leading into the central chamber. The main feature is a decorated slab in the entrance. The original is in Truro museum.

Managed by the Cornwall Heritage Trust.

OPENING TIMES
Any reasonable time

VISIT US

Direction: Located 2 miles SE of St Buryan, on B3315

Train: Penzance 5½ miles

Bus: Western Greyhound service 501, 504; First 1, 300

ACQ.1971 Parking (in lay-by).

MAP Page 336 (7B)
OS Map 203, 102: SW431244

TRETHEVY QUOIT
CORNWALL

This well-preserved and impressive Neolithic 'dolmen' burial chamber stands 2.7 metres (8.9 ft) high. There are five standing stones, surmounted by a huge capstone.

Managed by the Cornwall Heritage Trust.

OPENING TIMES
Any reasonable time

VISIT US

Direction: 1 mile NE of St Cleer, near Darite; off B3254

Train: Liskeard 3½ miles

Bus: Western Greyhound 573

ACQ.1931

Sheep may be grazing in field.

MAP Page 336 (6D)
OS Map 201, 109: SX259688

PENDENNIS CASTLE CORNWALL – TR11 4LP

Constructed between 1540 and 1545, Pendennis and its sister castle at St Mawes form the Cornish end of the chain of coastal castles built by Henry VIII to counter a threat from France and Spain. Pendennis was frequently adapted to face new enemies over 400 years, right through until World War II.

VISIT US

Address: Pendennis Castle,
Castle Close, Falmouth,
Cornwall TR11 4LP

Direction: On Pendennis
Headland, 1 mile SE of Falmouth

Train: Falmouth Docks ½ mile

Bus: First service 500; First service 41 also passes nearby

Tel: 01326 316594

Local Tourist Information:
0905 325 4534

NON-MEMBERS

Adult	£6.70
Concession	£6.00
Child	£4.00
Family	£17.40

Additional charges for members and non-members may apply on event days

OPENING TIMES

29 Mar-30 Jun, daily	10am-5pm*
1 Jul-31 Aug, daily	10am-6pm*
1 Sep-3 Nov, daily	10am-5pm*
*Castle closes at 4pm on Sat	
4 Nov-16 Feb, Sat-Sun	10am-4pm
17-21 Feb, daily	10am-4pm
22 Feb-31 Mar, Sat-Sun	10am-4pm
24-26 Dec and 1 Jan	Closed

Parts of the castle may close if an event is booked

Free guided tours of the Half Moon Battery, check availability on arrival

Wheelchair access to the grounds, but steep slopes or drops in places. There is also full wheelchair access to the shop, tearoom, Discovery Centre and the Barracks, which contains a virtual tour of the whole site.

Tearoom closes ½ hour before the castle.

MAP Page 336 (7C)
OS Map 204, 103/105: SW824318

Pendennis Castle is home to a collection of wartime cartoons by George Butterworth. The acclaimed cartoons, which appeared daily throughout World War II, lampooned both Hitler and Mussolini, enraging the Nazi leader so much that the cartoonist was put on his 'hit-list'. During your visit to Pendennis, set aside some time to view the cartoons, generously given to English Heritage by George Butterworth's widow, who lives nearby.

Visit www.
english-heritage.
org.uk/pendennis
for details of
special events.

In 1598, during Elizabeth I's reign, a new type of defensive rampart was added around the original fort. The castle was strengthened again prior to the Civil War and played host to the future Charles II in 1646, before he escaped to the Isles of Scilly. It then withstood five months of siege, before becoming the penultimate Royalist garrison on the British mainland to surrender.

Pendennis continued to play a vital role in Cornwall's defences throughout the late 19th and early 20th centuries, and saw significant action during World War II. Evidence of its fascinating history is on show throughout the site, and the Guardhouse has been returned to its World War I appearance. On the free guided tour you can visit the Half Moon Battery, including the underground magazine which is not normally open to the public, as well as the original 16th-century gun tower with its recreated Tudor gun deck.

The refurbished 1901 Royal Artillery Barracks houses an interactive exhibition, tracing the history of the castle, its people, and its links with Falmouth and the trade routes of the British Empire. There is a hands-on scale model of the castle and children can step into the shoes of a soldier on kit parade. A virtual tour in the Barracks brings the keep to life for visitors not able to fully explore the site.

After a busy day exploring, sample the delicious selection of refreshments and snacks in the tearoom, situated within the Royal Artillery Barracks.

The pre-bookable education suite with rooms for creative workshops can accommodate up to 70 children. The fully-equipped hospitality wing serves as both a conference centre and a stunning wedding venue, with the Fal Estuary as the backdrop.

🏠 HOLIDAY COTTAGES
   AT **PENDENNIS**

Enjoy the castle grounds in private after it closes to the public when you stay in the **Custodian's House** or **Callie's Cottage**.

🖵 Available for corporate and private hire
🔊 Licensed for civil wedding ceremonies

VISIT US

Direction: In St Mawes on A3078

Train: Penmere (Falmouth), 4 miles via Prince of Wales Pier and ferry

Bus: Western Greyhound service 550 ½ mile, but better to catch ferry from Falmouth

Ferry: St Mawes ferry from Falmouth

Tel: 01326 270526

Local Tourist Information
St Mawes: 01326 270440

NON-MEMBERS

Adult	£4.50
Concession	£4.10
Child	£2.70

OPENING TIMES

29 Mar–30 Jun, Sun–Fri	10am–5pm*
1 Jul–31 Aug, Sun–Fri	10am–6pm*
1–30 Sep, Sun–Fri	10am–5pm*
1 Oct–3 Nov, daily	10am–5pm
4 Nov–16 Feb, Sat–Sun	10am–4pm
17–23 Feb, daily	10am–4pm
24 Feb–31 Mar, Sat–Sun	10am–4pm

The Castle may close if an event is booked

24–26 Dec and 1 Jan	Closed

*Castle closed on Saturday if an event is booked. Please check with site in advance

ACQ.1961

MAP Page 336 (7C)
OS Map 204, 105: SW841328

St Mawes Castle is among the best-preserved of Henry VIII's coastal artillery fortresses, and the most elaborately decorated of them all. One of the chain of forts built between 1539 and 1545 to counter an invasion threat from Catholic France and Spain, it guarded the important anchorage of Carrick Roads, sharing the task with Pendennis Castle on the other side of the Fal estuary.

A charming clover-leaf shape surrounded by outer defences, St Mawes was designed to mount heavy 'ship-sinking' guns. But particular care was also taken with its embellishment, and it is still bedecked with carved Latin inscriptions in praise of Henry VIII and his son Edward VI. It owes its fine preservation for modern visitors to the fact that, unlike Pendennis Castle, it was little developed after its completion. Easily falling to landward attack by Civil War Parliamentarian forces in 1646, it remained neglected until partial re-arming during the 19th and early 20th centuries. Other coastal forts built by Henry VIII include Portland, Deal and Walmer Castles.

🏠 HOLIDAY COTTAGE AT **ST MAWES CASTLE**

The Fort House sleeps four and is ideal for families with young children, not least because the garden is fenced and wonderfully sheltered.

🍽 Available for corporate and private hire

🎩 Licensed for civil wedding ceremonies

Among the most spectacular historic sites in all Britain, Tintagel is inextricably linked with the legend of King Arthur.

VISIT US

Address: Tintagel Castle Castle Road, Tintagel, Cornwall PL34 0HE

Direction: On Tintagel Head, 600m (660 yards) along uneven track from Tintagel; no vehicles except Land Rover service (extra charge)

Bus: Western Greyhound 594 (with connections available at Wadebridge, Camelford and Boscastle)

Tel: 01840 770328

Local Tourist Information: Tintagel: 01840 779084

NON-MEMBERS

Adult	£5.90
Concession	£5.30
Child	£3.50
Family	£15.30

OPENING TIMES

29 Mar-30 Sep, daily	10am-6pm
1 Oct-3 Nov, daily	10am-5pm
4 Nov-16 Feb, Sat-Sun	10am-4pm
17-21 Feb, daily	10am-4pm
22 Feb-31 Mar, Sat-Sun	10am-4pm
24-26 Dec and 1 Jan	Closed

Beach Café closes ½ hour before the castle

ACQ. 1931

Disabled access is limited. A Land Rover service to the castle (Apr-Oct) is available at a separate charge. Please call the site for more details.

Parking (600 metres (660 yards) in the village) – not managed by EH.

MAP Page 336 (5C)
OS Map 200, 111: SX049891

A dramatic rocky headland now connected to the mainland only by a slender neck of rock, 'Din Tagell' – 'the fortress with the narrow entrance' – was clearly an important power-centre of local British-Celtic rulers between the 5th and 7th centuries, the post-Roman 'Dark Age' period when a historical Arthur may have flourished. Excavations here have uncovered fragments of luxury pottery and glass imported from lands round the Mediterranean, confirming the prosperity and high status of its inhabitants.

The link with King Arthur himself – perhaps stemming from traditions of Tintagel's Dark Age importance – is not however recorded until the 12th century, when the 'romantic novelist' Geoffrey of Monmouth wrote his largely fictional *History of the Kings of Britain*. According to Geoffrey, Duke Gorlois of Cornwall shut his wife Igerna (or Ygraine) away in Tintagel to protect her from the lusts of Uther Pendragon, King of Britain. But Merlin magically transformed Uther into the likeness of Ygraine's husband: in this disguise, Uther slept with her here, and fathered Arthur. By the 12th century, moreover, Tintagel was also linked with the separate legend of the tragic lovers, Tristan and Yseult (Isolde), whose husband (and Tristan's uncle) King Mark traditionally held court here.

It was almost certainly the Arthur connection which prompted the rich and ambitious Richard, Earl of Cornwall, younger brother of King Henry III, to build his castle here during the 1230s.

Visit www.
english-heritage.
org.uk/tintagel
for details of
special events.

Remote Tintagel had no strategic importance: but Richard may have wished to claim a link with a hero by then renowned throughout western Europe.

The atmospheric ruins of Richard's castle stand partly on the 'mainland', where two outer courtyards remain: and partly on the 'island' headland, the site of his great hall. Today a deep rocky chasm separates the two, the result of frequent landslips: but originally the two halves of the castle were linked by a fortified stone bridge. Visitors can approach the mainland castle via a relatively gentle slope, and then descend steep steps before crossing a modern bridge and ascending to the 'island': or they can ascend directly to either part of the castle from the ticket office. The climb is richly rewarded: for the windswept island displays not only Earl Richard's hall ruins but also the remains of many Dark Age houses and an atmospheric medieval chapel – as well as amazing views along the dramatic rocky coast.

Was Tintagel really connected with King Arthur?: this burning question is reviewed in the introductory audio-visual, *Searching*

for Arthur. Sir Thomas Malory's famous *Morte Darthur* reinforced the link in the later 15th century, when the statement that Arthur was born as well as conceived here also first appears. But perhaps the most influential association of Arthur with Tintagel was proclaimed in Alfred, Lord Tennyson's *Idylls of the King*, published in 1859-85 and enthusiastically illustrated by the Pre-Raphaelites. Great excitement was also provoked in 1998 by the discovery of a slate with a scratched 6th century inscription including the name 'Artognou'.

While considering these things, or enjoying a well-earned rest from exploring the ruins, visitors can enjoy excellent locally-sourced food and drink in the Beach Café, in a spectacular position overlooking Tintagel Haven and the legendary Merlin's Cave.

Access to the castle and (via many steep steps) the island is difficult for disabled visitors. A Land Rover service from the village (extra charge) can take visitors to the exhibition and shop.

DEVON

BAYARD'S COVE FORT:
SEE DARTMOUTH, BAYARD'S COVE FORT

BERRY POMEROY CASTLE
DEVON – TQ9 6LJ

Tucked away in a steep wooded valley, Berry Pomeroy Castle is the perfect romantic ruin. Within the 15th-century defences of the Pomeroy family castle, still displaying a wall painting of the Three Kings in its gatehouse chamber, looms the dramatic ruined shell of its successor, the great mansion of the Seymours. Begun in the 1560s and ambitiously enlarged from c. 1600, their mansion was intended to become the most spectacular house in Devon, a match for Longleat and Audley End.

Never completed, and abandoned by 1700, it became the focus of blood-curdling ghost stories, recounted in the audio tour.

NON-MEMBERS
Adult	£4.90
Concession	£4.40
Child	£2.90

OPENING TIMES
29 Mar-30 Sep, daily	10am-6pm
1 Oct-3 Nov, daily	10am-5pm
4 Nov-31 Mar, Sat-Sun	10am-4pm
24-26 Dec and 1 Jan	Closed

BERRY POMEROY CASTLE

VISIT US
Direction: 2½ miles E of Totnes off A385

Train: Totnes 3½ miles

Bus: Countrybus 149

Tel: 01803 866618

Local Tourist Information
Totnes: 01803 863168

ACQ.1977 🎧 ⬚ 🚶 🚻 🔪 **P** 🖼 📷
♿ 🍴 OVP

Disabled access (grounds and ground floor only).

Parking (no coach access) at end of long drive (approx. ¾ mile).

Café (not managed by EH) open Tue-Sun, Wed-Sun in Oct.

MAP Page 337 (6F)
OS Map 202, OL20/110: SX839623

BLACKBURY CAMP DEVON
An Iron Age hillfort with impressive ramparts and defended single entrance, now surrounded by woodland with delightful picnic area.

OPENING TIMES
Any reasonable time

VISIT US
Direction: Off B3174/A3052

Train: Honiton 6½ miles

Bus: Stagecoach Devon 52A, First X53 & X54 alight at Three Horseshoes on A3052 between Sidford & Seaton and then public footpath (steep climb c. 1 mile)

ACQ.1930 🔪 **P**

MAP Page 337 (5G)
OS Map 192/193, 115: SY187924

DARTMOUTH, BAYARD'S COVE FORT DEVON
Small Tudor artillery fort guarding Dartmouth's inner harbour, picturesquely sited on the quayside.

DARTMOUTH, BAYARD'S COVE FORT

OPENING TIMES
Any reasonable time

VISIT US
Direction: Located in Dartmouth, on the riverside

Train: Paignton 8 miles via ferry

Bus: First 90, 93 & X81, alternatively Stagecoach bus 22, 24 or 120 to Kingswear Banjo then cross the River Dart Lower or passenger ferry

ACQ.1954 🔪 ♿

Disabled access via town quay.

MAP Page 337 (6F)
OS Map 202, OL20: SX879509

DARTMOUTH CASTLE
SEE FEATURE – PAGE 110

GRIMSPOUND DEVON
The best known of many Dartmoor prehistoric settlements, Grimspound dates from the late Bronze Age. The remains of 24 stone houses survive within a massive boundary wall.

Managed by the Dartmoor National Park Authority.

OPENING TIMES
Any reasonable time

VISIT US
Direction: 6 miles SW of Moretonhampstead, off B3212

Bus: First summer only Transmoor Link service 82 Exeter St David's – Plymouth. Alight at Challacombe Cross then walk 1¼ mile. There is also a year-round service 98 operated by Beacon Bus between Tavistock and Bellever (Postbridge) which is 5 miles walk from Grimspound

ACQ.1977 🔪 **P**

MAP Page 336 (5E)
OS Map 191, OL28: SX701809

DARTMOUTH CASTLE DEVON – TQ6 0JN

VISIT US

Direction: 1 mile SE of Dartmouth off B3205, narrow approach road. No coach access

Train: Paignton 8 miles via ferry

Bus: First service 90, 93 & X81, alternatively Stagecoach bus 22, 24 or 120 to Kingswear Banjo then cross the River Dart Lower or passenger ferry

Tel: 01803 833588

Local Tourist Information
Dartmouth: 01803 834224

NON-MEMBERS

Adult	£5.00
Concession	£4.50
Child	£3.00
Family	£13.00

OPENING TIMES

29 Mar-30 Sep, daily	10am-6pm
1 Oct-3 Nov, daily	10am-5pm
4 Nov-31 Mar, Sat-Sun	10am-4pm
24-26 Dec and 1 Jan	Closed

ACQ. 1909

Parking (not owned by EH, charged).

Tearooms and toilets (not managed by EH).

MAP Page 337 (6F)
OS Map 202, OL20: SX887503

One of the most picturesquely-sited forts in England. For over six hundred years Dartmouth Castle has guarded the narrow entrance to the Dart Estuary and the busy port of Dartmouth.

This fascinating complex of defences was begun in 1388 by John Hawley, privateering mayor of Dartmouth and the prototype of the flamboyant 'Shipman' in Chaucer's *Canterbury Tales*. About a century later the townsmen added the imposing and well-preserved 'gun tower', probably the very first fortification in Britain purpose-built to mount 'ship-sinking' heavy cannon. Climb to the top for breathtaking views across the estuary, and see how this could be blocked in wartime by a heavy chain.

Unusually incorporating the fine church of St Petrox, the castle saw action during the Civil War and continued in service right up until World War II. Successive up-dating included the Victorian 'Old Battery' with its remounted heavy guns, guardrooms and maze of passages to explore. Here, a dramatic film-sequence recreates a Victorian gun-firing, and throughout the fortress displays retell the castle's six centuries of history.

Take the scenic boat trip to the castle from the bustling town quay.

Visit **www.english-heritage. org.uk/dartmouth** for details of special events.

HOUND TOR DESERTED MEDIEVAL VILLAGE DEVON

The remains of four 13th-century stone farmsteads, on land originally farmed in the Bronze Age. This isolated Dartmoor hamlet was probably abandoned in the early 15th century. A free downloadable audio tour is available from the English Heritage website.

Managed by the Dartmoor National Park Authority.

OPENING TIMES
Any reasonable time

VISIT US
Direction: 1½ miles S of Manaton, ½ mile from the Ashburton road

Bus: Countrybus Summer Saturday 'Haytor Hoppa' service 271 to Swallerton Gate. Otherwise the closest you will get by bus are the Country Bus 193 (Wed & Fri only) or 672 to Widecombe In The Moor (3 miles) (Wed only) or the Carmel Coaches service 671 (Wed only) to Manaton (2¼ mile)

ACQ.1972

Parking (½ mile walk across moor to monument).

MAP Page 336 (5E)
OS Map 191, OL28: SX746788

KIRKHAM HOUSE, PAIGNTON DEVON

This late medieval stone house, afterwards split into three cottages, was restored in the 1960s. Furnished with modern furniture, illustrating traditional craftsmanship and the original use of the rooms.

Managed in association with the Paignton Heritage Society.

KIRKHAM HOUSE

OPENING TIMES
| 29 Mar, 1 Apr, 6 & 27 May, 26 Aug & every Sun in Jul-Aug | 2pm-5pm |
| Heritage Open Days | 11am-4pm |

VISIT US
Direction: Located in Kirkham St, off Cecil Rd, Paignton

Train: Paignton ½ mile

Bus: From surrounding areas

ACQ.1948

MAP Page 337 (6F)
OS Map 202, OL20/110: SX885610

LYDFORD CASTLE, TOWN BANKS AND SAXON TOWN DEVON

Beautifully sited on the fringe of Dartmoor, Lydford boasts three defensive features. Near the centre is a small-scale Norman keep on a mound, built as a prison. It later became notorious for harsh punishments – 'the most annoyous, contagious and detestable place within this realm'. To the south is an earlier Norman earthwork castle; to the north, Saxon town defences. A free downloadable audio tour is available from the English Heritage website.

OPENING TIMES
Any reasonable time

VISIT US
Direction: In Lydford off A386; 8½ miles S of Okehampton

Bus: Beacon Bus 118 and Dartmoor Rover First bus service 187 (summer & Sun only)

ACQ.1934 Castle ACQ.1965 North of Town Banks
ACQ.1968 South of Town Banks
ACQ.1972 Norman Fort

MAP Page 336 (5E)
OS Map 191/201, OL28: SX509848

MERRIVALE PREHISTORIC SETTLEMENT DEVON

The remains of a Bronze Age settlement, alongside with several sacred sites, including three stone rows, a stone circle, standing stones and burial cairns, probably constructed over a long period between c. 2500 BC and 1000 BC.

Managed by the Dartmoor National Park Authority.

OPENING TIMES
Any reasonable time

VISIT US
Direction: 1 mile E of Merrivale

Train: Gunnislake 10 miles

Bus: Beacon Bus service 98 Yelverton-Tavistock (with connections from Plymouth)

ACQ.1973

MAP Page 336 (6E)
OS Map 191, OL28: SX554748

OKEHAMPTON CASTLE DEVON – EX20 1JA

OKEHAMPTON CASTLE

The remains of the largest castle in Devon, set on a wooded spur above the River Okement. Begun soon after the Norman Conquest as a motte and bailey castle with a stone keep, it was converted into a sumptuous residence in the 14th century by Hugh Courtenay, Earl of Devon, much of whose work survives. After the last Courtenay owner fell foul of Henry VIII in 1538, it declined into an allegedly haunted ruin. Riverside picnic area and woodland walks within the grounds and nearby.

NON-MEMBERS

Adult	£3.90
Concession	£3.50
Child	£2.30

OPENING TIMES

29 Mar-30 Jun, daily	10am-5pm
1 Jul-31 Aug, daily	10am-6pm
1 Sep-3 Nov, daily	10am-5pm
4 Nov-31 Mar	Closed

VISIT US

Direction: Located ½ mile SW of Okehampton town centre (signposted)). Turn into Castle Road by Post Office

Train: Dartmoor Railway, Okehampton (summer Sundays only) ½ mile

Bus: Stagecoach service X9, Beacon Bus service 118, Western Greyhound service 510 & 599; Dartline service 178 & Carmel service 318. Also Dartmoor Rover First service 187 (summer, Sun only)

Tel: 01837 52844

Local Tourist Information
Okehampton: 01837 53020

ACQ.1967

Audio Tour (also available for the visually impaired).
Woodland Walk Guide available from kiosk.

MAP Page 336 (5E)
OS Map 191, OL28/113: SX583942

ROYAL CITADEL, PLYMOUTH DEVON

A dramatic 17th-century fortress built to defend the coastline from the Dutch, and keep watch on a recently rebellious town. Still in use by the military today.

ENTRY

Non-member	£5.00
EH members and children	£4.00

OPENING TIMES

By Blue badge guided tour only, 7 May-26 Sep, Tue & Thu 2.30pm Meet outside the main entrance	
The Citadel is an operational military establishment, tours may be curtailed without notice. Photography is not permitted	

VISIT US

Direction: At E end of Plymouth Hoe

Train: Plymouth 1 mile

Bus: Plymouth Citybus 25

Local Tourist Information
Plymouth: 01752 304849

ACQ.1966

Parking on Plymouth Hoe. Allow 90 minutes for the tour. No large bags. Bags may be searched. No toilets on site.

MAP Page 336 (6E)
OS Map 201, OL20/108: SX480538

ST MARTIN'S CHURCH, EXETER
DEVON – EX1 1EZ

©CCT

ST MARTIN'S CHURCH, EXETER

This 1,000-year-old church in the shadow of the cathedral is one of the oldest buildings in Exeter. Its tiny parish – smaller than a football pitch – included workers and traders from the surrounding streets. The distinctive red and white exterior complements the light and simple interior.

Owned and managed by The Churches Conservation Trust.

OPENING TIMES

Mon-Fri	9.30am-4.30pm
Sat	10am-5pm

VISIT US

Train: Exeter Central 5 mins walk, Exeter St Davids 15 mins walk or a 5 mins bus ride

Bus: Exeter bus and coach station approx 7 mins walk. Bus services are operated by Stagecoach South West

30 mins from Hound Tor deserted medieval village

MAP Page 337 (5F)
OS Map 192, 114: SX922926

TOTNES CASTLE
DEVON –TQ9 5NU

A classic Norman motte and bailey castle, founded soon after the Conquest to overawe the Saxon town. A later stone shell-keep crowns its steep mound, giving sweeping views across the town rooftops to the River Dart.

NON-MEMBERS

Adult	£3.60
Concession	£3.20
Child	£2.20

TOTNES CASTLE

OPENING TIMES

29 Mar–30 Sep, daily	10am–6pm
1 Oct–3 Nov, daily	10am–5pm
4 Nov–31 Mar, Sat–Sun	10am–4pm
24–26 Dec and 1 Jan	Closed

VISIT US

Direction: In centre of Totnes, at Castle Street, off Station Road opposite railway station. From town centre, turn north off High Street

Train: Totnes ¼ mile

Bus: From surrounding areas

Tel: 01803 864406

Local Tourist Information
Totnes: 01803 863168

ACQ.1947 [symbols] OVP

Parking (charged, 64 metres (210 feet); cars only, narrow approach roads).

Keep accessible only via steep steps.

MAP Page 336 (6E)
OS Map 202, OL20/110: SX800605

UPPER PLYM VALLEY DEVON

Some 300 Bronze Age and medieval sites, covering 15½ square kilometres (6 square miles) of Dartmoor landscape.

OPENING TIMES

Any reasonable time

VISIT US

Direction: 4 miles E of Yelverton

ACQ.1978 [symbols]

Parking with ½ mile walk to monuments.

MAP Page 336 (6E)
OS Map 202, OL20/OL28: SX580660

ABBOTSBURY ABBEY REMAINS DORSET

Part of a monastic building, perhaps the abbot's lodging, of the Benedictine Abbey of Abbotsbury. St Catherine's Chapel is within half a mile.

OPENING TIMES

Any reasonable time

VISIT US

Direction: Located in Abbotsbury, off B3157, near the churchyard

Train: Upwey 7½ miles

Bus: First X53; Damory 61 (Wed only), 253

ACQ.1948 [symbols]

Parking (charged).

MAP Page 337 (5H)
OS Map 194, OL15: SY578852

ABBOTSBURY, ST CATHERINE'S CHAPEL DORSET

Set high on a hilltop overlooking Abbotsbury Abbey, this sturdily buttressed and barrel-vaulted 14th-century chapel was built by the monks as a place of pilgrimage and retreat.

ABBOTSBURY, ST CATHERINE'S CHAPEL

OPENING TIMES

Any reasonable time

VISIT US

Direction: ½ mile S of Abbotsbury; by path from village, off B3157

Train: Upwey 7 miles

Bus: First X53; Damory 61 (Wed only), 253

ACQ.1922 [symbols]

Parking (charged).

MAP Page 337 (5H)
OS Map 194, OL15: SY573848

CHRISTCHURCH CASTLE AND NORMAN HOUSE DORSET

The remains of Christchurch Castle include parts of the mound-top keep and, more unusually, the 12th-century riverside chamber block or 'Constable's House'. This very early example of domestic architecture includes a rare Norman chimney. There is an important 12th-century priory church nearby.

OPENING TIMES

Any reasonable time

VISIT US

Direction: Located in Christchurch, near the Priory

Train: Christchurch ¾ mile

Bus: More services X1 & X2; Yellow Bus 1A, 1B, 1C, 21, 33 & 111

ACQ.1946 [symbols]

MAP Page 337 (5K)
OS Map 195, OL22: SZ160927

FIDDLEFORD MANOR
DORSET

The principal parts of a small stone manor house, probably begun c. 1370 for William Latimer, Sheriff of Somerset and Dorset. The hall and solar chamber display outstandingly fine timber roofs.

Please note: The adjoining building is a private residence and is not open to visitors.

OPENING TIMES

29 Mar–3 Nov, daily	10am–6pm
4 Nov–31 Mar, daily	10am–4pm
24–26 Dec and 1 Jan	Closed

VISIT US
Direction: 1 mile E of Sturminster Newton off A357

Bus: Damory 310 & 368; More service X8

ACQ 1961 🕊 P 🏞

Disabled access (ground floor only – with 1 step).

Parking (no coach access).

MAP Page 337 (4H)
OS Map 194, 129: ST801136

JORDAN HILL ROMAN TEMPLE DORSET

The foundations of a 4th-century AD Romano-Celtic temple.

OPENING TIMES
Any reasonable time

VISIT US
Direction: Located 2 miles NE of Weymouth, off A353

Train: Upwey or Weymouth, 2 miles

Bus: First 4/4B, 31, X53

ACQ 1933 🕊 P

MAP Page 337 (5H)
OS Map 194, OL15: SY699821

KINGSTON RUSSELL STONE CIRCLE DORSET

A late Neolithic or early Bronze Age circle of 18 fallen stones, on a hilltop overlooking Abbotsbury and the sea.

KINGSTON RUSSELL STONE CIRCLE

OPENING TIMES
Any reasonable time

VISIT US
Direction: 2 miles N of Abbotsbury; 1 mile along a footpath off minor roads, not signposted, 1¾ miles

Train: Weymouth (10½ miles) or Dorchester South/West (8 miles)

Bus: First X53; Damory 61 (Wed only), 253 then 2 mile walk

ACQ 1887 🕊

Limited parking on road verge at access to farm. Access to Stone Circle on foot only via public footpaths, off minor roads. 1¾ mile. No off-road vehicle access.

MAP Page 337 (5H)
OS Map 194, OL15: SY578878

KNOWLTON CHURCH AND EARTHWORKS DORSET

The siting of this ruined medieval church at the centre of a Neolithic ritual henge earthwork symbolises the transition from pagan to Christian worship.

OPENING TIMES
Any reasonable time

VISIT US
Direction: SW of Cranborne on B3078

Bus: Damory service 300 serves Knowlton. Damory service 319 serve the nearby villages of Wimborne St Giles and Gussage All Saints

ACQ 1959 🕊 P

MAP Page 337 (4J)
OS Map 195, 118: SU024103

MAIDEN CASTLE DORSET

Among the largest and most complex Iron Age hillforts in Europe, Maiden Castle's huge multiple ramparts enclose an area equivalent to 50 football pitches, protecting several hundred residents. Past excavations have helped reveal the site's 4000-year history – from a Neolithic causewayed enclosure to a small Roman

MAIDEN CASTLE

temple built on the site in the 4th century AD – and produced evidence of an extensive late Iron Age cemetery. Information panels guide you around the hillfort, illustrating its long history, and a free downloadable audio tour is available on the website.

OPENING TIMES
Any reasonable time

VISIT US
Direction: 2 miles S of Dorchester, off A354, N of bypass

Train: Dorchester South/West (2 miles)

Bus: Damory service 1 to Maiden Castle Lane and then walk ½ mile. Alternatively First service 31 or Damory service 61 (Wed only) and alight between Martinstown and Poundbury and use footpath 1 mile

ACQ 1908 🕊 P

Sheep grazing on site.

MAP Page 337 (5H)
OS Map 194, OL15: SY669884

THE NINE STONES DORSET

Now in a wooded glade, this small prehistoric circle of nine standing stones was constructed around 4000 years ago. Winterbourne Poor Lot Barrows (p.117) are nearby.

OPENING TIMES
Any reasonable time

VISIT US
Direction: 1½ miles SW of Winterbourne Abbas, on A35

Train: Weymouth 4½ miles

Bus: First 31 Weymouth – 🚆 Axminster (passing 🚆 Dorchester South)

ACQ 1895 🕊 P

Park in Little Chef car park in Winterbourne Abbas and use permissive path parallel to A35.

MAP Page 337 (5H)
OS Map 194, OL15/117: SY611904

VISIT US

Direction: Overlooking Portland Harbour in Castletown, Isle of Portland

Train: Weymouth 4½ miles

Bus: First summer service 501 serves the castle direct. At other times South West Coaches service 210 & First service 1 pass close by

Ferry: From Weymouth Harbour, Good Fri-end Oct (weather permitting). Call the castle for details

Tel: 01305 820539

Local Tourist Information
Portland: 01305 861233

NON-MEMBERS

Adult	£4.80
Concession	£4.30
Child	£2.90
Family	£12.50

OPENING TIMES

29 Mar-30 Jun, daily	10am-5pm
1 Jul-31 Aug, daily	10am-6pm
1 Sep-3 Nov, daily	10am-5pm
4 Nov-31 Mar	Closed

Parts of the castle may be closed if an event is booked

Disabled access – Captain's House, ground floor of castle and Governor's Garden. Disabled toilet.

Captain's House Tearoom closes ½ hour before the castle.

Audio tours available.

The history of this Tudor fort, which overlooks Portland harbour, is diverse and fascinating. Built by Henry VIII to defend the anchorage against possible French and Spanish invasion, its squat appearance is typical of the artillery forts built in the early 1540s.

Unusually for a fort of this period the castle has seen much interior alteration, though the exterior remains largely unchanged. It first witnessed serious fighting during the Civil War, when it was seized in turn by Parliamentarians and Royalists.

It became a Seaplane Station during World War I, and was in the forefront of the D-Day preparations which helped to end World War II.

Recently-installed presentations and hands-on exhibits bring characters and stories from the long and fascinating history of the castle to life.

The Governor's Garden, designed by Christopher Bradley-Hole as part of the Contemporary Heritage Garden series, contains an impressive circular amphitheatre made from local Portland stone, with two-level seating for about 200 people. This perfectly sheltered spot is a great place to enjoy the dramatic sea and harbour views.

Enjoy a refreshing sea journey to Portland Castle from Weymouth aboard *My Girl*, a World War II veteran boat. 10% discount for EH members – valid 29 Mar to 30 Sept 2013. Tel: 01305 785000 or visit coastlinecruises.com

A range of trails take place throughout the year which are ideal to help families discover the history of the castle.

MAP Page 337 (6H)
OS Map 194, OL15: SY685744

⊤ Available for corporate and private hire

▲ Licensed for civil wedding ceremonies

ST CATHERINE'S CHAPEL, ABBOTSBURY: SEE
ABBOTSBURY,
ST CATHERINE'S CHAPEL –
PAGE 113

SHERBORNE OLD CASTLE
DORSET – DT9 3SA

Built by Bishop Roger of Salisbury in the 12th century as a strongly-defended palace, Sherborne Old Castle became a powerful Royalist base during the Civil War. Described as 'malicious and mischievous' by Cromwell, it fell in 1645 after a fierce eleven-day siege. Sherborne 'New' Castle is nearby (see p.143).

NON-MEMBERS

Adult	£3.60
Concession	£3.20
Child	£2.20

OPENING TIMES

29 Mar–30 Jun, daily	10am–5pm
1 Jul–31 Aug, daily	10am–6pm
1 Sep–3 Nov, daily	10am–5pm
4 Nov–31 Mar	Closed

VISIT US

Direction: Located ½ mile E of Sherborne, off B3145

Train: Sherborne ¾ mile

Bus: First 57, 58 & 58A and Damory services 35, 40, 74, 74A, 216 & 368 or South West Coaches service 42 to Sherborne town centre then ½ mile walk

Tel: 01935 812730

SHERBORNE OLD CASTLE

Local Tourist Information
Sherborne: 01935 815341

ACQ.1956 🚶 ♿ 🚼 🅿 🎫 📷 ♿
⚠️ OVP

Refreshments available.

Secure cycle parking available. National network route 26.

MAP Page 337 (4H)
OS Map 183, 129: ST648168

ST GEORGE'S CHURCH, PORTLAND
DORSET – DT5 2JP

© CCT

This vast solitary church rises from a rocky peninsula. Inspired by St Paul's Cathedral, it is one of Dorset's most magnificent 18th-century buildings. The interior is fabulously preserved, and the headstones in the sprawling churchyard are a treasure trove of tales of murder, piracy and adventure.

Owned and managed by The Churches Conservation Trust.

OPENING TIMES

May–Sept	2.30pm–5pm
At other times keyholder nearby	

VISIT US

Train: Weymouth 4½ miles

Bus: First bus services 1 & 10 and South West Coaches service 210

5 mins from Portland Castle

MAP Page 337 (6H)
OS Map 194, OL15: SY686720

WHITCOMBE CHURCH, WHITCOMBE
DORSET – DT2 8NY

© CCT

The setting of this medieval church evokes the rustic atmosphere of old Dorset life. Its great treasures are the stunning medieval wall paintings inside. However, the church still holds on to its final secret – its name – the dedication is lost in time.

Owned and managed by The Churches Conservation Trust.

OPENING TIMES
Open daily during daylight hours

VISIT US

Train: Dorchester West (2 miles)

Bus: Damory services 101 and 103

10 mins from Maiden Castle

MAP Page 337 (5H)
OS Map 194, OL15: SY716884

For information on events in the South West, visit **www.english-heritage.org.uk/events**

WINTERBOURNE POOR LOT BARROWS
DORSET

A 'cemetery' of 44 Bronze Age burial mounds of varying types and sizes, by the A35 main road.

OPENING TIMES
Any reasonable time

VISIT US
Direction: 2 miles W of Winterbourne Abbas, S of junction of A35 with a minor road to Compton Valence. Access via Wellbottom Lodge – 180 metres (200 yards) E along A35 from junction

Train: Dorchester West or South, both 7 miles

Bus: First 31 Weymouth – Axminster (passes ≠ Dorchester South)

ACQ.1961 ᛗ ⚠
No adjacent parking. Warning: cross road with care.

MAP Page 337 (5H)
OS Map 194, OL15/117: SY590907

Keep up to date with our plans to improve **Stonehenge**, including our new environmentally sensitive visitor centre.

BELAS KNAP LONG BARROW
GLOUCESTERSHIRE

A particularly fine example of a Neolithic long barrow of c. 3800 BC, featuring a false entrance and side chambers. Excavated in 1863 and 1865, when the remains of at least 38 people were found in the chambers. The barrow has since been restored. Managed by Gloucestershire County Council.

OPENING TIMES
Any reasonable time

VISIT US
Direction: Near Charlton Abbots; ½ mile on Cotswold Way

Train: Cheltenham 9 miles

Bus: Castleways service 606 & N.N.Cresswell's 656 to within 1¾ miles or Castleways 559 to Winchcombe village then walk

ACQ.1928 ᛗ **P**
Parking with ½ mile walk to monument.

MAP Page 337 (1J)
OS Map 163, OL45: SP021254

BLACKFRIARS, GLOUCESTER:
SEE GLOUCESTER, BLACKFRIARS – SEE RIGHT

CIRENCESTER AMPHITHEATRE
GLOUCESTERSHIRE

The earthwork remains of one of the largest Roman amphitheatres in Britain, built in the early 2nd century. It served the Roman city of Corinium (now Cirencester), then second only in size and importance to London, and had a capacity of around 8000 spectators. Later fortified against Saxon invaders.

Managed by Cirencester Town Council.

OPENING TIMES
Any reasonable time

VISIT US
Direction: Located W of Cirencester, next to the bypass. Access from the town, or along Chesterton Lane from the W end of the bypass, on to Cotswold Ave

Train: Kemble 4 miles

Bus: From surrounding areas

ACQ.1973 ᛗ

MAP Page 337 (2J)
OS Map 163, OL45/169: SP020014

GLOUCESTER, BLACKFRIARS
GLOUCESTERSHIRE

One of the most complete surviving friaries of Dominican 'black friars' in England, later converted into a Tudor house and cloth factory. Notable features include the church and the fine scissor-braced dormitory roof, as well as the earliest surviving purpose-built library in England, in the south range.

A free virtual tour and podcast are available on our website **www.english-heritage.org.uk/blackfriars**

Managed by Gloucester City Council.

NEW FOR 2013
New interpretation graphic panel on site.

OPENING TIMES
Mon & Sun	10am-4pm
24-26 Dec & 31 Dec-1 Jan	Closed

VISIT US
Direction: In Blackfriars Lane, off Ladybellegate St, off Southgate St, Gloucester

Train: Gloucester ½ mile

Bus: Short walk from Gloucester Bus Station

GLOUCESTER, BLACKFRIARS

Tel: 01452 503050

ACQ.1955 | P | ♿

Parking (adjacent. Charge applies, not managed by EH).

Guided tours available on Sundays in July and August at 2.30pm (charged) or tours can be booked on request.

MAP Page 337 (2J)
OS Map 162, 179: SO829184

GLOUCESTER, GREYFRIARS
GLOUCESTERSHIRE

Substantial remains of a medieval friary church of Franciscan 'grey friars' rebuilt in the Tudor period.

OPENING TIMES

Any reasonable time

VISIT US

Direction: On Greyfriars Walk

Train: Gloucester ½ mile

Bus: Gloucester Bus Station ½ mile

ACQ.1969 | ♿

MAP Page 337 (2J)
OS Map 162, 179: SO832184

GREAT WITCOMBE ROMAN VILLA GLOUCESTERSHIRE

The remains of a large and luxurious Roman villa built c. AD 250, with a bathhouse complex and possibly the shrine of a water spirit. Mosaics are preserved in a small building to the north east of the site.

OPENING TIMES

Exterior: Reasonable daylight hours

VISIT US

Direction: Located 5 miles SE of Gloucester off A46; ½ mile S of reservoir in Witcombe Park; 400 metres (440 yards) from Cotswold Way National Trail

Train: Gloucester 6 miles

Bus: Stagecoach service 46 to Green Street then 1 mile walk, or Stagecoach 10 to Brockworth

---

GREAT WITCOMBE ROMAN VILLA

and 2 mile walk. Also infrequent Swanbrook service 852 serves Witcombe

ACQ.1919 | P

Parking (no access for coaches. No parking permitted in the lane to or beyond the car park).

MAP Page 337 (2J)
OS Map 163, 179: SO899142

HAILES ABBEY
GLOUCESTERSHIRE
GL54 5PB

The Cistercian abbey of Hailes was founded in 1246 by Richard Earl of Cornwall, King Henry III's brother, in thanksgiving for deliverance from shipwreck, and dissolved on Christmas Eve 1539. Though never housing large numbers of monks, it had extensive and elaborate buildings, financed by pilgrims visiting its renowned relic, 'the Holy Blood of Hailes' – allegedly a phial of Christ's own blood.

Interpretation panels guide you around the abbey buildings, and an audio tour brings the site to life. Sculptures, stonework and other site finds are displayed in the museum. The adjacent parish church displays notable medieval wall-paintings. Hot drinks and snacks available in the shop.

Owned by the National Trust, managed and maintained by English Heritage.

NON-MEMBERS

Adult	£4.40
Concession	£4.00
Child	£2.60

National Trust members free, but charged for audio tour (£1) and special events

OPENING TIMES

29 Mar-30 Jun, daily	10am-5pm

HAILES ABBEY

1 Jul-31 Aug, daily	10am-6pm
1 Sep-3 Nov, daily	10am-5pm
4 Nov-31 Mar	Closed

VISIT US

Direction: 2 miles NE of Winchcombe off B4632. On the Cotswold Way National Trail

Train: Cheltenham 10 miles

Bus: Castleways service 606 from Cheltenham and occasional journeys on service 559 to within 1 mile

Tel: 01242 602398

ACQ.1948 | P | OVP

Disabled access (ramp to museum, disabled toilet).

Refreshments available.

MAP Page 337 (1J)
OS Map 150/163, OL45: SP050300

KINGSWOOD ABBEY GATEHOUSE
GLOUCESTERSHIRE

This 16th-century gatehouse, one of the latest monastic buildings in England, displays a richly sculpted mullioned window. It is the sole survivor of this Cistercian abbey.

OPENING TIMES

Exterior: open any reasonable time

Interior: key available from 3 Wotton Road, Kingswood 10am-3.30pm weekdays only

VISIT US

Direction: In Kingswood, off B4060; 1 mile SW of Wotton-under-Edge

Train: Yate 8 miles

Bus: First 311; Wessex 84 & 626; Mikes Travel 201

ACQ.1950 | P

Public toilets near to monument.

MAP Page 337 (2H)
OS Map 162/172, 167: ST747920

NYMPSFIELD LONG BARROW
GLOUCESTERSHIRE

A large Neolithic burial mound with spectacular vistas over the Severn Valley. Its internal burial chambers are uncovered for viewing.

A virtual tour and short film are available on our website **www.english-heritage.org.uk/ nympsfield**

Managed by Gloucestershire County Council.

OPENING TIMES
Any reasonable time

VISIT US
Direction: Located 1 mile NW of Nympsfield on B4066

Train: Stroud 5 miles

Bus: Cotswold Green 35 (weekdays) passes the site. Cotswold Green service 264 (Tue & Fri) also serves the village of Nympsfield (¾ mile from the site)

ACQ.1975

MAP Page 337 (2H)
OS Map 162, 167/168: SO794013

ODDA'S CHAPEL
GLOUCESTERSHIRE

One of the most complete surviving Saxon churches in England, this chapel was built in 1056 by Earl Odda, and rediscovered in 1865 subsumed into a farmhouse. Nearby is the equally famous Saxon parish church.

OPENING TIMES
29 Mar-3 Nov, daily	10am-6pm
4 Nov-31 Mar, daily	10am-4pm
24-26 Dec and 1 Jan	Closed

VISIT US
Direction: Located in Deerhurst off B4213, at Abbots Court; SW of parish church

Train: Cheltenham 8 miles

ODDA'S CHAPEL

Bus: Astons service 351 serves Apperley from there it is a 1½ mile walk

ACQ.1962

Parking (not EH, charges apply).

MAP Page 337 (1J)
OS Map 150, 179: SO869298

OFFA'S DYKE
GLOUCESTERSHIRE

A three-mile section of the great earthwork boundary dyke built along the Anglo-Welsh border by Offa, King of Mercia, probably during the 780s. This especially impressive wooded stretch includes the Devil's Pulpit, with fine views of Tintern Abbey.

OPENING TIMES
Any reasonable time

VISIT US
Direction: Located 3 miles NE of Chepstow, off B4228. Via Forest Enterprise Tidenham car park, 1 mile walk (waymarked) down to The Devil's Pulpit on Offa's Dyke (access is suitable only for those wearing proper walking shoes and is not suitable for the very young, old or infirm)

Train: Chepstow 7 miles

Bus: Forest Community Transport 707 (Tue, Thu & Fri only) passes the site. Alternatively Town & Country Bus/Stagecoach (Sun only) service 69 to Tintern then 1 mile walk or James Bevan 755 to Wibdon and then 1 mile walk

ACQ.1973

MAP Page 337 (2H)
OS Map 162, OL14/167
SO546011-ST549975

OVER BRIDGE
GLOUCESTERSHIRE

A single-arch stone bridge spanning the River Severn, built in 1825-30 by the great engineer Thomas Telford.

OVER BRIDGE

OPENING TIMES
Any reasonable time

VISIT US
Direction: 1 mile NW of Gloucester, at junction of A40 (Ross) and A417 (Ledbury)

Train: Gloucester 2 miles

Bus: Stagecoach 23, 24, 24A, 30, 31, 32, 33, 73, 132; Astons 351

ACQ.1978 Parking (in lay-by).

MAP Page 337 (1H)
OS Map 162, 179: SO816196

ST BRIAVELS CASTLE
GLOUCESTERSHIRE

The fine twin-towered gatehouse of this castle, built by Edward I in 1292, once defended a crossbow bolt factory which used local Forest of Dean iron. Once a prison, it is now a youth hostel in wonderful walking country.

A free podcast is available on our website **www.english-heritage.org.uk/stbriavelscastle**

NEW FOR 2013
New interpretation graphic panels on site.

OPENING TIMES
Exterior: Any reasonable time

Bailey	
1 Apr-30 Sep, daily	1pm-4pm

VISIT US
Direction: In St Briavels; 7 miles NE of Chepstow off B4228

Train: Chepstow 8 miles

Bus: Forest Community Transport service 701 or 707 (Tue, Thu, Fri only) and Geoff Willetts Coaches Monday service 787

Tel: 01594 530272

 ACQ.1982

MAP Page 337 (2H)
OS Map 162, OL14: SO559046

ST MARY'S CHURCH, KEMPLEY GLOUCESTERSHIRE

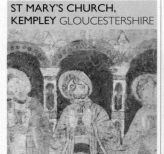

A delightful Norman church, displaying one of the most outstandingly complete and well-preserved sets of medieval wall-paintings in England, dating from the 12th–15th centuries.

Managed by the Friends of Kempley Church.

A free virtual tour is available on our website www.english-heritage.org.uk/stmaryskempley

OPENING TIMES

1 Mar-31 Oct, daily	10am-6pm
24-26 Dec and 1 Jan	Closed

VISIT US

Direction: 1 mile N of Kempley off B4024; 6 miles NE of Ross-on-Wye

Train: Ledbury 8 miles

Bus: Newent Community Link service 677 (Tue & Fri only)

Tel: 0117 975 0714/0709 for all group bookings and winter appointments

ACQ.1979 ☒ P ♿ Parking (in lay-by).

MAP Page 337 (1H)
OS Map 149, 189: SO670313

Don't forget to check opening times online before you visit.

www.english-heritage.org.uk/daysout/properties

ST NICHOLAS' CHURCH, GLOUCESTER
GLOUCESTERSHIRE
GL1 2PG

© CCT

This church beside Gloucester's (now vanished) west gate is known for its leaning, truncated white stone spire (damaged during the Siege of Gloucester in 1643). Formerly one of Gloucester's most prosperous parish churches, it was built for merchant traders, many of whom have memorials within.

Owned and managed by The Churches Conservation Trust.

OPENING TIMES

Tue-Sat	10am-5pm

Keys from Gloucester Folk Museum, opposite church on Westgate

VISIT US

Train: Gloucester ½ mile

Bus: Many bus services in Gloucester pass nearby. Most are operated by Stagecoach

5 mins walk from Greyfriars and Blackfriars; 10 mins walk from Over Bridge

MAP Page 337 (1H)
OS Map 162, 179: SO829188

ULEY LONG BARROW (HETTY PEGLER'S TUMP)
GLOUCESTERSHIRE

A partly reconstructed and recently restored Neolithic chambered mound, 37 metres (120 ft) long, atmospherically sited overlooking the Severn

Valley. 'Hetty Pegler' was its 17th-century landowner. The internal chambers are accessible – a torch is recommended.

A virtual tour and short film are available on our website www.english-heritage.org.uk/uley

Managed by Gloucestershire County Council.

OPENING TIMES

Exterior only – any reasonable time

VISIT US

Direction: Located 3½ miles NE of Dursley, on B4066. Take care crossing road

Train: Stroud 6 miles

Bus: Stagecoach in the Cotswolds service 20 Stroud – Uley (passes close to ☒ Stroud); Cotswold Green service 35 from Dursley. All to within 1 mile

ACQ.1883 ☒ P ⚠
Parking (in lay-by).

Warning: cross road with care.

MAP Page 337 (2H)
OS Map 162, 167/168: SO790000

WINDMILL TUMP LONG BARROW, RODMARTON
GLOUCESTERSHIRE

A Neolithic chambered tomb with an enigmatic 'false entrance'. Managed by Gloucestershire County Council.

OPENING TIMES

Any reasonable time

VISIT US

Direction: 1 mile SW of Rodmarton

Train: Kemble 5 miles

Bus: Cotswold Green service 881 Cirencester – Kemble ☒ Tetbury

ACQ.1979 ☒ P

Map Page 337 (2J)
OS Map 163, 168: ST933973

SOMERSET

ALL SAINTS' CHURCH, LANGPORT
SOMERSET – TA10 9QF

© CCT

All Saints' stands on a hill, overlooking the remains of a Benedictine abbey. Its bold pinnacled tower, bedecked with gargoyles known locally as 'Hunky Punks', is a local landmark. However, the church's special treasure is the largest collection of medieval stained glass in Somerset.

Owned and managed by The Churches Conservation Trust.

OPENING TIMES
Keyholder nearby

VISIT US
Train: Bridgwater 9½ miles

Bus: First service 54, Hatch Green Coaches service 16

3 mins from Muchelney Abbey

MAP Page 337 (4G)
OS Map 193, 129: ST423267

BUTTER CROSS, DUNSTER:
SEE DUNSTER, BUTTER CROSS – PAGE 122

CLEEVE ABBEY SOMERSET – TA23 0PS

The atmospheric Cistercian abbey of Cleeve boasts the most impressively complete and unaltered set of monastic cloister buildings in England. Standing roofed and two storeys high, they include the gatehouse; the 15th-century refectory with its glorious angel roof; an unusual 'painted chamber'; and the floor of an earlier refectory, decked from end to end with 13th-century heraldic tiles, the protection of which was the subject of a recent high profile English Heritage research project. The great dormitory is one of the finest examples in the country. Beneath it are the newly-vaulted warming room, and the sacristy with more early 13th-century tilework and decoration.

An exhibition and touch-screen virtual tour tell the story of abbey life, and a story bag, *Brother Cedric and the Missing Sheep*, is a fun way for families to explore the abbey together.

NON-MEMBERS

Adult	£4.40
Concession	£4.00
Child	£2.60

OPENING TIMES

29 Mar-30 Jun, daily	10am-5pm
1 Jul-31 Aug, daily	10am-6pm
1 Sep-3 Nov, daily	10am-5pm
4 Nov-31 Mar	Closed

VISIT US
Direction: Located in Washford, ¼ mile S of A39

Train: Washford ½ mile (West Somerset Steam Railway)

Bus: First 28 & Webber 18

Tel: 01984 640377

Local Tourist Information
Watchet: 01984 632101

Disabled access (grounds and ground floor only, plus toilet).

Dogs on leads (in grounds only).

Refreshments available.

MAP Page 337 (4F)
OS Map 181, OL9: ST047407

CHURCH OF ST MARY THE VIRGIN, STOCKLINCH OTTERSEY
SOMERSET – TA19 9JN

© CCT

This hillside landmark, made of golden Ham stone, is an atmospheric gem. St Mary's is linked to its sister church, St Mary Magdalene, by an old legend of two sisters who both fell in love with a vicar, each building a church for him.

Owned and managed by The Churches Conservation Trust.

OPENING TIMES
Open daily during daylight hours

VISIT US
Train: Crewkerne 6½ miles

Bus: No bus nearby

20 mins from Muchelney Abbey

MAP Page 337 (4G)
OS Map 193, 128: ST388172

DUNSTER, BUTTER CROSS
SOMERSET

The transplanted stump of a medieval stone cross, once a meeting-place for butter-sellers.

Managed by the National Trust.

OPENING TIMES
Any reasonable time

VISIT US
Direction: Beside minor road to Alcombe, 350 metres (400 yards) NW of Dunster parish church

Train: Dunster (West Somerset Railway) 1 mile

Bus: Beacon Bus service 398. Also Riddlers service 107 (Wed only) & Quantock service 564 (Mon & Fri only). First service 28 and

DUNSTER, BUTTER CROSS

WebberBus services 18 & 106 serve Dunster Steep from there it is about a ½ mile walk

ACQ. 1951

MAP Page 337 (4F)
OS Map 181, OL9: ST823604

DUNSTER, GALLOX BRIDGE
SOMERSET

This ancient stone bridge – originally 'gallows bridge'– once carried packhorses bringing fleeces to Dunster market.

Managed by the National Trust.

OPENING TIMES
Any reasonable time

VISIT US
Direction: Located off A396 at the S end of Dunster village

Train: Dunster ¾ mile (West Somerset Railway)

Bus: Beacon Bus service 398. Also Riddlers service 107 (Wed only) & Quantock service 564 (Mon & Fri only). First service 28 and WebberBus services 18 & 106 serve Dunster Steep from then about a ½ mile walk

ACQ. 1951

MAP Page 337 (4F)
OS Map 181, OL9: SS989432

DUNSTER, YARN MARKET
SOMERSET

This fine 17th-century timber-framed octagonal market hall is a monument to Dunster's once-flourishing cloth trade.

Managed by the National Trust.

OPENING TIMES
Any reasonable time

VISIT US
Direction: In Dunster High St

Train: Dunster (West Somerset Railway) ½ mile

Bus: Beacon Bus service 398. Also Riddlers service 107 (Wed only) & Quantock service 564 (Mon

DUNSTER, YARN MARKET

& Fri only). First service 28 and WebberBus services 18 & 106 serve Dunster Steep from there it is about a ½ mile walk

ACQ. 1951

MAP Page 337 (4F)
OS Map 181, OL9: SS992438

FARLEIGH HUNGERFORD CASTLE
SEE FEATURE OPPOSITE

GALLOX BRIDGE, DUNSTER:
SEE DUNSTER, GALLOX BRIDGE – SEE LEFT

GLASTONBURY TRIBUNAL
SOMERSET – BA6 9DP

A fine, late-15th-century stone town house, with an early Tudor façade and panelled interiors. Now contains a Tourist Information Centre and the Glastonbury Lake Village Museum.

Managed by Glastonbury Tribunal Ltd.

NON-MEMBERS
Museum:
Adult	£2.50
Concession	£2.00
Child	£1.00

OPENING TIMES
29-30 Mar, Mon-Sat (last entry 3.30pm)	10am-4pm
25-26 Dec and 1 Jan	Closed

Opening hours may be varied during winter season

VISIT US
Direction: In Glastonbury High St

Bus: Bakers-Dolphin service 668 passes site. First 29, 375, 376 & 377 and Frome Minibuses pass within ½ mile

Tel: 01458 832954

ACQ. 1932 P

Disabled access (ground floor – 2 steps).

Parking (charged, not EH).

MAP Page 337 (4H)
OS Map 182/183, 141: ST499389

FARLEIGH HUNGERFORD CASTLE
SOMERSET – BA2 7RS

Farleigh Hungerford was begun in the 1370s by Sir Thomas Hungerford, Speaker of the Commons, and extended in the 15th century by his son Walter, Lord Hungerford, distinguished soldier and statesman. The remains of their fortified mansion include two tall corner towers and a complete castle chapel, crowded with family monuments and bedecked with wall-paintings. In the chapel's crypt the coffins of many Hungerfords are still visible, several with attached 'death masks'.

The colourful Hungerford family included two members executed during the Wars of the Roses and another – who imprisoned his wife here for four years – beheaded by Henry VIII. A Tudor Lady Hungerford burnt her murdered husband's body in the castle's oven.

The story of Farleigh is told in an audio tour and extensive displays in the Priests House. There is a virtual tour for disabled visitors and family, plus educational facilities and a schools base with historic costumes.

NON-MEMBERS

Adult	£4.10
Concession	£3.70
Child	£2.50

OPENING TIMES

29 Mar-30 Sep, daily	10am-6pm
1 Oct-3 Nov, daily	10am-5pm
4 Nov-31 Mar, Sat-Sun	10am-4pm
24-26 Dec and 1 Jan	Closed

VISIT US

Direction: In Farleigh Hungerford, 9 miles SE of Bath; 3½ miles W of Trowbridge on A366

Train: Avoncliffe 2 miles; Trowbridge 3½ miles

Bus: Libra 94, 96 & X96 from Trowbridge (pass close Trowbridge ⊜) to Wingfield then 1½ miles walk

Tel: 01225 754026

Local Tourist Information
Trowbridge: 01225 710535

ACQ. 1915 🏠 🖼 🔅 💠 🖱 🚶 🚻 🖼 🗙 P 📷 ♿ ⚠ OVP

Disabled access (Chapel and Priest's House, ground floor only. Disabled toilet).

Refreshments available.

MAP Page 337 (3H)
OS Map 173, 143/156: ST801576

MEARE FISH HOUSE
SOMERSET

The only surviving building of comparable purpose in England, this housed Glastonbury Abbey's official in charge of the (then) adjacent lake fishery. Its design, miniaturising the components of larger medieval houses, is also unique.

OPENING TIMES

Any reasonable time. Key available from Manor Farm house

VISIT US

Direction: In Meare village, on B3151

Bus: Bakers-Dolphin service 668 Cheddar – Street

ACQ. 1911 🗙 P

MAP Page 337 (4G)
OS Map 182, 141: ST458417

MUCHELNEY ABBEY
SOMERSET – TA10 0DQ

This atmospheric and once-remote 'great island' amid the Somerset Levels has many rewards for visitors. Beside the clearly laid out foundations of the wealthy medieval Benedictine abbey (and its Anglo-Saxon predecessor) stands a complete early Tudor house in miniature. Originally the abbots' lodgings, this charming building includes a magnificent great chamber with ornate fireplace, carved settle and stained glass; two rooms with time-faded walls painted to

MUCHELNEY ABBEY

resemble cloth hangings; and a pair of kitchens with fine timber roof. Parts of the richly decorated cloister walk and refectory are incorporated, and nearby is the thatched two-storey monks' lavatory, unique in Britain.

Exhibitions illustrate monastic life with a fascinating collection of site finds, including decorated tiles and stonework. Much improved facilities for disabled visitors include a touch-screen tour. A 'story bag' is a fun way for families to explore the abbey together.

The adjacent parish church (with 17th-century painted ceiling) and medieval Priest's House are not managed by English Heritage.

NON-MEMBERS

Adult	£4.40
Concession	£4.00
Child	£2.60

OPENING TIMES

29 Mar-30 Jun, daily	10am-5pm
1 Jul-31 Aug, daily	10am-6pm
1 Sep-3 Nov, daily	10am-5pm
4 Nov-31 Mar	Closed

VISIT US

Direction: In Muchelney, 2 miles S of Langport via Huish Episcopi

Bus: Somerset County Transport 850 (Thu only); otherwise use First service 54 and walk 1 mile from Langport

Cycle: Sustrans: National Route 339

Tel: 01458 250664

Local Tourist Information
Langport: 01458 253527

ACQ.1927 🐕 E 💺 🚶 🚹 P 🚐 📷
♿ ⚠ OVP

Dogs on leads (in grounds only).

Disabled access (grounds and most of ground floor, adapted toilet).

MUCHELNEY ABBEY

Light refreshments available.

MAP Page 337 (4G)
OS Map 193, 129: ST429249

NUNNEY CASTLE
SOMERSET

The striking and picturesque moated castle of Nunney was built in the 1370s by Sir John de la Mere, a local knight who was beginning to enjoy royal favour. Extensively modernised in the late 16th century, the castle was held for the King during the Civil War, but quickly fell to Parliamentarian cannon in 1645: not until Christmas Day 1910, however, did the gun-damaged portion of the wall finally collapse.

OPENING TIMES

Any reasonable time

VISIT US

Direction: Located in Nunney, 3½ miles SW of Frome, off A361 (no coach access)

Train: Frome 3½ miles

Bus: First 161 Frome – Wells

ACQ.1926 🐕 ♿ ⚠

Parking by nearby church (not EH).

Disabled access (exterior only).

MAP Page 337 (3H)
OS Map 183, 142: ST737457

ST MARTIN OF TOURS, ELWORTHY
SOMERSET – TA4 3PY

© Robert Cutts

Tucked into the hillside above the road, this church has a distinctive battlemented tower with an unusual outside stairway. Inside, there is charming stained glass, and medieval and Jacobean woodwork, including a carved screen across the chancel arch.

Owned and managed by The Churches Conservation Trust.

OPENING TIMES

Open daily during daylight hours

VISIT US

Train: Taunton 10¾ miles or closer station at Stogumber then 2 mile walk on West Somerset Railway

Bus: No bus nearby

10 mins from Cleeve Abbey

MAP Page 337 (4F)
OS Map 181, OL09: ST082352

YARN MARKET, DUNSTER: SEE DUNSTER, YARN MARKET – PAGE 122

WILTSHIRE

BRADFORD-ON-AVON TITHE BARN WILTSHIRE

A spectacular 14th-century monastic stone barn, 51 metres (168 ft) long, with a sophisticated timber-cruck roof.

OPENING TIMES

Daily	10.30am–4pm
24-26 Dec and 1 Jan	Closed

VISIT US

Direction: Located ½ mile S of town centre off B3109

Train: Bradford-on-Avon ½ mile

Bus: Libra Travel service 96, 98A; Frome Minibuses service 98 & X96 to Frome Road canal bridge and then short walk

ACQ.1939 ⚑ P ♿

Parking (adjacent, not managed by EH – charge applies).

MAP Page 337 (3H)
OS Map 173, 156: ST823604

BRATTON CAMP AND WHITE HORSE WILTSHIRE

Below an Iron Age hillfort, enclosing a much earlier long barrow, lies the Westbury White Horse. Cut into the hillside in 1778, this replaced a slightly older horse, commemorating King Alfred's legendary victory over the Danes nearby.

OPENING TIMES

Any reasonable time

VISIT US

Direction: 2 miles E of Westbury off B3098, 1 mile SW of Bratton

Train: Westbury 3 miles

Bus: Faresaver/Libra 87/87A Trowbridge-Devizes (passes ≜ Westbury)

ACQ.1930 ⚑ P

Sheep grazing on site.

MAP Page 337 (3J)
OS Map 184, 143: ST900516

CHISBURY CHAPEL WILTSHIRE

A pretty, thatched and flint-walled 13th-century chapel, later used as a barn.

OPENING TIMES

Any reasonable time

VISIT US

Direction: Off unclassified road, ¼ mile E of Chisbury, off A4; 6 miles E of Marlborough

Train: Bedwyn 1 mile

Bus: Wiltshire Bus services 22 to Chisbury turn then ½ mile walk

ACQ.1982 ⚑ P Parking (in lay-by).

MAP Page 337 (3K)
OS Map 174, 157: SU280660

HATFIELD EARTHWORK (MARDEN HENGE) WILTSHIRE

Part of the earthworks of a Neolithic henge and monumental mound, by a loop in the River Avon.

OPENING TIMES

Any reasonable time

VISIT US

Direction: 5½ miles SE of Devizes, off A342; NE of village of Marden

Train: Pewsey 5 miles

Bus: Tourist Coaches 210 (Thu, Sat only) & 244 (Mon-Fri & Sun only)

ACQ.1972 ⚑

MAP Page 337 (3J)
OS Map 173, 130: SU092583

LUDGERSHALL CASTLE AND CROSS WILTSHIRE

The ruins and earthworks of a royal castle dating mainly from the 12th and 13th centuries, frequently used as a hunting lodge. The remains of the medieval cross stand in the centre of the village.

OPENING TIMES

Any reasonable time

VISIT US

Direction: Located on the N side of Ludgershall, off A342

Train: Andover 7 miles

Bus: Salisbury Red 'Active 8' service, Stagecoach 8 & 80

ACQ.1915 Castle ACQ.1952 Cross ⚑ P

Disabled access (part of site only and village cross).

Parking (limited).

MAP Page 337 (3K)
OS Map 184/185, 131: SU264512

NETHERAVON DOVECOTE
WILTSHIRE

A charming 18th-century brick dovecote, still with most of its 700 or more nesting boxes.

OPENING TIMES
Exterior viewing only from nearby roadside, as there is no access to the field in which dovecote is situated

VISIT US
Direction: In Netheravon, 4½ miles N of Amesbury on A345

Train: Pewsey 9 miles, Grateley 11 miles

Bus: Salisbury Reds service X5 Salisbury-Swindon (pass close Pewsey, Salisbury & Swindon ⬛)

ACQ 1939 ✈

MAP Page 337 (3J)
OS Map 184, 130: SU147484

OLD CHURCH ST MARY'S, WILTON
WILTSHIRE – SP2 0HQ

This 'old' church was partially demolished, leaving the surviving building standing surrounded by the romantic ruins of its arcades and tower arch. Apart from the charming 18th-century ceiling, there are some fascinating memorials to the people of Wilton inside.

Owned and managed by The Churches Conservation Trust.

OLD CHURCH ST MARY'S, WILTON

OPENING TIMES
Keyholder nearby

VISIT US
Train: Salisbury 2½ miles

Bus: Salisbury Red bus service 2, 25, 26 & 27; Wiltshire Buses service 24 & Wilton Park & Ride service 502

10 mins from Old Sarum, 20 mins from Stonehenge

MAP Page 337 (4J)
OS Map 184, 130: SU097313

OLD SARUM
SEE FEATURE – PAGE 128

OLD WARDOUR CASTLE
SEE FEATURE – PAGE 127

THE SANCTUARY: SEE AVEBURY – PAGE 131

SILBURY HILL: SEE AVEBURY – PAGE 131

ST ANDREW'S CHURCH, ROLLESTONE
WILTSHIRE – SP3 4HG

© Cameron Newham

ST ANDREW'S CHURCH, ROLLESTONE

This tiny, charming church, overlooking the River Till, was built of flint and stone chequerwork and has two large perpendicular windows. The church was owned by the religious crusading order of the Knights Hospitaller for 350 years, and still contains its original font.

Owned and managed by The Churches Conservation Trust.

OPENING TIMES
Open daily during daylight hours

VISIT US
Train: Salisbury 9 miles

Bus: Salisbury Reds services 2 & 4

5 mins from Stonehenge

MAP Page 337 (4J)
OS Map 184, 130: SU073431

STONEHENGE
SEE FEATURE – PAGE 134

WEST KENNETT AVENUE:
SEE AVEBURY – PAGE 132

WEST KENNETT LONG BARROW:
SEE AVEBURY – PAGE 132

WINDMILL HILL:
SEE AVEBURY – PAGE 132

VISIT US

Direction: Located off A30 3½ miles SW of Tisbury. Also accessible from A350 (narrow rural roads), coaches approach with care

Train: Tisbury 3½ miles

Bus: Salisbury Reds service 26 Salisbury – Shaftesbury (passes Tisbury 🚆)

Tel: 01747 870487

Local Tourist Information
Shaftesbury: 01747 853514

NON-MEMBERS

Adult	£4.10
Concession	£3.70
Child	£2.50

OPENING TIMES

29 Mar–30 Sep, daily	10am–6pm
1 Oct–3 Nov, daily	10am–5pm
4 Nov–31 Mar, Sat–Sun	10am–4pm
24–26 Dec and 1 Jan	Closed

Disabled access (grounds and ground floor only), disabled toilet.

Refreshments available.

MAP Page 337 (4J)
OS Map 184, 118: ST939263

Beautifully sited beside a lake, Old Wardour Castle was built in the late 14th century by John Lord Lovel as a lightly fortified but showy and luxurious residence. A hexagonal tower house ranged round a central courtyard, its form is very unusual in England.

Substantially updated by the staunchly Roman Catholic Arundell family after c. 1570, the castle saw much fighting during the Civil War. In 1643 the 60-year-old Lady Arundell was forced to surrender it to Parliament. But the new garrison was almost immediately besieged in turn by Royalist forces led by her son. After an eventful three months of bombardment and undermining, they finally capitulated in March 1644.

The abandoned castle became a romantic ruin, and was incorporated in the 18th century into the landscaped grounds of Lord Arundell's New Wardour House (not managed by English Heritage, no public access). The castle's setting in a Registered Landscape enhances the significance of this hidden jewel.

Visit the website for details of special events.

🔔 Licensed for civil wedding ceremonies

VISIT US

Direction: 2 miles N of Salisbury, off A345

Train: Salisbury 2 miles

Bus: Salisbury Reds service X5 (Stagecoach 5 on Sun), 8; Wiltshire Buses 501 Park and Ride service and Stonehenge Tour service. See www.thestonehengetour.info

Tel: 01722 335398

Local Tourist Information
Salisbury: 01722 334956

NON-MEMBERS

Adult	£3.90
Concession	£3.50
Child	£2.30

OPENING TIMES

29 Mar-30 Jun, daily	10am-5pm
1 Jul-31 Aug, daily	9am-6pm
1-30 Sep, daily	10am-5pm
1 Oct-31 Mar, daily	10am-4pm
24-26 Dec and 1 Jan	Closed

Disabled access (outer bailey and grounds only, disabled toilet).

Refreshments available.

MAP Page 337 (4J)
OS Map 184, 130: SU138327

The great earthwork of Old Sarum stands near Salisbury on the edge of Wiltshire's chalk plains. Its mighty ramparts were raised in about 500 BC by Iron Age peoples, and later occupied by the Romans, the Saxons and, most importantly, the Normans.

William the Conqueror paid off his army here in 1070, and in 1086 summoned all the great landowners of England here to swear an oath of loyalty. A Norman castle was built on the inner mound, and joined soon afterwards by a royal palace. By the middle of the 12th century a new town occupied much of the great earthwork, complete with a noble new Norman cathedral, the mother church of a huge diocese.

But Norman Sarum was not destined to thrive. Soldiers and priests quarrelled and life on the almost waterless hilltop became intolerable. The solution was a move downhill to the new settlement now known as

Salisbury, where a new cathedral was founded in 1220. Thereafter Old Sarum went into steep decline. Its cathedral was demolished and its castle was eventually abandoned. But the largely uninhabited site continued to 'elect' two MPs, becoming the most notorious of the 'Rotten Boroughs' swept away by the 1832 Reform Act.

Today, the remains of the prehistoric fortress and of the Norman palace, castle and cathedral evoke memories of thousands of years of history, which are interpreted by graphic panels throughout the site.

Visit the website for details of special events.

Combine your visit with a trip to Stonehenge, which is only 20 minutes away by car, or hop onto the Wilts & Dorset Stonehenge Tour bus service (www.thestonehengetour.info)

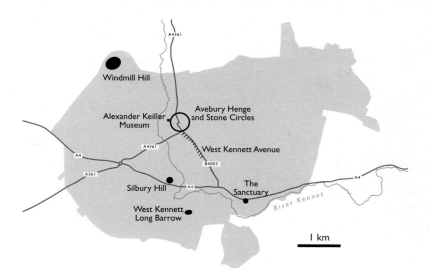

Stonehenge and Avebury and their associated sites were inscribed onto the UNESCO World Heritage List in 1986, one of the first of seven sites to be nominated by the UK that year. Stonehenge and Avebury stand alongside 962 other sites across the world – such as the Great Wall of China, the Taj Mahal of India and Machu Picchu in Peru – which have been selected for their 'outstanding universal value' to all the peoples of the world.

Stonehenge and Avebury were chosen for their outstanding prehistoric monuments. They help us to understand Neolithic and Bronze Age ceremonial and mortuary practices, and demonstrate around 2,000 years of continuous use and monument building between 3700 and 1600 BC.

Management Plans for both the Avebury and Stonehenge parts of the World Heritage site bring a whole range of organisations and individuals together. These work in partnership to manage the site and to protect and sustain its outstanding universal value.

Take some time to visit both parts of the World Heritage Site and you will be well rewarded. At Stonehenge itself, displays in the forthcoming new visitor centre will explore the amazing prehistoric landscape that surrounds this iconic

monument. View the rich collections in the Wiltshire Museum at Devizes and the Salisbury and South Wiltshire Museum, and learn more about the people who built the hundreds of prehistoric monuments of the World Heritage Site. Stay longer in the beautiful county of Wiltshire to experience a very different but equally rich visit to the Avebury area, with its 'sacred landscape' of prehistoric monuments and the Alexander Keiller Museum, displaying and interpreting finds from the immediate area.

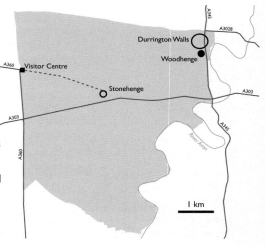

AVEBURY HENGE AND STONE CIRCLES
WILTSHIRE – SN8 1RF

Avebury henge and stone circles are one of the greatest marvels surviving from prehistoric Britain. The henge, built and altered over the centuries from about 2600 BC to 2400 BC, survives as a huge circular bank and ditch just over ¾ mile in circumference, enclosing an area of approximately 28 acres (11 hectares), including part of Avebury village. Long grassed over but once of gleaming chalk, this 'henge' ditch was originally nearly 30 feet (9 metres) deep, with a bank 13 feet (4 metres) high. Within it was a circle of originally about 100 great sarsen stones, making it the largest stone circle in Britain: 36 stones are now standing. This enclosed two more stone circles, each in turn enclosing a central stone setting.

The site's present appearance owes much to the marmalade heir Alexander Keiller, who

AVEBURY HENGE AND STONE CIRCLES WILTSHIRE

excavated and re-erected 21 stones during the 1930s, and whose archaeological collections are displayed in the site museum. Many stones had been deliberately broken or buried in medieval and later times, one possibly crushing its destroyer as it fell.

Avebury is part of a much wider complex of Neolithic and Bronze Age ceremonial and ritual sites. West Kennett Avenue joined it to the Sanctuary, and another stone avenue connected it with the Longstones enclosure and cove near Beckhampton. Older West Kennett Long Barrow and Windmill Hill are also nearby, as is later Silbury Hill, huge and mysterious. Many of these sites can be reached by pleasant walks from Avebury village. This extraordinary assemblage of monuments seemingly formed a huge 'sacred landscape', whose uses and purposes can still only be guessed at.

Avebury and its surroundings have, with Stonehenge, achieved international recognition as a World Heritage Site.

OPENING TIMES
Any reasonable time

VISIT US
See Alexander Keiller Museum

ACQ.1944   🅼 **P** ♿

Parking (see Alexander Keiller Museum).

MAP Page 337 (3J)
OS Map 173, 157: SU102700

AVEBURY, ALEXANDER KEILLER MUSEUM
WILTSHIRE – SN8 1RF

Set in traditional farm buildings on the edge of the picturesque village, the museum is a must for any visitor to the Avebury prehistoric landscape. The Stables Gallery houses one of the most important archaeological collections in Britain, including many notable finds from the World Heritage Site monuments. The Barn Gallery (itself a fine thatched, weatherboarded and timber-framed building) houses child-friendly interactive displays about the World Heritage Site and its people over the millennia, as well as Alexander Keiller's vintage car and a film about his colourful life. There are also a shop and a café, and directions and maps for walks to individual monuments within the World Heritage Site are available.

NON-MEMBERS

Adult	£4.40
Child	£2.20
Family (2+2)	£12.20
Family (1+3)	£7.90

Reduced price when arriving by cycle or public transport

OPENING TIMES

29 Mar-31 Oct, daily	10am-6pm
1 Nov-31 Mar, daily	10am-4pm
24-26 Dec and 1 Jan	Closed

VISIT US
Direction: In Avebury, 7 miles W of Marlborough

Train: Pewsey 10 miles; Swindon 11 miles

Bus: Stagecoach in Swindon service 49. Connect2 line 4

ACQ.1944 **E** 🧍 🚹 🅼 ✕ **P** ♿

AVEBURY, ALEXANDER KEILLER MUSEUM

Parking (Visitor car park free to EH members. S of Avebury off A4361. Free disabled visitors' parking in village car park).

MAP Page 337 (3J)
OS Map 173, 157: SU099700

DURRINGTON WALLS
SEE WOODHENGE AND DURRINGTON WALLS – PAGE 133

THE SANCTUARY
NEAR AVEBURY, WILTSHIRE

The Sanctuary as it may have appeared in the final phase Reconstruction by Judith Dobie.

Begun around 2500 BC, the Sanctuary was originally a complex concentric arrangement of six timber rings and two stone circles. These now-vanished components are today indicated by concrete slabs and posts. Various objects such as animal bones, pottery, flint tools and even human remains were deliberately buried at the site, but its function remains a mystery. Like the similar monuments at Woodhenge and Durrington Walls, it was probably a free-standing ceremonial structure rather than a building. Later, the West Kennett Avenue was constructed to connect it with Avebury, reinforcing the status of this enigmatic but clearly very important site. Part of the Avebury section of the WHS.

OPENING TIMES
Any reasonable time

VISIT US
Direction: ½ mile south of West Kennett, immediately beside s.side of the A4 road

Train: Pewsey 9 miles, Bedwyn 12 miles

Bus: Connect2 Wiltshire service 4 & 5 and Taxibus TL3. Tel 0845 652 5255; also limited service by A.D.Rains X76; also one journey on Tourist Coaches service 244 serves West Kennett village

ACQ 1944

Warning: Very limited parking in lay-by on S side of A4.

MAP Page 337 (3J)
OS Map 173, 157: SU118680

SILBURY HILL
NEAR AVEBURY, WILTSHIRE

SILBURY HILL

Unmistakably dominating the landscape around Avebury, mysterious Silbury Hill is the largest man-made prehistoric mound in Europe. At approximately 37 metres high and 500 metres round its base, it is comparable in height and volume with the roughly contemporary Egyptian pyramids. No doubt encouraged by tales of rich burials, antiquarians and archaeologists have dug three separate tunnels into the centre, but it contains no central grave. Recent conservation work has established that the mound was built in a series of stages over perhaps 100 years around 2400 BC, starting with a small gravel mound. The position of Silbury Hill near the source of the River Kennet was clearly important, but its purpose and significance remain unknown.

There is no access to the Hill itself. This is to prevent erosion of archaeological deposits and rare chalk grassland (the Hill is a Site of Special Scientific Interest). Part of the Avebury section of the WHS.

Find out more about the recent conservation project (2000-2008) at **www.english-heritage. org.uk/silbury**

OPENING TIMES
Viewing area during reasonable daylight hours. Strictly no access to the hill itself

VISIT US
Direction: 1 mile W of West Kennett on A4

USUAL FACILITIES MAY NOT BE AVAILABLE AROUND THE SUMMER SOLSTICE 20-22 JUNE. PLEASE CALL 01672 539250 BEFORE YOU VISIT.

SILBURY HILL

Train: Pewsey 9 miles, Swindon 13 miles

Bus: Stagecoach in Swindon service 49 passes within ¾ mile of the site. Also Connect2 Wiltshire services 4 & 5 and Taxibus TL3. Tel 0845 652 5255 for more details

ACQ.1883 🍽 P ♿

Disabled access (viewing area).

MAP Page 337 (3J)
OS Map 173, 157: SU100685

WEST KENNETT AVENUE
NEAR AVEBURY, WILTSHIRE

An 'avenue', originally of around 100 pairs of prehistoric standing stones, raised to form a winding 1½ mile ritual link between the pre-existing monuments of Avebury and the Sanctuary. The section nearest Avebury is the only part still visible. Many of the pairs, set around 20-30m from the next pair and around 15m apart, seem to follow a set form, with a large diamond-shaped stone matched with a slender straight-sided stone. Part of the Avebury section of the WHS.

OPENING TIMES

Any reasonable time

WEST KENNETT AVENUE

VISIT US

Direction: Runs alongside B4003

Train: Pewsey 9 miles, Swindon 12 miles

Bus: Connect2 Wiltshire service 4 & 5 and Taxibus TL3. Tel 0845 652 5255. Also limited service by A.D.Rains X76; also one journey on Tourist Coaches service 244 serves West Kennett village

ACQ.1944 🍽 P ♿

Parking (in lay-by, or at Avebury).

Disabled access (on roadway).

MAP Page 337 (3J)
OS Map 173, 157: SU105695

WEST KENNETT LONG BARROW
NEAR AVEBURY, WILTSHIRE

One of the largest, most impressive and most accessible Neolithic 'long barrow' chambered tombs in Britain: crowning a ridge above the River Kennet, it is an oasis of wild flowers in summer. Its five atmospheric internal burial chambers, constructed of massive boulders, can still be explored.

Built around 3650 BC, it is among the oldest visible monuments in the Avebury prehistoric landscape. The fragmented remains of around 50 people

WEST KENNETT LONG BARROW

were deposited here, mainly during a short period of time and according to a system: children predominate in some chambers, adults in others. Part of the Avebury section of the WHS.

OPENING TIMES

Any reasonable time

VISIT US

Direction: ¾ mile SW of West Kennett, along footpath off A4. 10-15 minutes uphill walk, on gravel and then grass track.

Train: Pewsey 9 miles, Swindon 13 miles

Bus: Connect2 Wiltshire service 4 & 5 and Taxibus TL3. Tel 0845 652 5255. Also limited service by A.D.Rains X76; also one journey on Tourist Coaches service 244 serves West Kennett village.

ACQ.1883 🍽 P

Warning: Very limited parking in lay-by off S of A4.

MAP Page 337 (3J)
OS Map 173, 157: SU105677

WINDMILL HILL
NEAR AVEBURY, WILTSHIRE

The classic Neolithic 'causewayed enclosure', built around 3675 BC and thus pre-

WINDMILL HILL

dating the Avebury henge. Its three concentric but intermittent ditches cover an area of approximately nine hectares (22 acres). Large quantities of animal bones, cereal crops, stone tools, artefacts and pottery were found here, suggesting the communal gathering of people to feast, trade and carry out ritual ceremonies. Can be reached by a 40-50 minute walk from Avebury village, along footpaths. Part of the Avebury section of the WHS.

OPENING TIMES
Any reasonable time

VISIT US
Direction: 1¼ miles NW of Avebury

Train: Swindon 11 miles

Bus: Stagecoach in Swindon service 49 passes within ¾ mile of the site. Alight between Winterbourne Monkton and Avebury and use footpath

ACQ.1944

MAP Page 337 (3J)
OS Map 173, 157: SU087714

WOODHENGE AND DURRINGTON WALLS
WILTSHIRE

WOODHENGE AND DURRINGTON WALLS

Woodhenge is a late Neolithic monument, where concrete markers now indicate the location of six concentric oval rings of timber posts. The timber structure is surrounded by a circular bank and ditch and is aligned north-east towards the summer solstice sunrise. A small central flint cairn marks the location of a child burial.

Nearby is Durrington Walls, a massive circular earthwork henge 500 metres in diameter. It was also built in the late Neolithic period, in about 2500 BC. Excavations here have revealed two concentric timber monuments, similar to Woodhenge, and the remains of many small buildings, possibly the houses where the builders or users of Stonehenge lived.

Part of the Stonehenge section of the World Heritage Site.

OPENING TIMES
Any reasonable time

Usual facilities may not be available around the summer solstice 20-22 June. Please call 0870 333 1181 before your visit

VISIT US
Direction: 1½ miles N of Amesbury, signposted off A345, just S of Durrington

Train: Salisbury 9 miles

Bus: Salisbury Reds services X5

ACQ.1971 Durrington Walls

ACQ.1932 Woodhenge

🐾 P ♿

Warning: Limited car parking.

MAP Page 337 (4J)
OS Map 184, 130: SU151434

AVEBURY MONUMENTS: OWNERSHIP, GUARDIANSHIP AND MANAGEMENT

Avebury Henge and Stone Circles; the Alexander Keiller Museum; West Kennett Avenue and Windmill Hill are in the freehold ownership of the National Trust: the Sanctuary is in Department of Culture, Media and Sport (DCMS) ownership: and Silbury Hill and West Kennett Long Barrow are in private ownership.

All the sites are in English Heritage guardianship, in the case of Alexander Keiller Museum on behalf of DCMS: the museum collection is on loan from DCMS.

All the sites (except Silbury Hill) are managed by the National Trust on behalf of English Heritage, and the two organisations share the cost of managing and maintaining the properties.

STONEHENGE WILTSHIRE – SP4 7DE

A World Heritage Site, Stonehenge and its surrounding prehistoric monuments remain powerful witnesses to the once great civilisations of the Neolithic and Bronze Ages, between 6000 and 3500 years ago.

VISIT US

Address: Stonehenge, Off A344 Road, Amesbury, Wiltshire SP4 7DE

Direction: 2 miles W of Amesbury on junction of A303 and A344. Note: from June 2013 road diversions will be in place, please follow the signage

Train: Salisbury 9½ miles

Bus: Wilts & Dorset Stonehenge Tour service (alight Salisbury train or bus station). See thestonehengetour.info

Tel: 0870 333 1181 (Customer Services)

Local Tourist Information Amesbury: 01980 622833; and Salisbury: 01722 334956

NON-MEMBERS

Adult	£8.00
Concession	£7.20
Child	£4.80
Family	£20.80

NT members admitted free

Please note: All education groups must be pre-booked

OPENING TIMES

29 Mar-31 May, daily	9.30am-6pm
1 Jun-31 Aug, daily	9am-7pm
1 Sep-15 Oct, daily	9.30am-6pm
16 Oct-15 Mar, daily	9.30am-4pm
16-31 Mar, daily	9.30am-6pm
26 Dec and 1 Jan	10am-4pm
24-25 Dec	Closed

Opening times from 20-22 June may be subject to change due to summer solstice. Please call 0870 333 1181 before your visit

Recommended last admission time no later than 30 minutes before the advertised closing time

When weather conditions are bad, access may be restricted and visitors may not be able to use the walkway around the stone circle

Stone Circle Access outside normal opening hours by advance booking only. Book during weekday office hours on telephone 0870 333 0605

Audio tours (complimentary – available in ten languages and hearing loop: subject to availability).

Catering, hot and cold refreshments available throughout the year.

New completely revised guidebook.

Guidebooks (available to purchase in French, German, Japanese and Spanish). Large print and Braille guidebooks available to loan (English version only).

No dogs allowed (except guide and hearing dogs).

Parking (Seasonal parking –Jun to end of Aug, half term and Easter is charged, refundable on entry).

MAP Page 337 (4J)
OS Map 184, 130: SU122422

This information relates to the existing admission arrangements and facilities. During 2013, we will be working to dramatically improve the visitor experience, culminating in the opening of a stunning new visitor centre in late 2013: this will feature lively new exhibits, improved catering facilities and expanded retail space. See pages 137-138 for more information. If you are planning to visit in late 2013 and beyond, please check our website or call for up-to-date information.

The great and ancient stone circle of Stonehenge is unique; an exceptional survival from a prehistoric culture now lost to us. The monument was begun around 3000 BC in the Neolithic period and construction activities continued until about 1600 BC in the Bronze Age. It is aligned with the rising and setting of the sun at the solstices, but its exact purpose remains a mystery.

Over many centuries, there has been intense debate about the significance and uses of Stonehenge. Certainly it became the focal point of a landscape filled with prehistoric ceremonial and burial sites. It also represented an enormous investment of labour and time.

A huge and extraordinarily well co-ordinated communal effort was needed to carry the stones tens — and on occasion hundreds — of miles by land and water, and then to shape and raise them. Only a sophisticated society could have mustered so large a workforce, and produced the design and construction skills necessary to build Stonehenge and its surrounding monuments.

Stonehenge's orientation in relation to the rising and setting sun has always been one of its most remarkable features. Yet it remains uncertain whether this was because its builders came from a sun-worshipping culture, or because the sun had some other meaning for them.

What cannot be denied is the ingenuity of the builders of Stonehenge. With only very basic tools such as antler picks at their disposal, they dug the enclosing ditch and raised the bank, later using similar tools to dig the holes for the stones. Stone tools were used to dress the stones, and shape the mortises and tenons linking the uprights with the horizontal lintels.

Some of these tools will soon be displayed, together with other artefacts including personal material from graves, in the new Stonehenge

visitor centre. Many items are being loaned by the Salisbury and South Wiltshire Museum and the Wiltshire Museum in Devizes, both well worth visiting.

The first monument at Stonehenge (around 3000 BC) consisted of a circular ditch and bank (c. 120m in diameter), with a ring of 56 wooden or stone posts, the pits for which are now called Aubrey Holes, named after the 17th-century antiquarian, John Aubrey, who discovered them. Some 500 years later the first stones were brought to the site. These were small bluestones, transported over 240km (150 miles) from the Preseli Hills in Pembrokeshire, and larger sarsen stones, some weighing 30 tonnes or more, from the Marlborough Downs over 27km (16 miles) to the north. The bluestones were probably erected as a double circle, and the sarsens were placed in an outer circle, composed of 30 sarsen uprights with joining lintels. Within this were five sarsen trilithons (pairs of uprights with a lintel across each) arranged in a horseshoe shape, with an open end towards midsummer sunrise. Later the bluestones were re-arranged to form an outer setting and an inner oval setting. The effort and ingenuity needed not only to erect the mighty sarsens but also to lift the lintels into position are astonishing tributes to the creators of Stonehenge.

The remains that can be seen today are a remarkable survival of this ancient monument in its final phase.

Stonehenge is surrounded by 827 hectares of land cared for by the National Trust, with visible remains of many different types of prehistoric monuments. These include long barrows; the ceremonial approach way called the avenue; the long rectangular earthwork known as the Greater Cursus (once thought to resemble a Roman chariot racecourse) and the henge monuments at Woodhenge and Durrington Walls (p.133). There are also hundreds of Bronze Age round barrows, which were built during the period after the large sarsens were erected at Stonehenge.

By removing modern intrusions, the changes now being implemented by English Heritage will do much to restore Stonehenge's prehistoric relationship with these monuments and with its surrounding landscape.

Artist impression of the new visitor centre (right) and an image showing the restored landscape around Stonehenge without the intrusion of the A344.

Great changes are now in hand at Stonehenge, which will much enhance the visitor experience. No part of the site will close while the new facilities are being built, and the switchover will be overnight. The date of the changeover in late 2013 will be announced in the media and on our website. Alternatively, call our Stonehenge team for more information on 0870 333 1186.

Stonehenge is one of the most important, most visited and best-known ancient monuments in the world. But its current setting is far from ideal. Now a long-awaited new environmental improvements scheme, spearheaded by English Heritage and supported by a wide range of partners, will at last restore the dignity of Stonehenge, providing visitors with a much enhanced impression of the monument our prehistoric ancestors knew.

A RICHER EXPERIENCE AND ENHANCED APPROACH

At present the A344 main road passes very close to the stones, also cutting them off from their landscape setting. This road will be closed and the part nearest the stones grassed over. Apart from reducing traffic noise and visual intrusion, this will re-unite Stonehenge with its ancient processional avenue, and help restore its relationship with the wider prehistoric landscape.

The current clutter of modern buildings and car parks greatly detract from the atmosphere of Stonehenge. This car park and visitor facilities will be removed, and the area returned to grass. Only a minimal security/operations base will be left near the stones. These landscape works will start in 2013 and continue through to 2014 after the opening of the new visitor centre.

Artist impressions of the new visitor centre.

SPACIOUS AND WELL DESIGNED FACILITIES

A new visitor centre and car park is being built some 2km (1.5 miles) from Stonehenge, invisible from the circle. Sensitively designed to echo the rolling form of the surrounding landscape and admit changing patterns of sun and shade, the new, fully-accessible visitor building will house museum-quality displays, a spacious café with indoor and outdoor seating, and a far bigger shop with a wider range of books and souvenirs.

The new approach to the circle from the visitor centre will be via a 10-minute journey by visitor shuttle, allowing visitors the opportunity to appreciate the landscape of the World Heritage Site and view the surrounding prehistoric monuments. Visitors can choose to walk all or part of their way to the circle, with one stop en route at Fargo Plantation, from which the Stones may be viewed. Meanwhile, a new timed ticket system will ensure that the the site is never excessively crowded.

MUSEUM-QUALITY INTERPRETATION AND DISPLAYS

The new visitor centre will provide high-quality interpretation telling the story of Stonehenge and its prehistoric landscape. An introductory 360° film will enable visitors to experience standing inside the famous stone circle and see the relationship between Stonehenge and the solstice. An exhibition gallery will display important objects excavated at or near Stonehenge – including many on loan from the Salisbury and South Wiltshire Museum and the Wiltshire Museum. Using models, graphics and video displays, the exhibition will help tell the story of Stonehenge and the people who built it, as well as exploring the possible meaning of the site. Outside, we will recreate three Neolithic houses of the type probably used by the people who built Stonehenge, based on those recently excavated at Durrington Walls. There will also be a varied programme of temporary exhibitions, and a multi-functional education space will provide space for school and other group workshops and hands-on activities.

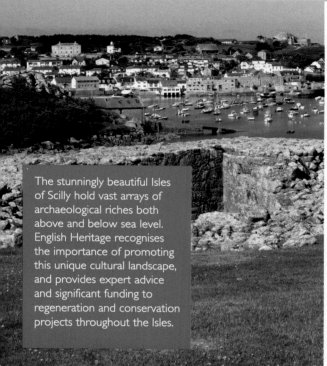

The stunningly beautiful Isles of Scilly hold vast arrays of archaeological riches both above and below sea level. English Heritage recognises the importance of promoting this unique cultural landscape, and provides expert advice and significant funding to regeneration and conservation projects throughout the Isles.

THE HERITAGE OF SCILLY

VISIT US

Bus: Details from St Mary's TIC on 01720 422536

Tel: 0117 9750700 (Regional office)

OPENING TIMES

All EH properties on the Scillies are open at any reasonable time

This compact archipelago of about 100 islands lies around 28 miles to the south-west of Land's End. None of them is any bigger than three miles across and only five are inhabited. Despite their landmass of only 16 square kilometres (6.18 square miles), these islands contain a remarkable number of historic sites. These range from traditional farmhouses and dwellings to ritual burial monuments, cist grave cemeteries and Romano-Celtic shrines. Early settlements provide evidence of a distinctive Scillonian culture which thrived in the island group 2000 years ago. More recently, defensive monuments constructed during the Civil War and World War II stand as testament to the strategic importance of the islands. The Gulf Stream keeps the climate warm, enabling exotic plants and wildlife to thrive.

King Charles' Castle

Cromwell's Castle

St Martin's

Old Blockhouse

Bryher

o New Grimsby

Tresco

Eastern Isles

Bants Carn Burial Chamber

Innisidgen Burial Chambers

Samson

St Mary's

Harry's Walls

Garrison Walls

o Hugh Town

Porth Hellick Down

Annet

Gugh

St Agnes

Western Isles

BANT'S CARN BURIAL CHAMBER AND HALANGY DOWN ANCIENT VILLAGE
ST MARY'S, ISLES OF SCILLY

The remains a Romano-British village in a wonderfully scenic location. On the hill above stands a Bronze Age burial mound with entrance passage and inner chamber.

OPENING TIMES
Any reasonable time

VISIT US
Direction: 1 mile N of Hugh Town

MAP Page 336 (5B)
OS Map 203, 101: SV910123

CROMWELL'S CASTLE
TRESCO, ISLES OF SCILLY

Standing on a rocky promontory guarding the lovely anchorage between Bryher and Tresco, this round tower is one of the few surviving Cromwellian fortifications in Britain, built after the conquest of the Royalist Scillies in 1651.

OPENING TIMES
Any reasonable time

VISIT US
Direction: On the shoreline, approach with care, ¾ mile NW of New Grimsby

MAP Page 336 (4A)
OS Map 203, 101: SV882159

GARRISON WALLS
ST MARY'S, ISLES OF SCILLY

You can enjoy a two-hour walk alongside the ramparts of these defensive walls and earthworks, dating from the 16th to 18th centuries. Other remains include Elizabethan Star Castle and defences from both World Wars.

GARRISON WALLS

OPENING TIMES
Any reasonable time

VISIT US
Direction: Around the headland W of Hugh Town

MAP Page 336 (5A)
OS Map 203, 101: SV898104

HARRY'S WALLS
ST MARY'S, ISLES OF SCILLY

An unfinished artillery fort, built above St Mary's Pool harbour in 1552-53.

OPENING TIMES
Any reasonable time

VISIT US
Direction: ¼ mile NE of Hugh Town

ACQ.1950 P

MAP Page 336 (5B)
OS Map 203, 101: SV909109

INNISIDGEN LOWER AND UPPER BURIAL CHAMBERS
ST MARY'S, ISLES OF SCILLY

Two Bronze Age communal burial cairns of Scillonian type, with fine views. The upper cairn is the best preserved on the islands.

OPENING TIMES
Any reasonable time

VISIT US
Direction: 1¾ miles NE of Hugh Town

ACQ.1950

MAP Page 336 (5B)
OS Map 203, 101: SV922127

KING CHARLES'S CASTLE
TRESCO, ISLES OF SCILLY

The ruins of a mid 16th-century coastal artillery fort, later garrisoned – hence the name –

KING CHARLES'S CASTLE

by Civil War Royalists. Reached from New Grimsby by footpath.

OPENING TIMES
Any reasonable time

VISIT US
Direction: Located ¾ mile NW of New Grimsby. Coastal location, approach with care

ACQ.1950

MAP Page 336 (4A)
OS Map 203, 101: SV882161

OLD BLOCKHOUSE
TRESCO, ISLES OF SCILLY

Substantial remains of a small 16th-century gun tower protecting Old Grimsby harbour, vigorously defended during the Civil War.

OPENING TIMES
Any reasonable time

VISIT US
Direction: Located on Blockhouse Point, at the S end of Old Grimsby harbour

ACQ.1950

MAP Page 336 (4A)
OS Map 203, 101: SV897155

PORTH HELLICK DOWN BURIAL CHAMBER
ST MARY'S, ISLES OF SCILLY

A large and imposing Scillonian Bronze Age entrance grave, with kerb, inner passage and burial chamber all clearly visible.

OPENING TIMES
Any reasonable time

VISIT US
Direction: 1¾ miles E of Hugh Town

ACQ.1950

MAP Page 336 (5B)
OS Map 203, 101: SV928108

DISCOUNTED ATTRACTIONS: **SOUTH WEST**

Use your membership to get exclusive discounts at these independent attractions in the South West. Please remember to show your card as proof of membership.

Discount applies to:

| KEY | ⊞ MEMBERS | OVP OVP HOLDERS | 👪? NO. OF MEMBER'S CHILDREN |

Terms and conditions may apply, so make sure you check the individual pages on our website or call the individual property for more details.

2 FOR 1 ENTRY

⊞ 👪1
AMERICAN MUSEUM
Bath BA2 7BD
Home to the finest collection of Americana outside the United States; features 17th-19th century Period Rooms, outstanding quilt collection, inspiring Folk Art and Native American craft.
www.americanmuseum.org
T. 01225 460503

20% DISCOUNT ON ENTRY

⊞ OVP 👪4
THE ARTHURIAN CENTRE
Cornwall PL32 9TT
Walk through to the unique, 1500-year-old 'King Arthur's Stone' on the site of Arthur and Mordred's last battle of 'Camlann'. Great visit for all ages. See website for details.
www.arthur-online.co.uk
T. 01840 213947

50% OFF TOWER TOURS

⊞ 👪6
BATH ABBEY
Somerset BA1 1LT
There is nowhere else like Bath Abbey. Come and experience the special atmosphere of this holy and uplifting place.
www.bathabbey.org
T. 01225 422462

10% DISCOUNT ON ENTRY

⊞ 👪4
BODMIN & WENFORD RAILWAY
Cornwall PL31 1AQ
The only standard gauge heritage railway in Cornwall still regularly worked by steam locomotives. A great family attraction!
www.bodminrailway.co.uk
T. 01208 73555

25% DISCOUNT ON ENTRY

⊞ OVP 👪6
COLDHARBOUR MILL WORKING WOOL MUSEUM – Devon EX15 3EE
This 200-year old spinning mill still produces knitting yarns and weaves tartan cloth as it tells the story of the once flourishing West Country woollen industry.
www.coldharbourmill.org.uk
T. 01884 840960

25% DISCOUNT ON ENTRY

⊞ 👪6
FLEET AIR ARM MUSEUM
Somerset BA22 8HT
Get up close and personal with Europe's largest collection of naval aircraft and see the first British Concorde.
www.fleetairarm.com
T. 01935 840565

DISCOUNTED ATTRACTIONS:

Use your membership to get exclusive discounts at these independent attractions in the South West. Please remember to show your card as proof of membership.

£1 OFF EXHIBITION ENTRY

⊞ OVP

HOLBURNE MUSEUM
Bath BA2 4DB
At the Holburne Museum you will find a beautiful and fascinating art collection in one of Bath's great buildings. Open daily, free admission. Ticketed exhibition programme.
www.holburne.org
T. 01225 388569

50% DISCOUNT ON ENTRY

⊞ OVP ⛓ 6

KENTS CAVERN PREHISTORIC CAVES
Devon TQ1 2JF
Britain's oldest human fossil was found at Kents Cavern, making it one of the top Stone Age sites in the world.
www.kents-cavern.co.uk
T. 01803 215136

2 for 1 ADULT ENTRY

⊞ OVP

LULWORTH CASTLE & PARK
Dorset BH20 5QS
Enjoy wide open spaces, historic buildings, stunning landscapes, park and woodland walks. Castle displays, children's activity room and unrivalled views.
www.lulworth.com
T. 0845 450 1054

10% DISCOUNT ON ENTRY

⊞ OVP

NATIONAL MARITIME MUSEUM CORNWALL
Cornwall TR11 3QY
Celebrating its 10th anniversary in 2013, this multi-award-winning museum has 15 galleries over five floors dedicated to the sea, boats and Cornwall.
www.nmmc.co.uk
T. 01326 313388

10% DISCOUNT ON ENTRY

⊞ OVP ⛓ 3

PORTHCURNO TELEGRAPH MUSEUM – Cornwall TR19 6JX
Award-winning family-friendly attraction set in secret WWII tunnels. Explore the sights and sounds of the world's largest telegraph cable station. Check website for opening.
www.porthcurno.org.uk
T. 01736 810966

20% DISCOUNT ON ENTRY

⊞ OVP ⛓ 6

POWDERHAM CASTLE
Devon EX6 8JQ
Family home of the Earl of Devon. Entertaining tours, stunning views, play area, animals, treasure trails, nature trails, shops, tearoom and Toby Buckland's plant centre.
www.powderham.co.uk
T. 01626 890243

SOUTH WEST CONTINUED

Discount applies to:

| KEY | ⊞ MEMBERS | OVP OVP HOLDERS | ⋔?⋔ NO. OF MEMBER'S CHILDREN |

Terms and conditions may apply, so make sure you check the individual pages on our website or call the individual property for more details.

50% DISCOUNT ON ENTRY

⊞ ⋔4⋔

SALISBURY AND SOUTH WILTSHIRE MUSEUM
Wiltshire SP1 2EN
Situated in the medieval King's House, within the glorious setting of Salisbury Cathedral Close. Fantastic collections, events and exhibitions.
www.salisburymuseum.org.uk
T. 01722 332151

30% OFF GARDENS ONLY ENTRY

⊞ OVP ⋔4⋔

SHERBORNE CASTLE
Dorset DT9 5NR
Built by Sir Walter Raleigh in 1594, the castle displays magnificent state rooms, Raleigh's kitchen and a museum. Superb 'Capability' Brown lake landscape and gardens.
www.sherbornecastle.com
T. 01935 812072 – Ext 2

20% DISCOUNT ON STANDARD ENTRY

⊞ ⋔6⋔

SUDELEY CASTLE
Gloucestershire GL54 5JD
Described as 'The Queen of the Cotswolds', Sudeley is the former home and final resting place of Tudor Queen, Katherine Parr. Sudeley's award-winning gardens make it a must-see.
www.sudeleycastle.co.uk
T. 01242 603208

2 for 1 ENTRY

⊞ OVP ⋔6⋔

WHEAL MARTYN
Cornwall PL26 8XG
UK's only China Clay mining Museum, Cornwall's largest waterwheel, preserved Victorian clay works, woodland walks, vintage vehicles, mining in action, café, shop, dogs welcome.
www.wheal-martyn.com
T. 01726 850362

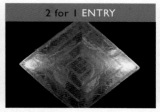

2 for 1 ENTRY

⊞ OVP ⋔6⋔

WILTSHIRE MUSEUM
Wiltshire SN10 1NS
New Prehistory galleries opening Summer 2013 feature the ceremonial finds from Bush Barrow – gold from the time of Stonehenge.
www.wiltshiremuseum.org.uk
T. 01380 727369

£1 OFF ADMISSION

⊞ OVP

WOODCHESTER MANSION
Gloucestershire GL10 3TS
Abandoned by its builders before completion. Enjoy a unique opportunity to explore a neo-Gothic building 'frozen' in mid-assembly.
www.woodchestermansion.org.uk
T. 01453 861541

EAST OF ENGLAND

Audley End House and Gardens

Remember to check opening times before you visit any of our properties **www.english-heritage.org.uk/daysout**

Details of local public transport information in England are available from Traveline **www.traveline.org.uk** or call 0871 200 2233.

Audley End House & Gardens

Norfolk

33 25 26 Cromer
24 22
31
36
King's Lynn
29 30
Norwich 32
28
34 Great Yarmouth
23 27
Wisbech
Downham Market
37
Peterborough
Lowestoft
8
Cambridgeshire
41 35
40 39
38
Ely
7
Huntingdon
Southwold
5
47
Bury St Edmunds
49 43 45
42
Cambridge
Newmarket
Suffolk
Aldeburgh
Bedfordshire
1
48
Bedford
6
46 Ipswich
3
9 Saffron Walden
15
Felixstowe
2 4
16
Harwich 44
Luton Stevenage
Colchester 10
14 11
Hertford
Essex
Clacton
19 20 St Albans
Harlow
Chelmsford
Hemel Hempstead
21
18 13
Hertfordshire
Basildon
12
Southend
Tilbury 17

Make the most of your membership and keep up to date with upcoming events, the latest news and special offers by subscribing to our e-newsletter. Register online now at **www.english-heritage.org.uk/newsletter**

HIGHLIGHTS FOR 2013/14 IN THE **EAST OF ENGLAND**

p.154

p.149

p.172

Audley End House & Gardens: a spectacular stately home explores life above and below stairs.

Wrest Park: discover the magnificently restored gardens and new Dairy sculpture gallery.

Framlingham Castle: climb to the very top of the castle for beautiful views of the surrounding mere and Framlingham town.

PROPERTIES

BEDFORDSHIRE

BUSHMEAD PRIORY
BEDFORDSHIRE – MK44 2LD

A rare survival of the complete refectory of an Augustinian priory, with fine timber roof and notable 14th-century wall paintings.

NON-MEMBERS

Adult	£5.70
Concession	£5.10
Child	£3.40

OPENING TIMES

1 May-31 Aug, entry on the first Sat of the month only. Tel: 01525 860000 (Option 2) to book

VISIT US

Direction: Located off B660, 2 miles S of Bolnhurst

Train: St Neots 6 miles

Bus: Grant Palmer 28 & 29

ACQ.1974

MAP Page 340 (4E)
OS Map 153, 225: TL115607

CHURCH OF ST MARGARET OF ANTIOCH, KNOTTING
BEDFORDSHIRE MK44 1AF

© CCT

This small rural church tucked into the landscape is quintessentially English. The spiked chancel gates were added in 1637 to stop cockfighting and betting, for which the rector of the day was de-frocked! In the churchyard stands a World War I memorial to the men of Knotting.

CHURCH OF ST MARGARET OF ANTIOCH, KNOTTING

Owned and managed by The Churches Conservation Trust.

OPENING TIMES
Open daily during daylight hours

VISIT US
Train: Wellingborough 6¾ miles

Bus: Grant Palmer 26, Bedford Borough Council 30 and Nene Valley County Collect R16 (operated by Centrebus, Tel: 0845 456 4474 to book) all serve the church

15 mins from Chichele College

MAP Page 340 (4E)
OS Map 153, 224: TL004636

DE GREY MAUSOLEUM, FLITTON
BEDFORDSHIRE – MK45 5EJ

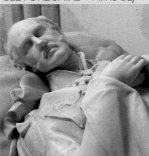

Among the largest sepulchral chapels attached to any English church, this cruciform mausoleum houses a remarkable sequence of 17 sculpted and effigied monuments, spanning nearly three centuries (1615-1859), to the De Grey family of Wrest Park. You can download the audio tour prior to visiting from the English Heritage website.

OPENING TIMES
Weekends only. Contact the key keeper in advance: Mrs Stimson, 3 Highfield Road, Flitton MK45 5EB. Tel: 01525 860094

DE GREY MAUSOLEUM, FLITTON

VISIT US
Direction: Attached to Flitton church; through Flitton, on an unclassified road 1½ miles W of A6 at Silsoe

Train: Flitwick 2 miles

Bus: A limited service is provided by Flittabus (of Ampthill); Cedar service 146 (Fri only); Centrebus 20; Grant Palmer service 44 & 77 (Tue only)

Tel: 01525 860094 (weekends only)

ACQ.1979

MAP Page 340 (5E)
OS Map 153, 193: TL059359

HOUGHTON HOUSE
BEDFORDSHIRE – MK45 2EZ

The shell of a 17th-century mansion commanding magnificent views, reputedly the inspiration for the 'House Beautiful' in John Bunyan's *Pilgrim's Progress*. Built around 1615 for Mary, Dowager Countess of Pembroke, in a mixture of Jacobean and Classical styles; the ground floors of two Italianate loggias survive, possibly the work of Inigo Jones.

Information panels describe the house, its owners and the surrounding hunting estate. A free downloadable audio tour is available from the English Heritage website.

OPENING TIMES
Any reasonable time

VISIT US
Direction: 1 mile NE of Ampthill off B530, 8 miles S of Bedford

Train: Flitwick or Stewartby, both 3 miles

Bus: Stagecoach in Northants service 42; Grant Palmer service 42, 44, 197 & 200; Flittabus F5, F6B, F8; Cedar 146

Tel: 01604 735464

ACQ.1938

MAP Page 340 (5E)
OS Map 153, 193: TL039395

There is now even more to see at magnificent Wrest Park, English Heritage's latest star garden attraction. Wrest Park is among the most vastly impressive of all English gardens. Telling the story of England's love affair with landscape, it is a unique place displaying over two hundred years of garden history and design.

VISIT US

Address: Wrest Park, Silsoe, Luton, Bedfordshire MK45 4HR

Direction: ¾ mile E of Silsoe off A6, 10 miles S of Bedford

Train: Flitwick 4 miles

Bus: Grant Palmer 44 & 77 (Tue only); Stagecoach in Northants service 81 Bedford – Luton; Cedar 146 (Fri only); Flittabus

Tel: 01525 860000

NON-MEMBERS

Adult	£8.80
Concession	£7.90
Child	£5.30
Family	£22.90

OPENING TIMES

29 Mar-3 Nov, daily	10am-6pm
4 Nov-31 Mar, Sat-Sun	10am-4pm
17-23 Feb, daily	10am-4pm
24-26 Dec and 1 Jan	Closed

Last entry one hour before closing

The house may be closed if an event is booked. Entry to the gardens may also be restricted earlier than the usual 'one hour before closing' time, although access to the gardens for those who have already arrived will continue until normal closing times. Please call to check

Mobility cart available for disabled visitors.
New guidebook.

MAP Page 340 (5E)
OS Map 153, 193: TL091355

Wrest's 90-acre gardens were developed over more than two centuries by the aristocratic de Grey family, and have now been re-awakened in an ambitious 20-year-long restoration project supported by the Heritage Lottery Fund. The most recent addition is a garden sculpture gallery, imaginatively housed in the ornamental Dairy.

The gardens are enlivened throughout by charming architectural features, unexpected vistas and a wealth of statuary. More sculptures, too delicate to remain

outdoors, are now displayed in the Dairy, a lovely 1830s building never before open to the public.

Visitors can stroll beside the Long Water to the beautiful Baroque 'Archer Pavilion': the focus of the main garden walks, it still retains its outstanding interior decoration. The intricate woodland paths of the 18th-century Great Garden reveal Classical altars, a Chinese Temple and a secluded Dogs' Cemetery for de Grey family pets. And yet more walks lead to the splendid 1830s Orangery; the colonnaded Bowling Green House; and Jemima, Marchioness Grey's enchanting Bath House, disguised as a thatched Classical ruin. Nearer the great mansion are the Rose Garden and the vibrantly-planted Italian Garden: while immediately below the terrace the formal French Parterre has now been restored to its appearance as at the turn of the 20th century.

In addition to the gardens, some of the ground floor of the French-style mansion designed and

NEW FOR 2013

Now open 7 days a week so you can visit when you like!

- ⊤ Available for corporate and private hire
- ◢ Licensed for civil wedding ceremonies

built by Thomas, Earl de Grey in 1834-9,
is open to visitors. Its unfurnished but
opulently decorated State Rooms
include the Library which served as
the de Grey family's living room,
and the Drawing Room with
its ceiling paintings of wispily-
draped 1830s ladies.

Countess Henrietta's Sitting Room, chintzily
furnished as it may have appeared in the1840s,
looks through to a lofty Conservatory,
unusually built as an integral part of the
mansion. An interactive exhibition traces
the history of the de Grey family and
their estate.

The Visitor Centre in the Walled Garden
also offers a spacious café with
indoor and outdoor tables,
overlooking a children's play
area inspired by the house and
gardens.

Please note:
No flash photography or stiletto
heels in the house.

DON'T MISS…

Our St George's Day
Festival event here
on 20 & 21 Apr 2013,
the largest in the
country.

CAMBRIDGESHIRE

ALL SAINTS' CHURCH, CAMBRIDGE

CAMBRIDGESHIRE
CB5 8BP

© Paul Raeside.
BBC Homes & Antiques magazine

The pale stone spire of All Saints' is a prominent landmark in the heart of Cambridge. The interior is a dramatic blast of colour and pattern – light gleams through stained-glass windows by leading Arts and Crafts artists and almost every surface has painted, stencilled or gilded decoration.

Owned and managed by The Churches Conservation Trust.

OPENING TIMES

Open daily during daylight hours

VISIT US

Train: Cambridge 1 mile

Bus: From surrounding areas

15 mins from Denny Abbey and the Farmland Museum

MAP Page 341 (4F)
OS Map 154, 209: TL453587

DENNY ABBEY AND THE FARMLAND MUSEUM CAMBRIDGESHIRE – CB25 9PQ

Founded in 1159 as a Benedictine monastery, it then became a retirement home for elderly Knights Templars. After the Templars' suppression for alleged heresy in 1308, it next passed to the Countess of Pembroke, who converted part into a house and established in the rest a convent of 'Poor Clare' Franciscan nuns. This in turn was dissolved by Henry VIII in 1539, whereafter the buildings became a farm until the 1960s, with the nuns' great refectory as its barn. Among its tenants was Thomas Hobson, the horse-hirer whose refusal to allow customers to select their mounts gave rise to the expression 'Hobson's choice'.

All these changes are still traceable in the building: they are now interpreted for visitors by graphic panels illustrated by local artist Anne Biggs, together with a time-line tracing the site's history from 4000 BC, a viewing platform and displays of site finds. Family-friendly activities include imaginative hands-on interactives about medieval tiles, stained glass and arches.

Denny's later farming story is continued by Walnut Tree Cottage, furnished as a labourer's home of the 1940s. The site's Farmland Museum also features a fenman's hut, farrier's hut and wheelwright's workshops, a village shop display and many other aspects of Cambridgeshire rural life.

Managed by the Farmland Museum Trust.

NON-MEMBERS

Museum and Abbey

Adult	£5.00	Concession	£4.00
Child	£3.00	Family	£13.00

Free entry for children under 5

Museum charge

Adult	£4.00	Concession	£3.50
Child	£2.00	Family	£9.00

Free entry for children under 5

The abbey is free for members with reduced entry for the museum. There will be a premium payable by all visitors, including members, on special event days – please check www.dennyfarmlandmuseum. org.uk for details.

OPENING TIMES

31 Mar-31 Oct, Mon-Fri   12pm-5pm
Sat-Sun & Bank Hols   10.30am-5pm

VISIT US

Direction: Located 6 miles N of Cambridge on A10

Train: Waterbeach 3 miles

Bus: Stagecoach Cambridge 9

Tel: 01223 860988

Disabled access (museum and abbey ground floor only).

Dogs on leads (restricted areas only).

Tearoom/restaurant (weekends and bank holidays only).

MAP Page 341 (4F)
OS Map 154, 226: TL492685

DUXFORD CHAPEL
CAMBRIDGESHIRE – CB2 4NL

A modest but complete and attractive 14th-century chantry chapel, perhaps originally a hospital.

Managed by South Cambridgeshire District Council.

OPENING TIMES
Any reasonable time

VISIT US
Direction: Adjacent to Whittlesford station off A505

Train: Whittlesford, adjacent

Bus: Stagecoach Cambridge Citi7. Also Myall service 101 (Tue only) & 132 (Sun only)

Tel: 01604 735464

ACQ.1947

MAP Page 341 (4F)
OS Map 154, 209: TL485473

ISLEHAM PRIORY CHURCH
CAMBRIDGESHIRE – IP28 7DP

The best example in England of a small Norman Benedictine priory church, surviving in a surprisingly unaltered state despite later conversion into a barn.

OPENING TIMES
Any reasonable time. Contact the key keeper, Mrs R Burton, 18 Festival Road, Isleham CB7 5SY – 5 min walk

VISIT US
Direction: Located in centre of Isleham, 16 miles NE of Cambridge on B1104

Train: Newmarket 8½ miles, Ely 9 miles

Bus: Freedom Travel service 203 (Tue and Sat only) & 204

Tel: 01604 735464

ACQ.1944

MAP Page 341 (4G)
OS Map 143, 226: TL642743

LONGTHORPE TOWER
CAMBRIDGESHIRE – PE3 6LU

Longthorpe Tower displays one of the most complete and important sets of 14th-century domestic wall paintings in northern Europe. This varied 'spiritual encyclopaedia' of worldly and religious subjects includes the Wheel of Life, the Nativity and King David.

Managed by Vivacity Culture & Leisure.

NON-MEMBERS

Adult	£3.00
Concession	£2.00
Child	£2.00
Family	£8.00

There will be a premium payable by all visitors, including members, on special event days – please visit www.vivacity-peterborough.com/museums-and-heritage/longthorpe-tower for details

OPENING TIMES

6 Apr-31 Jul, Sat-Sun & Bank Hols	10am-5pm
1-31 Aug, Thu-Sun & Bank Hols	10am-5pm
1 Sep-31 Oct, Sat-Sun	10am-5pm

Last admission 30 mins before closing

Guided tours will be available on the first Saturday of every month and are included in the entrance fee. Call during office hours to book

A guide or costumed interpreter will be on site on the first Sunday of the month, Apr-Oct

VISIT US
Direction: Located 2 miles W of Peterborough on A47

Train: Peterborough 1½ miles

Bus: Location is a short walk from Peterborough Bus Station. Centrebus R47; Kimes service 9, Enterprise Managed Services service 406 and Stagecoach service 2 bus nearby

LONGTHORPE TOWER

Tel: 01733 864663

ACQ.1947

Parking (not at site).
No wheelchair access.

MAP Page 340 (3E)
OS Map 142, 227/235: TL162984

ST PETER'S CHURCH, CAMBRIDGE
CAMBRIDGESHIRE
CB3 0AJ

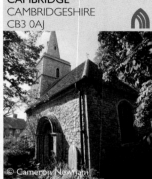
© Cameron Newham

Tiny, tall-spired St Peter's is tucked into a quiet corner of Cambridge, a haven of tranquillity amid the busy streets around it. Mermen, carved into the stone font, may have an ancient link to St Peter, patron saint of fishermen.

Owned and managed by The Churches Conservation Trust.

OPENING TIMES
Open Mon-Fri during the morning; other times key available from Kettle's Yard Gallery next door

VISIT US
Train: Cambridge 2 miles

Bus: Drummer Street Bus Station 10 mins walk from church. Many buses pass close by

30 mins from Audley End House and Gardens

MAP Page 341 (4F)
OS Map 154, 209: TL445592

Among the the most delightful of English Heritage's treasures, Audley End is probably the best place in the country to experience not only the sumptuous lifestyle enjoyed by the aristocratic owners of a great country house – but also how their indoor and outdoor servants made it happen.

VISIT US

Address: Audley End House & Gardens, Off London Road, Saffron Walden, Essex CB11 4JF

Direction: 1 mile W of Saffron Walden on B1383 (M11 exit 8 or 10)

Train: Audley End 1¼ miles. Note: Footpath is beside busy main road

Bus: First 302; Hedingham 417, 418, 419; Stephensons 1, 5, 301. C.J.Myall service 101, 132; Stephensons 59; Excel 5, 301; Four Counties Buses 59, 313; Freedom Travel 18; Regal 322; Viceroy 11, 34, 59, 443, 444, 445, 590; Walden Travel 91, 94 all pass within ¼ mile of entrance

Tel: 01799 522842 (info line)

Local Tourist Information
Saffron Walden: 01799 524002
Cambridge: 01223 464732

NON-MEMBERS

Adult	£13.40
Concession	£12.10
Child	£8.00
Family	£34.80

OPENING TIMES

29 Mar–3 Nov, daily	10am–6pm
4 Nov–31 Mar, Sat–Sun	10am–4pm
17–23 Feb, daily	10am–4pm
24–26 Dec and 1 Jan	Closed

Last entry one hour before closing. House will close at 5pm in September and October due to low light levels. Gardens only prices available when house closed in winter (Nov–Mar)

The house will be accessible for guided tours only on certain days. Please call or check our website for more details

Disabled access (grounds, Great Hall, Stable Yard and Service Wing only. Please call for more information).

MAP Page 341 (5F)
OS Map 154, 195: TL525382

The house takes its name from Sir Thomas Audley, Henry VIII's Lord Chancellor, who adapted the buildings of suppressed Walden Abbey as his mansion. His grandson Thomas Howard, first Earl of Suffolk and James I's Lord Treasurer, rebuilt the house on a massive scale between 1603 and 1614. This immense double-courtyard 'Palace of Audley End' was three times its present size, and one of the largest mansions in England: 'too big for a king', quipped James during a visit in 1614, 'though it might suit a Lord Treasurer'. But in 1618 Suffolk fell from favour, and his vast mansion went into decline.

Charles II bought Audley End in 1668 as a base for attending Newmarket races: his Queen Catherine of Braganza held court here that autumn. When repairs proved ruinously costly, William III returned Audley End to the Suffolk family in 1701. The witty and accomplished Henrietta Howard lived here, before leaving her 'obstinate, drunken and brutal' husband, the 9th Earl, for a royal lover and her new Thames-side villa, Marble Hill House (see p.38).

After the Suffolk line died out in 1745, the estate was bought by the Countess of Portsmouth for her nephew and heir, later first Baron Braybrooke. He made extensive changes, adding a suite of neo-Classical rooms designed by Robert Adam and a Gothick chapel. Meanwhile, 'Capability' Brown was employed to remodel the grounds. Today the house's interior largely represents the taste of the third Baron Braybrooke, who redecorated many of its rooms in the Jacobean style during the 1820s. He installed his extensive picture collection and filled the rooms with inherited furnishings.

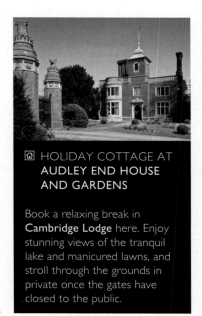

⌂ HOLIDAY COTTAGE AT
**AUDLEY END HOUSE
AND GARDENS**

Book a relaxing break in **Cambridge Lodge** here. Enjoy stunning views of the tranquil lake and manicured lawns, and stroll through the grounds in private once the gates have closed to the public.

The Service Wing

The Victorian Service Wing gives a unique insight into the 'below stairs' working of this great household during the 1880s. The kitchens, dairy, dry larder and laundries are fully equipped with original and reproduction Victorian fixtures and fittings, and vividly animated with lifelike sights and sounds, film projection and even examples of foods eaten in the era. They provide a strikingly atmospheric picture of daily life for the people who once toiled here – from butler down to dairy maid and lowly houseboy. Incorporating research into the real lives of the 25 or so indoor servants employed here, the Service Wing illustrates how familiar household tasks were conducted on a near-industrial scale for the Braybrooke family and their retinue. Watch out for special days when visitors can see and hear from costumed interpreters cooking, washing and ironing in traditional ways (Every weekend, June-September plus other days throughout the year).

The Stables

The lovely gabled red-brick early 17th-century stables, recently re-opened after many decades, are the latest of Audley End's many attractions. Once housing the horses, grooms, coaches, and other equipment needed to service the demands of this great country house, they are now set as in the 1880s.

The horses are back, and there are daily riding displays, plus talks, stables tours and hands-on demonstrations of grooming and horse-care, in which children can take part. Lively interactive displays here trace the development of the estate, and allow visitors to 'virtually' meet the Victorian outdoor staff of Audley End, including the land steward, head gardener, gamekeeper, cowman and groom.

The Gardens

Audley End's park and fine gardens also offer a series of varied delights. Visitors can stroll by the lake through the cascaded Elysian Garden; walk up to the Classical Temple of Concord to view the house in its wonderful setting; visit the memorial to Polish 'underground' resistance soldiers who trained here in World War II; or admire the restored 19th-century formal parterre garden at the back of the house. For practical gardeners, Audley End's massive and renowned walled organic kitchen garden, growing fruit and vegetable varieties from Victorian times, is also an unmissable attraction. Next to it are the new children's play area and Cart Yard Café.

Please note: in some rooms, light levels are reduced to preserve vulnerable textiles and other collections. No photography or stiletto heels allowed in the house.

COLCHESTER, ST BOTOLPH'S PRIORY
ESSEX – CO2 7EE

The remains of one of the first Augustinian priories in England, founded c. 1100. An impressive example of early Norman architecture, built in flint and re-used Roman brick, the church displays massive circular pillars and round arches and an elaborate west front. Later badly damaged by cannon fire during the Civil War siege of 1648.

Managed by Colchester Borough Council.

OPENING TIMES
Any reasonable time

VISIT US
Direction: Nr Colchester Town station

Train: Colchester Town, adjacent

Bus: Bus services to/from Colchester are provided by Beestons (of Hadleigh) Chambers (of Bures), First Essex, Hedingham Omnibuses, Regal Busways, Stephensons of Essex and Network Colchester. Priory is 2 minutes walk from the bus station

Tel: 01206 282929

 ACQ.1912

MAP Page 341 (5H)
OS Map 168, 184: TL999249

COLCHESTER, ST JOHN'S ABBEY GATE
ESSEX – CO1 1RQ

This pinnacled gatehouse, elaborately decorated in East Anglian 'flushwork', is the sole survivor of the wealthy Benedictine abbey of St John. It was built c. 1400 to strengthen the abbey's defences following the Peasants' Revolt. Later part of the mansion of the Royalist Lucas family, the gatehouse was bombarded and stormed by Parliamentarian soldiers during the Civil War siege.

Managed by Colchester Borough Council.

OPENING TIMES
Any reasonable time

VISIT US
Direction: S side of central Colchester

Train: Colchester Town ¼ mile

Bus: Bus services to/from Colchester are provided by Beestons (of Hadleigh) Chambers (of Bures), First Essex, Hedingham Omnibuses, Regal Busways, Stephensons of Essex and Network Colchester.

Tel: 01206 282929

 ACQ.1983

MAP Page 341 (5H)
OS Map 168, 184: TL998248

HADLEIGH CASTLE
SEE FEATURE – PAGE 159

HILL HALL
ESSEX – CM16 7QQ

This fine Elizabethan mansion features some of the earliest external Renaissance architectural detail in the country, and two rare and outstanding sets of 16th-century wall paintings of mythical and Biblical subjects. Hill Hall has now been divided into private houses, but parts remain open to the public by prior arrangement.

NON-MEMBERS
Adult	£5.70
Concession	£5.10
Child	£3.40

OPENING TIMES
1 Apr-30 Sep. Pre-booked guided tours on Wednesdays only

Tel: 01799 522842 to book

VISIT US
Direction: 3 miles SE of Epping. Entrance ½ mile N of Theydon Mount Church

Bus: Closest bus services are Arriva 375; Blue Triangle 575 to Passingford Bridge (2¾ miles)

Train: Epping or Theydon Bois 2½ miles

ACQ.1976

MAP Page 341 (6F)
OS Map 167/177, 174: TQ489995

LEXDEN EARTHWORKS
– CO3 5EF **BLUEBOTTLE GROVE** – CO3 4DU
ESSEX

The banks and ditches of a series of late Iron Age defences protecting the western side of Camulodunum – pre-Roman Colchester. There are also many pre-Roman graves hereabouts, including Lexden Tumulus, allegedly the burial place of the British chieftain Cunobelinus.

Managed by Colchester Borough Council.

OPENING TIMES
Any reasonable time

VISIT US
Direction: 2 miles W of Colchester off A604. Lexden Earthworks are on Lexden Straight Rd. To visit Bluebottle Grove from Lexden, turn left into Heath Rd, left into Church Lane, right into Beech Hill and follow the signs to the site

Train: Colchester or Colchester Town, both 2½ miles

Bus: Hedingham 4 and 15

Tel: 01206 282929

ACQ.1925

MAP Page 341 (5H) OS Map 168,184
Lexden Earthworks: TL965246
Bluebottle Grove: TL975245

MISTLEY TOWERS
ESSEX – CO11 1HB

MISTLEY TOWERS

Two porticoed Classical towers, which stood at each end of a grandiose but highly unconventional Georgian church, designed by Robert Adam in 1776.

Managed by Mistley Thorn Residents' Association.

OPENING TIMES
| Daily | 10am-4pm |

Key available from Mistley Quay Workshops: 01206 393884
Please call in advance

VISIT US
Direction: Located on B1352, 1½ miles E of A137 at Lawford, 9 miles E of Colchester

Train: Mistley ¼ mile

Bus: Hedingham service 2, 85 (Wed only); Carters 93C, 96; First 103, 104, 193; Network Colchester 102 & 104;

Tel: 01206 393884

ACQ.1958

Disabled access (exterior only).

Dogs on leads (restricted areas).

MAP Page 341 (5H)
OS Map 168/169,184/197: TM116320

PRIOR'S HALL BARN, WIDDINGTON
ESSEX – CB11 1SB

One of the finest surviving medieval barns in eastern England, tree-ring dated to the mid-15th century, with a breathtaking aisled interior and crown-post roof, the product of some 400 oaks.

OPENING TIMES
| 1 Apr-30 Sep, Sat-Sun | 10am-6pm |

VISIT US
Direction: In Widdington, on unclassified road 2 miles SE of Newport, off B1383

Train: Newport 2 miles

Bus: TGM Stansted 301; Regal 322

Tel: 01604 735464

PRIOR'S HALL BARN
ACQ.1976

MAP Page 341 (5F)
OS Map 167, 195: TL537318

ST BOTOLPH'S PRIORY
ESSEX: SEE COLCHESTER, ST BOTOLPH'S PRIORY – PAGE 157

ST JOHN'S ABBEY GATE
ESSEX: SEE COLCHESTER, ST JOHN'S ABBEY GATE – PAGE 157

WALTHAM ABBEY GATEHOUSE AND BRIDGE
ESSEX – EN9 1XQ

A fine 14th-century gatehouse, bridge and other remains of the abbey refounded by Harold, last Saxon King of England.

Managed by Lee Valley Regional Park Authority.

OPENING TIMES
Any reasonable time

VISIT US
Direction: In Waltham Abbey off A112

Train: Waltham Cross 1¼ miles

Bus: Regal 211, 212, 213 & 240; Regal/Arriva 250 & 251; Network Harlow 505; Roadrunner 255; TWH 555

Tel: 08456 770600

ACQ.1976

Sensory trail guide.

MAP Page 341 (6F) OS Map 166,174
Gatehouse: TL381007
Harold's Bridge: TL382009

VISIT US

Direction: ¾ mile S of A13 at Hadleigh

Train: Leigh-on-Sea 1½ miles by footpath

Bus: First, First/Regal and Arriva from surrounding areas to within ½ mile

Tel: 01604 735464

OPENING TIMES

Any reasonable time

ACQ.1948

Castle access is restricted as entry is via a 'kissing gate' only.

MAP Page 341 (7G)
OS Map 178, 175: TQ810860

The romantic ruins of a royal castle on a ridge overlooking the Essex marshes and the Thames estuary. The first castle was begun in about 1215 by Hubert de Burgh, King John's powerful Justiciar, probably as a towered octagonal enclosure. But in 1239 it was confiscated by Henry III, and thereafter remained in royal ownership or gift for over three centuries.

Conveniently accessible from London by royal barge, Hadleigh Castle was extensively rebuilt by Edward III during the 1360s, to which period most of the surviving remains belong. Edward's refurbished castle was intended partly to reinforce the defences of the Thames Estuary against French invasion: the towers looking towards the estuary would have presented a strong impression of power and security. Yet the now ageing king's main use of the castle was probably as a personal retreat, where he could stay in privacy and comfort: excavated remains of Edward's great hall, with its 'solar' or private withdrawing room, can still be seen here.

After Edward III's death in 1377 his successors took little interest in Hadleigh, whose tenancy passed to a series of mainly absentee royal relations, including three of Henry VIII's queens. Eventually the castle was sold in 1551, and substantially demolished for building materials. Yet Edward III's two big eastern drum towers still remain, the south-east tower – allegedly used by Georgian revenue men looking out for smugglers – still commandingly standing three storeys high.

VISIT US

Direction: Located ½ mile E of Tilbury off A126, close to the Port of Tilbury

Train: Tilbury Town 1½ miles

Bus: Ensignbus service 99 connects with trains at Tilbury Town and passes the fort

Ferry: Gravesend – Tilbury Ferry, then ¼ mile

Tel: 01375 858489

NON-MEMBERS

Adult	£4.60
Concession	£4.10
Child	£2.80
Family	£12.00

OPENING TIMES

29 Mar-3 Nov, Wed-Sun	10am-5pm
4 Nov-31 Mar, Sat-Sun	10am-4pm
24-26 Dec and 1 Jan	Closed

ACQ 1948

Disabled access (exterior, magazines and fort square).

Dogs on leads (restricted areas).

MAP Page 341 (7G)
OS Map 177/178,162/163: TQ651753

The great artillery fort at Tilbury on the Thames estuary defended London's seaward approach from the 16th century through to World War II. Henry VIII built the first fort here, and Queen Elizabeth I famously rallied her army nearby to face the threat of the Armada. The present fort was begun in 1672 under Charles II: it is much the best example of its type in England, with its complete circuit of moats and bastioned outworks still substantially surviving. The fort mounted powerful artillery to command the river, as well as landward defences. The east magazine houses an exhibition which traces its role in the defence of London.

Visitors can now enter the north-east bastion. There are displays of guns and gunpowder barrels, and information on advances in military engineering. The audio tour includes Elizabeth I's Armada speech, and a description of life at Tilbury by 'Nathan Makepiece', the fort's Master Gunner. Our interactive oral history programme provides a fascinating insight into Tilbury, and also includes 360 degree views of inaccessible areas.

Sharpe, the TV historical drama set during the Napoleonic Wars.

HERTFORDSHIRE

BERKHAMSTED CASTLE
HERTFORDSHIRE – HP4 1HH

The substantial remains of a strong and important motte and bailey castle dating from the 11th to 15th centuries, with surrounding walls, ditches and earthworks. Lived in by Thomas Becket in the 12th century; Richard Earl of Cornwall added a 13th-century palace complex.

OPENING TIMES

Summer, daily	10am-6pm
Winter, daily	10am-4pm
25 Dec and 1 Jan	Closed

VISIT US
Direction: Near ⊒ Berkhamsted

Train: Berkhamsted, adjacent

Bus: Arriva The Shires service 354 and Little Jim's service 532 pass the castle

Tel: 01604 735464

ACQ.1929 🐕

MAP Page 340 (6D)
OS Map 165, 181: SP995082

CHURCH OF ST MARY THE VIRGIN, LITTLE HORMEAD
HERTFORDSHIRE
SG9 0LS

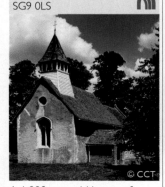
© CCT

A 1,000-year-old haven of tranquillity set in a churchyard encircled by trees. Atmospheric St Mary's is a rare and precious

CHURCH OF ST MARY THE VIRGIN, LITTLE HORMEAD

survival with a rare Norman chancel arch, and some wonderful craftsmanship in wood and ironwork, including an original Norman door.

Owned and managed by The Churches Conservation Trust.

OPENING TIMES
Please see Churches Conservation Trust website for current opening times

VISIT US
Train: Bishop's Stortford 7½ miles, Stansted Airport 7¾ miles, Royston 8 miles

Bus: Richmonds Coaches 27 (Wed only), 28 (Mon only), 334 (Fri only) or 386 (Thu only) and Arriva The Shires 331

25 mins from Audley End House and Gardens

MAP Page 341 (5F)
OS Map 166, 194: TL398291

OLD GORHAMBURY HOUSE
HERTFORDSHIRE – AL3 6AH

The remains of a once immense mansion built in 1563-8 by Sir Nicholas Bacon, Queen Elizabeth's Lord Keeper, and visited by the queen on at least four occasions. Its elaborately

OLD GORHAMBURY HOUSE

decorated Classical two-storey porch survives, with parts of the hall, chapel and clock-tower.

OPENING TIMES
All year (except 1 Jun & Saturdays 1 Sep-1 Feb), 8am-6pm. Access by car limited to Thu May-Sep 2pm-5pm, but access is possible on foot via a 2 mile path on all days when house is open

VISIT US
Direction: Just off A4147 on western outskirts of St Albans. Walk up 2 mile drive on permissive path. Access by car is limited

Train: St Albans Abbey 3 miles, St Albans 3½ miles

Bus: Arriva/Uno services 300, 301 pass start of drive

Tel: 01604 735464

ACQ.1959 🐾

MAP Page 340 (6E)
OS Map 166, 182: TL110076

ROMAN WALL, ST ALBANS
HERTFORDSHIRE – AL3 4BL

A section of the two-mile-long wall built between AD 265 and 270 to defend the Roman city of Verulamium, including the foundations of towers and the London Gate.

OPENING TIMES
Any reasonable time

VISIT US
Direction: Located on the S side of St Albans, ½ mile from the centre, off the A4147

Train: St Albans Abbey ½ mile, St Albans 1¼ miles

Bus: Uno services S8 & S9 operate close to the Roman Wall site

Tel: 01604 735464

ACQ.1931 🐕

MAP Page 340 (6E)
OS Map 166, 182: TL137066

NORFOLK

BACONSTHORPE CASTLE
NORFOLK – NR25 6LE

Surrounded by a reedy moat and a wildfowl-haunted mere, the evocative ruins of this fortified manor house chronicle the rise and fall of the ambitious Heydon family over two centuries. The wealthy but 'crafty and quarrelsome' John Heydon built the imposing inner gatehouse and first castle in the 1450s, during the troubled Wars of the Roses period, and his son Sir Henry extended the gunport-defended castle to include a garden court. Subsequent generations converted part of the site into a textile factory, and added the turreted Elizabethan outer gatehouse, but the family eventually succumbed to bankruptcy and sold their mansion for salvage.

The castle stands astride walking and cycle trails. Download a free audio tour from our website before you visit.

OPENING TIMES
Any reasonable time

VISIT US
Direction: ¾ mile N of village of Baconsthorpe off unclassified road, 3 miles E of Holt

Train: Sheringham 4½ miles

Bus: Sanders service 16 (Tue and Fri only) or 17 (Thu only) and the Baconsthorpe Community Bus (Wed and Fri only) serve the village

Tel: 01604 735464

ACQ.1966

MAP Page 341 (1H)
OS Map 133, 252: TG121382

BERNEY ARMS WINDMILL
NORFOLK

One of Norfolk's best and largest extant marsh mills, built to grind a constituent of cement and in use until 1951, finally pumping water to drain surrounding marshland.

Access to Berney Arms Windmill is currently by pre-booked group tours only, for further information please call the Great Yarmouth Row Houses on 01493 857900.

OPENING TIMES
Access by pre-arranged booking – please ring 01493 857900 for details

VISIT US
Direction: 3½ miles NE of Reedham on the N bank of River Yare. Accessible by hired boat, or by footpath from Halvergate (3½ miles)

Train: Berney Arms ¼ mile

Tel: 01493 857900

ACQ.1950

MAP Page 341 (3K)
OS Map 134, OL40: TG465049

BINHAM MARKET CROSS
NORFOLK – NR21 0DW

The tall shaft of a 15th-century cross, on the site of an annual fair held from the 1100s until the 1950s.

Managed by Binham Parochial Church Council.

OPENING TIMES
Any reasonable time

BINHAM MARKET CROSS

VISIT US
Direction: Located on the Binham village green adjacent to the Priory

Bus: Sanders service 13 (Thu only) and 46

Tel: 01604 735464

ACQ.1949

MAP Page 341 (1H)
OS Map 132, 251: TF984396

BINHAM PRIORY
NORFOLK – NR21 0DQ

Among the most impressive monastic sites in East Anglia, Binham Priory retains its nave – now the parish church – virtually complete, with a striking 13th-century west front and triple tiers of late Norman arches within, along with screens revealing medieval saints peeping through later overpainting. The extensive ruins beyond, notably the massive piers of the fallen church tower, emphasise the original size of this Benedictine priory.

Major recent enhancements, carried out by local initiatives with English Heritage support, make a visit even more worthwhile. They include much improved disabled access, a fascinating display of site finds, toilets, and a children's activity area.

Managed by Binham Parochial Church Council.

OPENING TIMES
Binham Priory (monastic ruins):
Any reasonable time

Priory Church:	
Summer, daily	9am-6pm
Winter, daily	9am-4pm

VISIT US
Direction: ¼ mile NW of village of Binham on road off B1388

Bus: Sanders service 13 (Thu only) & 46

BINHAM PRIORY

Tel: 01328 830362

ACQ.1933 E ⛪ 🚶 P ♿

Toilets available in Church.

MAP Page 341 (1H)
OS Map 132, 251: TF982399

BLAKENEY GUILDHALL
NORFOLK – NR25 7NA

A relic of Blakeney's medieval prosperity, the remains of a flint 15th-century merchant's house with complete brick-vaulted undercroft. Later the Guildhall of the port's fish merchants.

Managed by Blakeney Parish Council.

OPENING TIMES

Any reasonable time

VISIT US

Direction: In Blakeney off A149

Train: Sheringham 9 miles

Bus: Norfolk Green Coasthopper service (CH3), Sanders service 13 (Thu only) and 46

Tel: 01263 741106

ACQ.1956 🐾

MAP Page 341 (1H)
OS Map 133, 251: TG028441

BURGH CASTLE
NORFOLK – NR21 9QG

The imposing stone walls, with added towers for catapults, of a Roman 3rd-century 'Saxon Shore' fort. Panoramic views over Breydon Water, into which the fourth wall long since collapsed.

A free podcast is available on our website **www.english-heritage.org.uk/burghcastle**

Managed by Norfolk Archaeological Trust.

OPENING TIMES

Any reasonable time

BURGH CASTLE

VISIT US

Direction: At far W end of Breydon Water on unclassified road, 3 miles W of Great Yarmouth

Train: Great Yarmouth 5 miles

Bus: First 5 from Great Yarmouth then a short walk

Tel: 01604 735464

ACQ.1929 🐾

MAP Page 341 (3K)
OS Map 134, OL40: TG475047

CAISTER ROMAN FORT
NORFOLK – NR30 5JS

The partial excavated remains of a Roman 'Saxon Shore' fort, including wall and ditch sections and building foundations. Built around AD 200 for a unit of the Roman army and navy, and occupied until the end of the 4th century.

Managed by Great Yarmouth Borough Council.

OPENING TIMES

Any reasonable time

VISIT US

Direction: From Great Yarmouth, follow the A149 northbound and then the A149 Caister Bypass. Follow brown tourist signs for Caister Roman Fort. From other directons follow signs for Great Yarmouth and then brown tourist signs from the Caister Bypass roundabout. Parking and the entrance to the Fort are situated off a lay-by on Norwich Road ¼ mile from the roundabout

Train: Great Yarmouth 3 miles

Bus: First services 1, 1A, 4 pass the site; Sanders 6 and Anglian 586 pass within ½ mile.

Tel: 01493 846534

ACQ.1954 🐾

MAP Page 341 (2K)
OS Map 134, OL40: TG517123

CASTLE RISING CASTLE
NORFOLK – PE31 6AH

One of the biggest, most complete and most lavishly decorated Norman keeps in England, with an impressive entrance forebuilding, surrounded by stupendous earthworks. Begun in 1138 by William d'Albini for his wife, the widow of Henry I, in the 14th century it became the luxurious prison of Queen Isabella, widow (and alleged murderess) of Edward II.

Owned and managed by Lord Howard of Rising.

www.castlerising.co.uk

NON-MEMBERS

Adult	£4.00
Concession	£3.30
Child	£2.50
Family (2+2)	£12.00

There will be a premium payable by all visitors, including members, on special event days – please check www.castlerising.co.uk for details

OPENING TIMES

1 Apr–1 Nov, daily (or dusk if earlier in Oct)	10am–6pm
2 Nov–31 Mar, Wed–Sun	10am–4pm
24–26 Dec	Closed

VISIT US

Direction: Located 4 miles NE of King's Lynn off A149

Train: King's Lynn 4½ miles

Bus: Norfolk Green 11 to Castle Rising

Tel: 01553 631330

ACQ.1958 🐾 🚶 P 📷 ♿ ⚠

Disabled access (exterior only, toilets).

Dogs on leads (restricted areas).

MAP Page 341 (2G)
OS Map 132, 250: TF666246

The delightful village of Castle Acre boasts an extraordinary wealth of history.

Situated on the Peddar's Way, a major trade and pilgrim route to Thetford, Bromholm Priory and Walsingham, it is a very rare and complete survival of a Norman planned settlement, including a castle, town, fine parish church and associated monastery. All this is the work of a powerful Norman baronial family, the Warennes, mainly during the 11th and 12th centuries.

First came the castle, founded soon after the Conquest by the first William de Warenne, probably as a stone 'country house'. During the first half of the 12th century, however, more disturbed conditions prompted its progressive conversion into a strong keep, further defended by stone walls and an immense system of earthworks. These massive ramparts and ditches are perhaps the finest castle earthworks anywhere in England.

Meanwhile, the 'planned town', deliberately established outside the castle, was also protected by ditched earthwork defences with stone gates. The north or Bailey Gate survives, with the main road into the village still running between its towers.

Visitors to Castle Acre can likewise trace the ancient street layout of this now peaceful village, lined with attractive flint or brick houses, before exploring both the great castle earthworks and the extensive priory remains. A village and castle trail can be downloaded from the Castle Acre Priory page of the English Heritage website.

CASTLE ACRE CASTLE AND BAILEY GATE
NORFOLK – PE32 2AJ

VISIT US
Direction: Located at the E end of Castle Acre, 5 miles N of Swaffham

Bus: West Norfolk Community Transport (weekdays); Freestone Coaches 32; Peelings 1 (Tue)

Tel: 01604 735464

OPENING TIMES
Any reasonable time

ACQ.1970 Castle ACQ.1938 Bailey Gate 🐾 ⚠ (Castle only)

MAP Page 341 (2G) OS Map 132, 236/238
Bailey Gate: TF819152 Castle: TF819152

VISIT US

Direction: ¼ mile W of village of Castle Acre, 5 miles N of Swaffham

Bus: West Norfolk Community Transport (weekdays); Freestone Coaches 32; Peelings 1 (Tue)

Tel: 01760 755394

NON-MEMBERS

Adult	£5.80
Concession	£5.20
Child	£3.50
Family	£15.10

OPENING TIMES

29 Mar-3 Nov, daily	10am-5pm
4 Nov-31 Mar, Sat-Sun	10am-4pm
24-26 Dec and 1 Jan	Closed

Disabled access (ground floor and grounds only).

Toilets (a short walk. Not accessible for wheelchairs; 50 metres from entrance, with single step for access).

MAP Page 341 (2G)
OS Map 132, 236/238: TF814148

Among the largest and best-preserved monastic sites in all England, Castle Acre Priory often surprises new visitors by its immense size and variety. Its foundation in about 1090 by William de Warenne II reflected his family's devotion to the famous French monastery of Cluny: the Cluniac order's love of architectural decoration is displayed in the beautiful west front of the great 12th-century priory church, bedecked with tiers of intersecting round arches. Beyond extend the impressive remains of the cloister and monks' living quarters, including a gigantic, two-storey, 24-seater toilet block.

Best preserved of all is the west range, virtually complete and fully roofed. Its timber-framed and flint-chequered porch and oriel-windowed prior's lodging form an outstandingly attractive grouping with the church's west front. A mansion in itself, the lodging includes a chamber sumptuously revamped in early Tudor times for one of the last priors; with decorated fireplace, ceiling painted with Tudor roses, and two massive timber chests still in place. The adjacent prior's chapel was once even more elaborately adorned, with traces of medieval wall paintings still visible.

There is much more to see, including our exhibition and display of archaeological finds, site model and audio tour featuring a 15th-century chant from a Castle Acre song book. The recreated herb garden grows plants the monks would have used for medicinal and culinary purposes. There is also a large activities barn for schools. A priory terrain guide can be downloaded from the Castle Acre Priory page of the English Heritage website.

CHURCH OF ST JOHN, MADDERMARKET, NORWICH
NORFOLK – NR2 1DS

© CCT

500-year-old St John's, which survived a gas explosion in 1876, is squeezed ingeniously into a cramped site. The almost square, light-filled interior is crowded with marvellous monuments, furnishings and rich stained glass. One of three CCT churches in Norwich.

Owned and managed by The Churches Conservation Trust.

OPENING TIMES
Please see Churches Conservation Trust website for current opening times

VISIT US
Train: Norwich ½ mile

Bus: Many bus services pass nearby

1 mile from Cow Tower

MAP Page 341 (2J)
OS Map 134, 237: TG229087

CHURCH OF THE HOLY SEPULCHRE, THETFORD, NORFOLK:
SEE THETFORD, CHURCH OF THE HOLY SEPULCHRE – PAGE 169

COW TOWER, NORWICH
NORFOLK – NR1 4AA

One of the earliest purpose-built artillery blockhouses in England, this brick tower was built in c. 1398-9 to command a strategic point in Norwich's city defences External viewing only.

Managed by Norwich City Council.

OPENING TIMES
Any reasonable time

VISIT US
Direction: In Norwich, near cathedral (approx. 1 mile walk)

Train: Norwich ½ mile

Bus: From surrounding areas

Tel: 01603 706229

ACQ.1950

MAP Page 341 (2J)
OS Map 134, OL40/237: TG240092

CREAKE ABBEY
NORFOLK – NR21 9LF

Tranquil ruins of an Augustinian abbey church, unusual because visibly reduced in size after a serious fire in the 15th century.

Managed by Mr and Mrs A C Scott.

OPENING TIMES
Any reasonable time

VISIT US
Direction: N of North Creake off B1355

CREAKE ABBEY

Bus: Sanders service 27

Tel: 01604 735464

ACQ.1950

MAP Page 341 (1H)
OS Map 132, 251: TF856395

GRIME'S GRAVES
SEE FEATURE – PAGE 168

NORTH ELMHAM CHAPEL
NORFOLK – NR19 2AP

A place with an unusual story, illustrated on graphic panels. The small Norman chapel here stands on the site of an earlier timber church, probably the Saxon cathedral of East Anglia. In the 14th century it was converted into a fortified manor house by Henry Despenser, the unpopular Bishop of Norwich who brutally suppressed the Peasants' Revolt of 1381.

Managed by North Elmham Parish Council.

OPENING TIMES
Any reasonable time

VISIT US
Direction: Located 6 miles N of East Dereham on B1110

Bus: Konectbus service 18, 21 & 22; Carters service 9 (Wed only)

Tel: 01604 735464

ACQ.1948

MAP Page 341 (2H)
OS Map 132, 238: TF988216

VISIT US

Direction: Great Yarmouth, follow signs for Historic Quay. The houses are directly behind the Norfolk Nelson Museum on the Historic South Quay

Train: Great Yarmouth ½ mile

Bus: Bus services to Great Yarmouth are operated by Anglian (of Beccles), Ambassador Travel and First in Suffolk & Norfolk and Sanders of Holt

Tel: 01493 857900

NON-MEMBERS

Adult	£4.30
Concession	£3.90
Child	£2.60
Family	£11.20

OPENING TIMES

29 Mar–30 Sep, Mon–Fri 11am–4pm

Access to Greyfriars' Cloisters is by pre-arrangement only

ACQ.1950

Living space was very much at a premium in early 17th-century Great Yarmouth, then among the most prosperous fishing ports in England. Hence the inhabitants crowded into the town's distinctive 'Rows', a network of narrow alleyways linking Yarmouth's three main thoroughfares. Many 'Row houses' were damaged by World War II bombing or demolished during post-War clearances, but two surviving properties in the care of English Heritage show what these characteristic dwellings looked like at various stages in their history.

Both Row 111 and the Old Merchant's House were originally built in the early 17th century as wealthy merchants' residences, but later sub-divided into tenements. The Old Merchant's House, which has spectacular Jacobean plaster ceilings in two of its rooms, is presented as it was in the 1850s, when fish merchant Simon Fleet and his wife occupied one half of the property, and in the 1890s when the other half was occupied by Martha King and her family – represented here by models. Adjacent Row 111 house is shown as it was in about 1942 (just before it

received a direct hit from an incendiary bomb), likewise with figures of the three families which then occupied parts of it. Both houses also display a wonderful collection of fixtures and fittings – including painted panels, elaborate wall-ties and door-knockers – rescued from other now-demolished Row dwellings, a treasure trove for lovers of period decoration.

Nearby stands Greyfriars' Cloisters, the remains of a 13th-century friary of Franciscan 'grey friars', later swallowed up by Row development and converted into a number of dwellings large and small. Traces of their interior features can still be seen on the brick-built walls of parts of the cloister and church, laid bare by wartime bombing. Early 14th-century wall-paintings were discovered here in the 1960s. Access to the cloister is limited to pre-booked group tours only.

MAP Page 341 (2K)
OS Map 134, OL40
Houses: TG525072
Cloisters: TG524073

VISIT US

Direction: Located 7 miles NW of Thetford off A134

Train: Brandon 3½ miles

Bus: Only public transport is Coach Services of Thetford service 40. Ask driver to set you down at Lynford

Tel: 01842 810656

NON-MEMBERS

Adult	£3.50
Concession	£3.20
Child	£2.10
Family	£9.10

No entry to the mines for children under 5 years of age

OPENING TIMES

29 Mar–29 Sep, daily	10am–5pm
30 Sep–3 Nov, Wed–Sun	10am–5pm
4 Nov–28 Mar	Closed

 ACQ.1931 🐕 ♿ ⌂ 🚶 ♿ **P** 🏪 ♿
⚠ OVP

Disabled access (exhibition area only; access track rough).

Dogs on leads (restricted areas).

Visitors intending to descend the shaft should wear flat shoes.

Grime's Graves is the only Neolithic flint mine open to visitors in Britain. A grassy lunar landscape of over 400 shafts, pits, quarries and spoil dumps, they were first named Grim's Graves by the Anglo-Saxons – meaning the pagan god Grim's quarries, or 'the Devil's holes'.

It was not until one of them was excavated by Canon Greenwell in 1870 that they were identified as flint mines dug over 5000 years ago, during the later Neolithic and Early Bronze Ages.

What the prehistoric miners sought here was the fine quality, jet-black flint floorstone, which occurs some nine to twelve metres below surface level. Digging with red-deer antler picks, they sank shafts and dug radiating galleries which followed the seams of flint. Today visitors can descend 9 metres (30 ft) by ladder into one excavated shaft – an unforgettable experience.

Grime's Graves flint was prized for its distinctive colour and easily 'knapped' qualities. Rough-outs of axes and other tools were made on site, but then traded on and finished elsewhere.

Set amid the distinctive Breckland heath landscape, Grime's Graves is also a Site of Special Scientific Interest: the habitat of a variety of rare and distinctive plants and animals. The Breckland flora are especially attractive from April to July.

A small introductory exhibition in the visitor centre includes information about Neolithic mining, a virtual tour of the mines and landscape, and touchable reproduction Neolithic tools. A trail leaflet guides visitors round the multi-period site, explaining features from the earliest times until today.

The family explorer kit will enable you to read vital clues about the site.

See the Neolithic mine, and the plants and creatures which thrive in this unique landscape.

MAP Page 341 (3G)
OS Map 144, 229: TL817899

ST MARY'S CHURCH, EAST BRADENHAM
NORFOLK – IP25 7QL

This simple church has a powerful tower and stands at the end of an avenue of lime trees. The bold, buttressed exterior in its grassy graveyard setting is striking. Inside, it is plainly furnished and gloriously lit, with several lovely memorials to local people.

Owned and managed by The Churches Conservation Trust.

OPENING TIMES
Open during daylight hours summer Sat & Sun

At other times keyholder nearby

VISIT US
Train: Attleborough 11¼ miles

Bus: Konectbus service 17 (Tue and Fri only)

20 mins from Castle Acre Priory and Castle Acre

MAP Page 341 (2H)
OS Map 144, 237: TF931084

ST NICHOLAS' CHAPEL, KING'S LYNN
NORFOLK – PE30 1NH

Nine centuries of dazzling treasures can be found in England's largest chapel. Startlingly life-like painted figures celebrate Kings Lynn's seamen, merchants, mayors and shopkeepers, and stunning carved woodwork adorns the interior, including the earliest known portrayal of an instrument in a church carving.

Owned and managed by The Churches Conservation Trust.

OPENING TIMES
Mid Jun-end Sep,
Tue & Sat   10.30am-4.30pm

VISIT US
Train: King's Lynn 10 mins walk

ST NICHOLAS' CHAPEL, KING'S LYNN

Bus: Bus station in Vancouver Centre by Sainsbury's 10 mins walk. Main bus services in Kings Lynn are operated by Norfolk Green, Konectbus and First

30 mins from Castle Rising Castle

MAP Page 341 (2G)
OS Map 132, 236/249/250: TF618204

ST OLAVE'S PRIORY
NORFOLK – NR31 9HE

The wonderfully complete, 14th-century, brick-vaulted refectory undercroft – later a cottage occupied until 1902 – of a small Augustinian priory.

OPENING TIMES
Any reasonable time

VISIT US
Direction: Located 5½ miles SW of the town of Great Yarmouth on A143

Train: Haddiscoe 1¼ miles

Bus: Ambassador service 577; Anglian services 581 & 581A

Tel: 01604 735464

ACQ.1921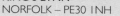

Dogs on leads (restricted areas only).

MAP Page 341 (3K)
OS Map 134, OL40: TM459996

THETFORD, CHURCH OF THE HOLY SEPULCHRE
NORFOLK – IP24 3PW

The only surviving remains in England of a priory of Canons of the Holy Sepulchre, who aided pilgrims to Christ's tomb: the ruined nave of their 14th-century church, later used as a barn. Managed by Thetford Town Council.

OPENING TIMES
All year, daily   10am-5pm
(or dusk whichever is earlier)

25 Dec   Closed

THETFORD, CHURCH OF THE HOLY SEPULCHRE

VISIT US
Direction: Located on the W side of Thetford on A134

Train: Thetford ¾ mile

Bus: Coach Services of Thetford 40, 84, 86, 190, T1, T1A

Tel: 01842 754038

ACQ.1977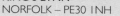

MAP Page 341 (3H)
OS Map 144, 229: TL865831

THETFORD PRIORY
NORFOLK – IP24 2NA

The extensive remains of one of the most important East Anglian monasteries, the Cluniac Priory of Our Lady of Thetford, burial place of the earls and dukes of Norfolk for 400 years. Founded in the early 12th century, it owed much of its prosperity to a miraculous appearance of the Virgin Mary, whose statue here was discovered to conceal relics of saints, and became a magnet for pilgrims. Two of the greatest men in early Tudor England, Thomas Howard, victor of Flodden, and Henry Fitzroy, illegitimate son of Henry VIII, were buried near her shrine. Survivals include the lower walls of the church and cloister, along with the impressive shell of the priors' lodging and, reached by a pathway from the main site, an almost complete 14th-century gatehouse.

Managed by Thetford Town Council.

OPENING TIMES
1 Apr-30 Sep, daily	8am-6pm
1 Oct-31 Mar, daily	8am-4pm
25 Dec	Closed

VISIT US
Direction: Near Thetford station

THETFORD PRIORY

Train: Thetford ¼ mile

Bus: Coach Services of Thetford 40, 84, 86, 190, T1, T1A

Tel: 01842 754038

ACQ.1932

MAP Page 341 (3G)
OS Map 144, 229: TL865831

THETFORD WARREN LODGE NORFOLK

Probably built c. 1400 by the Prior of Thetford, this defensible lodge protected gamekeepers and hunting parties against armed poachers. Much later used by the local 'warreners' who harvested rabbits here.

OPENING TIMES
Any reasonable time

VISIT US
Direction: Located 2 miles W of Thetford off B1107

Train: Thetford 2½ miles

Bus: See above

Tel: 01604 735464

ACQ.1948

MAP Page 341 (3G)
OS Map 144, 229: TL839984

WEETING CASTLE
NORFOLK – IP27 0RQ

The ruins of a substantial early medieval moated manor house, built in local flint.

OPENING TIMES
Any reasonable time

VISIT US
Direction: Located 2 miles N of Brandon off B1106

Train: Brandon 1¼ miles

Bus: Coach Service 40

Tel: 01604 735464

ACQ.1926

MAP Page 341 (3G)
OS Map 144, 229: TL778891

SUFFOLK

BURY ST EDMUNDS ABBEY
SUFFOLK – IP33 1UZ

The extensive remains of the wealthiest and most powerful Benedictine monastery in England, shrine of St Edmund. They include the complete 14th-century Great Gate and Norman Tower, and the impressive ruins and altered west front of the immense church.

Managed by St Edmundsbury Borough Council.

OPENING TIMES
Any reasonable time

VISIT US
Direction: E end of town centre

Train: Bury St Edmunds 1 mile

Bus: Services to the town are operated by H.C.Chambers, Coach Services of Thetford, Galloway European, High Suffolk Community Transport, Mulley's Motorways, Stagecoach in Cambridge, Simonds of Diss, Stephensons of Essex and Suffolk Travel Services

Tel: 01284 764667

ACQ.1955

MAP Page 341 (4G)
OS Map 155, 211: TL857642

CHURCH OF ST MARY THE VIRGIN, STONHAM PARVA
SUFFOLK – IP14 5JL

© CCT

Spectacular and airy, this medieval flint-work church lies behind the village and beside the Old Hall. The nave and chancel are impressively high, and the double hammerbeam roof is a splendid example of medieval craftsmanship.

Owned and managed by The Churches Conservation Trust.

OPENING TIMES
Open daily during daylight hours

VISIT US
Train: Needham Market 3½ miles

Bus: Simonds service 114 to Little Stonham

30 mins from Framlingham Castle

MAP Page 341 (4H)
OS Map 155, 211: TM115601

FRAMLINGHAM CASTLE
SEE FEATURE – PAGE 172

LANDGUARD FORT SUFFOLK – IP11 3TW

The site of the last opposed seaborne invasion of England in 1667 and the first land battle of the Royal Marines. The current fort was built in the 18th century and modified in the 19th century with substantial additional 19th/20th-century outside batteries.

Guided tours and audio tours of the fort are supplemented by an audio-visual presentation of the site's history, and by guided tours of the outside batteries.

Managed by Landguard Fort Trust.

The nearby submarine mining building houses Felixstowe Museum's collections of local interest. (For museum opening times and prices see felixstowemuseum.org, or call 01394 674355.)

NON-MEMBERS

Adult	£4.00
Concession	£3.00
Child	£1.50

Free entry for children under 5 and wheelchair users

There may be a premium payable by all visitors, including members, on event days – please check www.landguard.com for details

OPENING TIMES

29 Mar-31 Jun, daily	10am-5pm
1 Jul-31 Aug, daily	10am-6pm
1 Sep-3 Nov, daily	10am-5pm

Last admission 1 hour before closing

VISIT US

Direction: 1 mile S of Felixstowe town centre – follow signs to Landguard Point

Train: Felixstowe 2½ miles

Bus: First service 77

Tel: 01394 675900

Route 51 cycle route comes to site.

MAP Page 341 (5J)
OS Map 169, 197: TM284319

LEISTON ABBEY
SUFFOLK – IP16 4TD

The mainly 14th-century remains of an abbey of Premonstratensian canons. Among Suffolk's most impressive monastic ruins, with some spectacular architectural features.

Managed by Pro Corda Trust.

OPENING TIMES

Any reasonable time

VISIT US

Direction: N of Leiston off B1069

Train: Saxmundham 5 miles

Bus: Minibus Coach Hire 196 passes the site; First services 64; Anglian service 165 and Nightingale of Beccles service 521 all serve Leiston (1½ mile walk)

Tel: 01728 831354

ACQ.1964

MAP Page 341 (4K)
OS Map 156, 212: TM445642

LINDSEY ST JAMES'S CHAPEL
SUFFOLK – IP7 6QA

A pretty, thatched, 13th-century chapel with lancet windows.

OPENING TIMES

All year, daily	10am-4pm

VISIT US

Direction: Located on an unclassified road ½ mile E of Rose Green and 8 miles E of Sudbury

Train: Sudbury 8 miles

Bus: Hadleigh Community Transport 'Suffolk Links Cosford' demand-responsive bus service: telephone 01473 828202 to book

Tel: 01604 735464

ACQ.1930

Disabled access (single step).

MAP Page 341 (5H)
OS Map 155, 196: TL9784444

FRAMLINGHAM CASTLE SUFFOLK – IP13 9BP

Framlingham is a magnificent example of a late 12th-century castle. Built by Roger Bigod, Earl of Norfolk, one of the most influential people at the court of the Plantagenet kings, the castle, together with Framlingham Mere, was designed both as a stronghold and a proclamation of power and status. Architecturally, the fortress is notable for its curtain wall with regular mural towers, being an early example of this style.

VISIT US

Address: Framlingham Castle, Church Street, Framlingham, Suffolk IP13 9BP

Direction: In Framlingham on B1116

Train: Wickham Market 6½ miles; Saxmundham 7 miles

Bus: First in Suffolk & Norfolk service 63; Galloway European 118, 119; Nightingale 482

Tel: 01728 724189

Local Tourist Information
Woodbridge: 01394 382240

NON-MEMBERS

Adult	£6.70
Concession	£6.00
Child	£4.00
Family	£17.40

OPENING TIMES

29 Mar-3 Nov, daily	10am-5pm
4 Nov-26 Dec, Sat-Sun	10am-4pm
27-31 Dec, Fri-Tue	10am-4pm
1 Jan-14 Feb, Sat-Sun	10am-4pm
15-23 Feb, daily	10am-4pm
24 Feb-31 Mar, Sat-Sun	10am-4pm

The property may close early if an event is booked, please ring in advance for details

Disabled access (grounds and ground floor only).

Parking charge, refundable to EH members and paying visitors on admission.

MAP Page 341 (4J)
OS Map 156, 212: TM287637

The castle has fulfilled a number of roles. It was at the centre of the struggle between the Bigod barons and the Crown, and Mary Tudor mustered her supporters here in 1553, before being crowned Queen. At the end of the 16th century it was used to imprison enemies of the monarch; later still a Poorhouse was built within the walls. Today the imposing stone walls and crenellated towers with their ornate Tudor chimneys dominate, while the grassy earthworks around the castle are subdued reminders of its outer defences. To the west, the Mere provides a stunning setting.

Visitors can explore over 800 years of life at Framlingham Castle in an introductory exhibition in the Poorhouse, which tells the story of the people who lived in the castle during its long and varied history. The displays illustrate the struggle for power between monarchs and the lords of Framlingham,

including Thomas Howard, 3rd Duke of Norfolk and uncle to Anne Boleyn and Catherine Howard, both married to and beheaded by Henry VIII; the accession of Queen Mary Tudor; and the Poorhouse, still in use until 1839.

The Poorhouse Kitchen provides an area where visitors can enjoy a selection of factual and fictional books relating to Framlingham Castle. Entry also includes access to the Lanman Trust's Museum of Local History.

Embark on a self-guided journey of discovery around the site with our lively audio tour, and explore the Mere, the castle's outer courts and the wall-walk with its spectacular views over the surrounding landscape. Younger visitors can discover more about life in the castle with a variety of themed games and interactives.

MOULTON PACKHORSE BRIDGE SUFFOLK

A pretty, four-arched, late medieval bridge spanning the River Kennet on the old route from Cambridge to Bury St Edmunds.

OPENING TIMES
Any reasonable time

VISIT US
Direction: In Moulton off B1085, 4 miles E of Newmarket

Train: Kennett 2 miles

Bus: Stephensons 312, 400 & 401; Suffolk CC service 310, 311A & 311B

Tel: 01604 735464

ACQ.1977 🐾 P ♿

MAP Page 341 (4G)
OS Map 154, 210/226: TL698645

ST PETER'S CHURCH, CLAYDON
SUFFOLK – IP6 0EQ

This originally Saxon church has wonderful views over the Gipping Valley, and is full of stunning, vibrant stained glass and extravagant carvings. A rector was responsible for the design of some of the stained glass, and it is possible he carved some of the stonework too.

Owned and managed by The Churches Conservation Trust.

OPENING TIMES
Open daily during daylight hours

VISIT US
Train: Westerfield 2¾ miles, Ipswich 4 miles

Bus: First 88/88a; Galloway 87 (Sun only), 110; Simons 113/114

35 mins from Framlingham Castle

MAP Page 341 (4J)
OS Map 169, 197: TM137499

SAXTEAD GREEN POST MILL
SUFFOLK – IP13 9QQ

This fine four-sailed corn-grinding 'post mill', whose whole body – turned by a secondary windmill or 'fantail' – revolves on its three-storey roundhouse base, is of a type characteristic of Suffolk since around the 13th century. It originates from about 1796, but has been three times rebuilt and raised: in 1854 it was given a full set of new cast-iron machinery. Though commercial milling ceased when the last miller died in 1947, the mill is still in full working order. Climb the stairs to the various floors, which are full of fascinating mill machinery. Framlingham Castle is nearby.

NON-MEMBERS
Adult	£3.60
Concession	£3.20
Child	£2.20

OPENING TIMES
30 Mar-29 Sep,
Fri-Sat & Bank Hols   12pm-5pm

VISIT US
Direction: 2½ miles NW of Framlingham on A1120

Train: Wickham Market 9 miles

Tel: 01728 685789

ACQ.1951 🏛 🐾 📷 ⚠ OVP

MAP Page 341 (4J)
OS Map 156, 212: TM253644

VISIT US

Direction: In Orford on B1084, 20 miles NE of Ipswich

Train: Wickham Market 8 miles

Bus: PF Travel service 71

Tel: 01394 450472

Local Tourist Information
Woodbridge: 01394 382240

NON-MEMBERS

Adult	£6.00
Concession	£5.40
Child	£3.60
Family	£15.60

OPENING TIMES

29 Mar-3 Nov, daily	10am-5pm
4 Nov-26 Dec, Sat-Sun	10am-4pm
27 Dec-31 Dec, daily	10am-4pm
1 Jan-31 Mar, Sat-Sun	10am-4pm

ACQ.1962 🎧 ⚒ 🏛 **P** 📷 ⚠ OVP

MAP Page 341 (4J)
OS Map 169, 212: TM419499

The unique polygonal tower keep of Orford Castle stands beside the pretty town and former port, which Henry II also developed here in the 1160s. His aim was to counterbalance the power of turbulent East Anglian barons like Hugh Bigod of Framlingham, and to guard the coast against foreign mercenaries called to their aid.

An 18-sided drum with three square turrets and a forebuilding reinforcing its entrance, the keep was built to a highly innovative design. The progress of its construction between 1165 and 1173 is extensively recorded in royal documents. Both exterior and interior survive almost intact, allowing visitors to explore the basement, with its vital well, and the lower and upper halls – the latter the principal room of the castle. Around these polygonal rooms is a maze of passages leading to the chapel, kitchen and other chambers in the turrets. From the roof there are magnificent views seaward to Orford Ness.

Recent archaeological work has provided a clearer understanding of how the castle worked, and a painting by Frank Gardiner shows how the keep and its vanished outer defences looked in their heyday. The upper hall now houses a display by the Orford Museum Trust, including local finds of Roman brooches, medieval seals and coins and some of the borough's regalia. Graphic panels display maps, documents, pictures and photographs, illustrating Orford's history up to the 20th century.

DISCOUNTED ATTRACTIONS:

Use your membership to get exclusive discounts at these independent attractions in the East of England. Please remember to show your card as proof of membership.

2 for 1 ENTRY

⊞ OVP

ELIZABETHAN HOUSE
Great Yarmouth, Norfolk
This handsome 16th-century home invites to you to look into the lives of the families who lived there from Tudor through to Victorian times.

www.museums.norfolk.gov.uk
T. 01493 855746

20% OFF ADULT TICKET

⊞

FELIXSTOWE MUSEUM
Suffolk IP11 3TW
Fourteen display rooms, local, social and military history, housed within 1878-built Submarine Mining Establishment. Shop, tearoom. Three new exhibitions.

www.felixstowemuseum.org
T. 01394 674355

20% DISCOUNT ON ENTRY

⊞ ⛹ 2

HOLKHAM HALL
Norfolk NR23 1AB
Surrounded by acres of rolling parkland, this grand 18th-century Palladian Hall is full of stunning architecture and art, original furniture and classical statuary.

www.holkham.co.uk
T. 01328 710227

2 for 1 ADULT ENTRY*

⊞   *Terms & conditions apply.

IWM DUXFORD
Cambridgeshire CB22 4QR
Discover the history of aviation in times of war and peace in one of the world's finest aviation heritage sites; explore over 200 aircraft including Spitfire and Concorde.

www.iwm.org.uk
T. 01223 835000

£1 OFF

⊞ OVP ⛹ 2

KELVEDON HATCH SECRET NUCLEAR BUNKER
Essex CM15 0LA
Visit this restored ex Government Cold War Bunker, to have been used in the event of a war. Open all year.

www.secretnuclearbunker.com
T. 01277 364883

£1 OFF STANDARD TICKET

⊞ OVP

LAYER MARNEY TOWER
Essex CO5 9US
England's tallest Tudor gatehouse, built in 1523. Climb the Tower, children's play areas, gardens, parkland, walks. Gift shop and tearoom. See website for events throughout the summer.

www.layermarneytower.co.uk
T. 01206 330784

EAST OF ENGLAND

Discount applies to:

KEY ⊞ **MEMBERS** OVP **OVP HOLDERS** 👪? **NO. OF MEMBER'S CHILDREN**

Terms and conditions may apply, so make sure you check the individual pages on our website or call the individual property for more details.

2 for 1 ENTRY

⊞ OVP

OLIVER CROMWELL'S HOUSE
Cambridgeshire CB7 4HF
Visit the former Lord Protector's family home. Experience what domestic life would have been like in the 17th century.
www.olivercromwellshouse.co.uk
T. 01353 662062

2 for 1 ENTRY

⊞ OVP 👪4

RAF AIR DEFENCE RADAR MUSEUM
Norfolk NR12 8YB
Featuring the once Top Secret Cold War Ops Room, we cover the history of Air Defence 1935 to today. A great day out!
www.radarmuseum.co.uk
T. 01692 631485

3 for 2
ON HALL TOUR AND GARDEN

⊞

SOMERLEYTON HALL & GARDENS
Suffolk NR32 5QQ
Twelve acres of landscaped gardens. Ancient yew hedge maze. Paxton glasshouses. Guided Hall tours. Excellent tearooms and giftshop.
www.somerleyton.co.uk
T. 0871 222 4244

£1 OFF ADULT TICKET

⊞

STOW MARIES AERODROME
Essex CM3 6RJ
An English Heritage Angel award winner, this unique aerodrome is the only WWI aerodrome with over 20 of its original buildings in their original context.
www.stowmaries.com
T. 01245 808744

15% DISCOUNT WEEKDAYS ONLY AND NOT VALID ON EVENT DAYS

⊞

WOBURN ABBEY
Bedfordshire MK17 9WA
Home to the Duke of Bedford and birthplace of Afternoon Tea. Enjoy priceless art and treasures and beautiful gardens, all set in 3000 acres of deer park.
www.woburn.co.uk/abbey
T. 01525 290333

GIVE THE GIFT OF MEMBERSHIP

Give friends and family the opportunity to enjoy these fantastic discounts too!

- Free entry to over 400 historic properties
- Kids go free (up to six per adult in a family group)
- Free or discounted entry to hundreds of events, activities and other attractions
- Free handbook worth £10.95
- Exclusive members' magazine

EAST
MIDLANDS

Bolsover Castle

Remember to check opening times before you visit any of our properties **www.english-heritage.org.uk/daysout**

Details of local public transport information in England are available from Traveline **www.traveline.org.uk** or call 0871 200 2233.

Bolsover Castle

Make the most of your membership and keep up to date with upcoming events, the latest news and special offers by subscribing to our e-newsletter. Register online now at **www.english-heritage.org.uk/newsletter**

Glossop
23
14 Gainsborough
Market Rasen
7
Worksop
Lincolnshire
Buxton
Bakewell
Chesterfield
2
15 Lincoln
1
5
8
3
6
4
24
13 Skegness
9
Mansfield
17
16
Nottinghamshire
Boston
Derbyshire
Nottingham
Grantham
Derby
Spalding
10
Loughborough
Leicestershire
12
11 Leicester
Oakham
Rutland
25
21
18
Market Harborough
22
20
Kettering
Northamptonshire
19
Daventry
Northampton
Brackley

Hardwick Old Hall

HIGHLIGHTS FOR 2013/14 IN THE **EAST MIDLANDS**

p.184

p.192

p.186

Bolsover Castle: horses return for spectacular historic displays this summer.

Kirby Hall: one of England's greatest Elizabethan houses, with exceptional views.

Peveril Castle: stunning views over the Peak District from this Norman fortress.

PROPERTIES

DERBYSHIRE

ALL SAINTS' CHURCH, KEDLESTON
DERBYSHIRE – DE22 5JH

© CCT

All Saints' church is all that remains of the medieval village of Kedleston. A dazzling marble tomb, with life-size figures, floats on a sea of green translucent quartz, in its own chapel with spectacular stained glass windows. Carved monsters surround the Norman doorway.

Owned and managed by The Churches Conservation Trust.

OPENING TIMES
26 Mar–30 Oct, Mon-Wed during daylight hours;
Sat-Sun   11am-5pm

VISIT US
Train: Derby 5 miles

Bus: Arriva Derby Bus 109

30 mins from Wingfield Manor

MAP Page 342 (3E)
OS Map 119/128, 259: SK313404

ARBOR LOW STONE CIRCLE AND GIB HILL BARROW
DERBYSHIRE – DE45 1JS

The region's most important prehistoric site, Arbor Low is a Neolithic henge monument atmospherically set amid high moorland. Within an earthen bank and ditch, a circle of some 50 white limestone slabs, all now fallen, surrounds a central stone 'cove' – a feature found only in major sacred sites. Nearby is enigmatic Gib Hill, a large burial mound.

Please note: The farmer who owns access to the property will levy a charge for entry.

Managed by Peak District National Park Authority.

OPENING TIMES
Any reasonable time

Access charge of £1 per person to cross private land to the monument

VISIT US
Direction: ½ mile E of A515, 2 miles S of Monyash

Train: Buxton 10 miles

Bus: High Peak services 42/42A and Warringtons 449 both serve Parsley Hay which is within a 1 mile walk to the two locations

Tel: 01629 816200

ACQ.1884

MAP Page 342 (2E)
OS Map 119, OL24: SK160636

BOLSOVER CASTLE
SEE FEATURE – PAGE 184

BOLSOVER CUNDY HOUSE
DERBYSHIRE – S44 6BQ

This charming cottage-like 17th-century conduit house, with vaulted stone-slab roof, once supplied water to Bolsover Castle.

Managed by Bolsover Civic Society.

OPENING TIMES
Any reasonable time

VISIT US
Direction: Off M1 at junction 29A, follow signs for Bolsover Castle. At junction of Craggs Rd and Houghton Rd, Bolsover, 6 miles E of Chesterfield on A362

Train: Chesterfield 6 miles or Langwith – Whaley Thorns 4½ miles

Bus: Stagecoach in Chesterfield service 82 & TM Travel Bolsover town services B2 & B3 actually pass the property. Stagecoach Chesterfield services 53, 53A serve Hilltop Avenue a short walk from the Cundy House

Tel: 01246 822844 (Bolsover Castle)

ACQ.1945

MAP Page 343 (2F)
OS Map 120, 269: SK471709

HARDWICK OLD HALL DERBYSHIRE S44 5QJ

The imposing shell of the remodelled family home of Bess of Hardwick, one of the most remarkable and most formidable women of Elizabethan England. Born on this site the daughter of an impoverished country squire, she rose via four increasingly advantageous marriages and much social manoeuvring to become Countess of Shrewsbury, and perhaps the richest woman in England. A friend and then enemy of Mary Queen of Scots, she was treated with respect even by Queen Elizabeth.

To celebrate her success and proclaim her status, Bess transformed her birthplace from a modest medieval manor house into a luxurious Elizabethan mansion. Completed by 1591, perhaps largely to Bess's own designs, the Old Hall was almost immediately superseded by her grander New Hall which stands beside it, becoming a guest and service wing to the newer mansion.

Though the Old Hall is now roofless, you can still ascend through four storeys to admire surviving decorative plasterwork and overmantels in the former staterooms, and view the kitchen and service rooms. An exhibition describes Bess's adventures in architecture, and on the ground floor there is a virtual tour of the first floor rooms (which are only accessible via steps).

Managed by English Heritage and owned by the National Trust.

NON-MEMBERS

Adult	£5.20
Concession	£4.70
Child	£3.10
Family	£13.50

National Trust members admitted free, but small charge at EH events. Tickets for the New Hall (the National Trust) and joint tickets for both properties available at extra cost

OPENING TIMES

29 Mar-3 Nov, Wed-Sun & Bank Hols	10am-5pm
4 Nov-14 Feb, Sat-Sun	10am-4pm
15-23 Feb, Wed-Sun	10am-4pm
24 Feb-31 Mar, Sat-Sun	10am-4pm

VISIT US

Direction: 9½ miles SE of Chesterfield, off A6175 (J29 of M1)

Train: Chesterfield 8 miles

Bus: Trent Barton/Stagecoach 'Pronto' service or G&J Hallmark service 49 (alight Glapwell 'Young Vanish', then 2 mile walk) or Stagecoach /TM Travel serices 96 to Hardstoft and 2 mile walk

Tel: 01246 850431

ACQ.1959

MAP Page 343 (2F)
OS Map 120, 269: SK462637

Holiday cottage available to let – see opposite

HOB HURST'S HOUSE
DERBYSHIRE – DE4 2NT

A square prehistoric burial mound with earthwork ditch and bank, amid remote moorland. Named after a local goblin.

Managed by the Peak District National Park Authority.

OPENING TIMES
Any reasonable time

VISIT US
Direction: On open moorland from unclassified road off B5057, 9 miles W of Chesterfield

Train: Chesterfield 9 miles

Bus: TM Travel services 214 & 215 to Beeley then walk 2 miles

Tel: 01629 816200

ACQ.1884

MAP Page 342 (2E)
OS Map 119, OL24: SK287692

NINE LADIES STONE CIRCLE
DERBYSHIRE – DE4 2LS

A small, early Bronze Age stone circle traditionally believed to represent nine ladies turned to stone as a penalty for dancing on Sunday. Their fiddler became the nearby King Stone. Part of an extensive complex of prehistoric remains on Stanton Moor.

Managed by Peak District National Park Authority.

OPENING TIMES
Any reasonable time

VISIT US
Direction: From an unclassified road off A6, 5 miles SE of Bakewell

Train: Matlock 4½ miles

Bus: Hulleys service 172 to Stanton in Peak (within 1 mile)

Tel: 01629 816200

ACQ.1883

MAP Page 342 (2E)
OS Map 119, OL24: SK249635

There is nothing else in Britain quite like Bolsover Castle – a unique survival of a 17th-century fantasy mansion intended solely for pleasure and extravagant display.

VISIT US

Address: Bolsover Castle, Castle Street, Bolsover, Derbyshire S44 6PR

Direction: In Bolsover, 6 miles E of Chesterfield on A632. Off M1 at junction 29A (signposted)

Train: Chesterfield 6 miles

Bus: G&J Holmes service 49; TM Travel 53A (Sun only), B2 & B3; Stagecoach services 53, 53A, 82 & 83 pass close to the castle entrance

Tel: 01246 822844

Local Tourist Information (Chesterfield): 01246 345777

NON-MEMBERS

Adult	£8.50
Concession	£7.70
Child	£5.10
Family	£22.10

OPENING TIMES

29 Mar-3 Nov, daily	10am-5pm
4 Nov-16 Feb, Sat-Sun	10am-4pm
17-21 Feb, daily	10am-4pm
22 Feb-31 Mar, Sat-Sun	10am-4pm
24-26 Dec and 1 Jan	Closed

Part of the castle may close for 1 hour if an event is booked. Please call to check

Parking (in castle car park, off main gate. Charge payable, refundable to EH members and paying visitors on admission). The coach drop-off point is in the council car park opposite.

There is good access to the grounds, but please note that the Little Castle is not accessible to wheelchairs.

MAP Page 343 (2F)
OS Map 120, 269: SK470707

☒ Available for corporate and private hire

⬛ Licensed for civil wedding ceremonies

Visit the fairytale Little Castle and our new discovery centre. Building work is taking place in the Little Castle between November 2013 and March 2014 so some restrictions may apply. Please contact the site for further information.

NEW FOR 2013

The horses are coming back to Bolsover's famous Riding School. Every Saturday and Sunday between 1 Apr and 1 Sep (excluding Aug Bank Holiday weekend), riders in 17th-century attire will give two spectacular performances of 'classical dressage', which takes horse and rider years to learn. There will also be chances for you to meet some of Bolsover's horses.

Dominating the countryside from its hilltop like a great ship, Bolsover occupies the site of a medieval castle built by the Peverel family. Sir Charles Cavendish bought the old fortress in 1612 and began work on his Little Castle project. Though playfully battlemented and pinnacled, his creation was not designed for defence, but as a fashionable retreat into an imaginary golden age of chivalry, courtly love – and opulent wealth.

His son William – playboy, poet, courtier and later Royalist general and first Duke of Newcastle – inherited the Little Castle in 1617 and set about its completion, assisted by the architect John Smythson. The exquisitely carved fireplaces and richly-coloured murals and panelling of its interiors still take the visitor on an allegorical journey from earthly concerns to heavenly (and erotic) delights.

William also added the immense Terrace Range, now a dramatic roofless shell. To show off his

achievement, in 1634 he invited King Charles I and his court to *Love's Welcome to Bolsover*, a masque specially written by Ben Jonson for performance in the Fountain Garden. Finally he constructed the cavernous Riding House, among the finest surviving indoor riding schools in the country. It is still easy to imagine Bolsover as the setting for Cavendish's lavish lifestyle, attended by armies of servants.

An interactive exhibition in the Riding House stables introduces the site and celebrates the legacy of William Cavendish, his passion for horses and his contribution to the modern art of dressage. An audio visual display explores the links between horse menage and dressage. There are dressing-up clothes and a replica 17th-century saddle children can sit on, plus a model and film about the Little Castle and a lavish banquet held there in 1634.

VISIT US

Direction: Via the market place in Castleton; 15 miles W of Sheffield on A6187

Train: Hope 2½ miles

Bus: Hulley's 68,173, 174, 272, 273, 274, 276; First 272; TM Travel service 242, 272, 273, 274 all to Castleton then short walk

Tel: 01433 620613

Local Tourist Information:
01629 816572

NON-MEMBERS

Adult	£4.60
Concession	£4.10
Child	£2.80
Family	£12.00

OPENING TIMES

29 Mar-3 Nov, daily	10am-5pm
4 Nov-16 Feb, Sat-Sun	10am-4pm
17-23 Feb, daily	10am-4pm
24 Feb-31 Mar, Sat-Sun	10am-4pm
24-26 Dec and 1 Jan	Closed

ACQ.1932 ⚠ OVP

Parking (in town).

MAP Page 342 (2E)
OS Map 110, OL1: SK149826

Perched high above the pretty village of Castleton, the castle offers breathtaking views of the Peak District. Founded soon after 1066 by William Peverel, one of William the Conqueror's most trusted knights, it played an important role in guarding the Peak Forest.

Henry II made a number of additions to 'Castle Peak' (as it was known in the Middle Ages). Most notable is the great square keep, with its round-headed windows, built in 1176. Thirteenth-century developments included the great hall, and though by 1400 the fortress had ceased to be strategically important, its impregnability guaranteed its continued use as a prison.

Displays in the visitor centre tell the story of Peveril as the focal point of the Royal Forest of the Peak, a royal hunting preserve since the 11th century.

Wheelchair access is available to the visitor centre only.

SUTTON SCARSDALE HALL
DERBYSHIRE – S44 5UR

The imposing shell of a grandiose Georgian mansion built in 1724-9, with an immensely columned exterior. Roofless since 1919, when its interiors were dismantled and some exported to America: but there is still much to discover within, including traces of sumptuous plasterwork. Set amid contemporary garden remains, including a ha-ha ditch and parish church.

OPENING TIMES

Summer, daily	10am-6pm
Winter, daily	10am-4pm
24-26 Dec and 1 Jan	Closed

VISIT US

Direction: Between Chesterfield and Bolsover, 1½ miles S of Arkwright Town

Train: Chesterfield 5 miles

Bus: G&J Holmes 'Hallmark' service 48

Tel: 01604 735464

ACQ.1971 P ⛽ ♿

MAP Page 343 (2F)
OS Map 120, 269: SK442689

ENGLISH HERITAGE PROPERTY GUIDEBOOKS

Want to know more about a property near you?

Visit www.english-heritage shop.org.uk

WINGFIELD MANOR DERBYSHIRE – DE55 7NH

The vast and immensely impressive ruins of a palatial medieval manor house arranged round a pair of courtyards, with a huge undercrofted Great Hall and a defensible High Tower 22 metres (72 feet) tall. This monument to late medieval 'conspicuous consumption' was built in the 1440s for the wealthy Ralph, Lord Cromwell, Treasurer of England and also builder of Tattershall Castle and College. Later the home of Bess of Hardwick's husband, the Earl of Shrewsbury, who imprisoned Mary Queen of Scots here in 1569, 1584 and 1585.

Please note: Wingfield Manor is part of a working farm and the owner's privacy should be respected at all times.

No access to the public except by pre-booked guided tours.

NON-MEMBERS

Adult	£5.50
Concession	£5.00
Child	£3.30

OPENING TIMES

Entry by pre-booked guided tours only, on the first Sat of the month from Apr-Sep. To book please call 0870 333 1181

Call for full details of opening times and other site facilities

VISIT US

Direction: 17 miles N of Derby; 11 miles S of Chesterfield on B5035; ½ mile S of South Wingfield. From M1 junction 28, W on A38, A615 (Matlock Road) at Alfreton, 1½ miles and turn onto B5035

Train: Alfreton 4 miles

Bus: Yourbus 140 & 142

Tel: 0870 333 1183 to book (Customer Services)

ACQ.1960 ✂ ⚠

Parking (none on site or in gateway).

MAP Page 342 (3E)
OS Map 119, 269: SK374548

VISIT US

Direction: In Ashby de la Zouch, 12 miles S of Derby on A511. Restricted parking on site, please park in town car park

Train: Burton on Trent 9 miles

Bus: Macpherson Coaches 1, 2 & 3; Arriva 8, 9A; Roberts 7; Paul S. Winson Travel 129; Arriva/Midland Classic 9

Local Tourist Information: 01530 411767

Tel: 01530 413343

NON-MEMBERS

Adult	£4.60
Concession	£4.10
Child	£2.80
Family	£12.00

OPENING TIMES

29 Mar-30 Jun, Wed-Sun	10am-5pm
1 Jul-31 Aug, daily	10am-5pm
1 Sep-3 Nov, Wed-Sun	10am-5pm
4 Nov-14 Feb, Sat-Sun	10am-4pm
15-23 Feb, Mon-Fri	10am-4pm
24 Feb-31 Mar, Sat-Sun	10am-4pm
24-26 Dec and 1 Jan	Closed

ACQ.1932

Disabled access (grounds only).

Parking (restricted on site, please park in town car park – charge applies).

MAP Page 342 (4E)
OS Map 128, 245: SK361166

Ashby Castle forms the backdrop to the famous jousting scenes in Sir Walter Scott's classic novel of 1819, *Ivanhoe*. Now a ruin, the castle began as a manor house in the 12th century. It only achieved castle status in the 15th century, by which time the hall and buttery had been enlarged with a solar to the east and a large integral kitchen added to the west.

Between 1474 and his execution by Richard III in 1483, Edward IV's Chamberlain Lord Hastings added the chapel and the impressive keep-like Hastings Tower – a castle within a castle. Visitors can climb the 24 metre (78 feet) high tower, which offers fine views. Later

the castle hosted many royal visitors, including Henry VII, Mary Queen of Scots, James I and Charles I.

A Royalist stronghold during the Civil War, the castle finally fell to Parliament in 1646, and was then then made unusable. An underground passage from the kitchen to the tower, probably created during this war, can still be explored today. Archaeologists recently investigated the mysterious castle garden, famous for its elaborately shaped sunken features.

Interpretation boards include beautiful illustrations evoking the splendour of Lord Hastings' additions to the castle. The audio guide provides an amusing account of the castle's dramatic history, drawing upon a masque performed here for Alice Spencer, Countess of Derby, in the early 17th century.

JEWRY WALL
LEICESTERSHIRE – LE1 4LB

A length of Roman bath-house wall over 9 metres (30 feet) high, near a museum displaying the archaeology of Leicester and its region. Graphic panels describe the Roman baths.

Managed by Leicester City Council Parks and Gardens.

OPENING TIMES
Any reasonable time

VISIT US
Direction: In St Nicholas St, W of Church of St Nicholas

Train: Leicester ¾ mile

Bus: Various services operated by First, Stagecoach, Thurmaston Bus, Arriva, NJ Travel, Kinch Bus, Robinson's and Coachcare

Tel: 01604 735464

 ACQ.1920

Parking (by museum, within St Nicholas Circle).

MAP Page 343 (4F)
OS Map 140, 233: SK582045

KIRBY MUXLOE CASTLE
LEICESTERSHIRE – LE9 2DH

The picturesque moated remains – including the fine gatehouse and a complete corner tower – of this brick-built fortified mansion have recently been extensively conserved by English Heritage. Begun in 1480 by Lord Hastings, the castle was left unfinished after his execution by Richard III in 1483.

NON-MEMBERS

Adult	£3.60
Concession	£3.20
Child	£2.20

OPENING TIMES
4 May-1 Sep, Sat-Sun
& Bank Hols   10am-5pm

VISIT US
Direction: 4 miles W of Leicester off B5380; close to M1 junction 21A, northbound exit only

Train: Leicester 5 miles

Bus: NJ Travel service 13A; Arriva Midlands 27 & 153

Tel: 01162 386886

 ACQ.1912   OVP

MAP Page 343 (4F)
OS Map 140, 233: SK524046

BOLINGBROKE CASTLE
LINCOLNSHIRE – PE23 4HH

The remains of a 13th-century hexagonal castle, birthplace in 1367 of the future King Henry IV, with adjacent earthworks. Besieged and taken by Cromwell's Parliamentarians in 1643.

Managed by Heritage Lincolnshire.

OPENING TIMES
Any reasonable time

VISIT US
Direction: In Old Bolingbroke, 16 miles N of Boston off A16

Train: Thorpe Culvert 10 miles

Bus: Translinc Spilsby Call Connect (TC Minicoaches) service 6S will operate to Old Bolingbroke on request. To book telephone 0845 234 3344

Tel: 01529 461499

ACQ.1949

MAP Page 343 (2J)
OS Map 122, 273: TF349650

GAINSBOROUGH OLD HALL
LINCOLNSHIRE – DN21 2NB

Gainsborough Old Hall is among the biggest and best-preserved medieval manor houses in England, part timber-framed but mostly brick-built.

GAINSBOROUGH OLD HALL

Later 15th-century with Elizabethan additions, it has an impressive kitchen with an enormous fireplace, a noble great hall, and an imposing lodgings tower. Many rooms are furnished as they may have appeared in the 15th century, and there is an exhibition tracing the Hall's later links with the Pilgrim Fathers.

Managed by Lincolnshire County Council.

NON-MEMBERS

Adult	£6.00
Child	£4.00
Family	£16.00
Free entry for children under 5	

OPENING TIMES

1 Mar-31 Oct, Mon-Fri	10am-5pm
Sat-Sun	11am-5pm
1 Nov-28 Feb, Mon-Fri	10am-4pm
Sat	11am-4pm

Last admission 30 mins before closure every day

Closed on the last two Saturdays and 1st Friday of each month from May to Sep 2013

VISIT US

Direction: In Parnell Road, Gainsborough, opposite the library

Train: Gainsborough Central ½ mile, Gainsborough Lea Road 1 mile

Bus: Stagecoach and YourBus operate services to Gainsborough bus station from surrounding areas. It is a short walk from there to the Old Hall

Tel: 01427 677348

Disabled access (most of ground floor).

MAP Page 343 (1G)
OS Map 112/121, 280: SK813900

LINCOLN MEDIEVAL BISHOPS' PALACE
LINCOLNSHIRE – LN2 1PU

Standing almost in the shadow of Lincoln cathedral, with sweeping views over the ancient city and the countryside beyond, the medieval bishops' palace was once among the most important buildings in the country. The administrative centre of the largest diocese in medieval England, stretching from the Humber to the Thames, its architecture reflected the enormous power and wealth of the bishops as princes of the church.

Begun in the late 12th century, the palace's most impressive feature is the undercrofted East Hall, initiated by Bishop St Hugh and completed in the 1230s. The chapel range and entrance tower were built by Bishop William Alnwick, who modernised the palace in the 1430s. Having hosted visits from Henry VIII and James I, the palace was sacked by Royalist troops during the Civil War.

Built on hillside terraces, the palace also boasts a Contemporary Heritage Garden, designed by Mark Anthony Walker. Its form was inspired by the cathedral's medieval vaulting, with trees shaped to echo spires. Award-winning audio tour.

The site is also the home of a working vineyard, donated to Lincoln City Council in 1972 by Lincoln's twinned city, Neustadt an der Weinstrasse in Germany. The vineyard was re-established in 2012 with the landscaping of the contemporary garden. The vines are tended by an active group of volunteers using traditional methods. Visit the palace at different times of the year to see how the vines are progressing.

NON-MEMBERS

Adult	£4.60
Concession	£4.10
Child	£2.80
Family	£12.00

OPENING TIMES

29 Mar-3 Nov, Wed-Sun & Bank Hols	10am-5pm
4 Nov-31 Mar, Sat-Sun	10am-4pm
24-26 Dec and 1 Jan	Closed

VISIT US

Direction: On the south side of Lincoln Cathedral. From the cathedral precinct gate, follow wall to your right to the gateway directly opposite cathedral south porch, then take tunnelled walkway (Chesney Gate). Entrance to the left down the pathway

Train: Lincoln 1 mile

Bus: From surrounding areas

Tel: 01522 527468

Parking (limited disabled parking on site).

MAP Page 343 (2H)
OS Map 121, 272: SK978717

SIBSEY TRADER WINDMILL
LINCOLNSHIRE – PE22 0SY

Built in 1877, this restored six-storey mill, with complete gear, sails and fantail, still works today. The award-winning tearoom sells produce made from the mill's organic, stone-ground flour.

Managed by Ian Ansell.

NON-MEMBERS

Adult	£2.50
Concession	£2.00
Child	£1.00

OPENING TIMES

2 Mar-30 Apr, Sat & Bank Hols	10am-6pm
Sun	11am-6pm
1 May-30 Sep, Tue, Sat & Bank Hols	10am-6pm
Sun	11am-6pm
1 Oct–30 Nov, Sat	10am-6pm
Sun	11am-6pm
1 Dec-28 Feb, Sat	11am-5pm
28 Dec	Closed

Group and education visits outside these hours by arrangement

VISIT US

Direction: ½ mile W of Sibsey off A16, 5 miles N of Boston

Train: Boston 5 miles

Bus: Brylaine 113 and Grayscroft 8 (Wed) to Sibsey, then ½ mile walk

Tel: 01205 460647/07718 320449

Disabled access (exterior only).

MAP Page 343 (3J)
OS Map 122, 261: TF345510

ST GEORGE'S CHURCH, GOLTHO
LINCOLNSHIRE
LN8 5JD

© CCT

The charming red-brick chapel of St George is situated beside one of Lincolnshire's lost Saxon villages. The name 'Goltho' is said to be Saxon for 'where the marigolds grow'. Inside, this tranquil atmospheric church contains rustic painted wooden pews and a sense of time stood still.

Owned and managed by The Churches Conservation Trust.

OPENING TIMES

Please phone 01904 709090 in advance of your visit to arrange collection of the key

VISIT US

Train: Market Rasen 7½ miles

Bus: Stagecoach Lincolnshire service 6 or 10 to Rand, Village Lane end stop and then it is c. ½ mile walk

25 mins from Lincoln Medieval Bishops' Palace

MAP Page 343 (2H)
OS Map 121, 273: TF116775

TATTERSHALL COLLEGE
LINCOLNSHIRE – LN4 4LJ

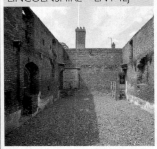

Remains of a grammar school for church choristers, founded in the mid-15th century by Ralph, Lord Cromwell, the builder of Wingfield Manor and nearby Tattershall Castle (National Trust).

The college is managed by Heritage Lincolnshire.

OPENING TIMES
Any reasonable time

VISIT US

Direction: In Tattershall, 14 miles NE of Sleaford on A153

Train: Ruskington 10 miles

Bus: Brylaine Interconnect service 5 and Translinc Call Connect service 65

Tel: 01529 461499

ACQ.1972

MAP Page 343 (2H)
OS Map 122, 261: TF213578

🏠 HOLIDAY COTTAGE AT
KIRBY HALL

Peacock Cottage gives you direct access to the ruins and the grounds at any time. This means that in winter, when Kirby is only open to the public at weekends, you will have days of undisturbed pleasure.

VISIT US

Direction: On an unclassified road off A43, 4 miles NE of Corby

Train: Corby 4 miles

Bus: There are no bus services to the property. The closest is Centrebus 67. Alight at Kirby Lodge from there it is a 1 mile walk. Otherwise Stagecoach services 2, 2A, 2B, X1 and X4 to Priors Hall from there it is a 2 mile walk

Tel: 01536 203230

NON-MEMBERS

Adult	£5.80
Concession	£5.20
Child	£3.50
Family	£15.10

OPENING TIMES

29 Mar-3 Nov, Wed-Sun & Bank Hols	10am-5pm
4 Nov-31 Mar, Sat-Sun	10am-4pm
24-26 Dec and 1 Jan	Closed

May close early for private events. Please call to check

ACQ.1930 🎧 🎭 ♨ ❄ 🖥 🚶 ♿ P
🏠 📷 ♿ ⚠

Disabled access (grounds, gardens and ground floor only).

Dogs on leads (restricted areas).

Kirby Hall is one of England's greatest Elizabethan and 17th-century houses. Begun by Sir Humphrey Stafford, it was purchased by Sir Christopher Hatton, one of Queen Elizabeth I's 'comely young men' and later her Lord Chancellor. Hatton hoped in vain to receive the Queen here during one of her annual 'progresses' around the country. Although this vast mansion is partly roofless, most of its walls survive to their full impressive height; as does the prodigious three-tier inner porch, begun following French pattern books and later embellished in the Classical style by the sculptor Nicholas Stone.

Kirby Hall's exceptionally rich decoration proclaims that its successive owners were always in the forefront of new ideas about architecture and design. The Great Hall and state rooms remain roofed and intact, their interiors refitted and redecorated to authentic 17th- and 18th-century specifications.

Sir Christopher Hatton the Fourth added the great gardens (described as 'the finest garden in England') in the late 17th century. They have been recreated as they may have appeared at that time, with elaborate period style 'cutwork', statues, urns, seating, topiary and other features.

The gardens and ground floor of the mansion are easily accessible by wheelchair users.

An audio tour guides visitors through the house and gardens, accompanied by commentaries from experts in garden history, conservation and country houses.

Owned by the Earl of Winchilsea and managed by English Heritage.

MAP Page 343 (5G)
OS Map 141, 224: SP926927

APETHORPE HALL
NORTHAMPTONSHIRE
PE8 5AQ

Among England's finest country houses, big and stately Apethorpe Hall was begun in the late 15th century. It contains one of the country's most complete Jacobean interiors, and hosted thirteen royal visits between 1565 and 1636.

While restoration work continues, English Heritage is pleased to offer access to visitors during 2013 on a limited, pre-booked and guided-tour basis only. For further details please visit our website or phone 0870 333 1181.

Please note: Apethorpe is still classed as a building site, and suitable footwear must be worn. There are lots of stairs, and no resting/seating points available. Children under 16 must be accompanied by an adult. We are unable to admit children under 5.

NON-MEMBERS
Please call for details

OPENING TIMES
By pre-booked tour only – please call 0870 333 1183 for details

VISIT US
Direction: Located off the A43 towards King's Cliffe. If entering Apethorpe via King's Cliffe Road,

APETHORPE HALL

advance to Laundry Lane, not the High Street. If entering via Bridge St, pass the stone cross and turn left into Laundry Lane

Train: Stamford 11 miles or Peterborough 14 miles

Bus: CallConnect services 4P, 4S Mon-Sat (Tel: 0845 263 8153); or Centrebus service C24 (Tel: 0845 456 4474). Bus services must be booked in advance

Tel: 0870 333 1181

ACQ.2004 P

Access via narrow residential lane – please observe 10mph speed limit at all times.

MAP Page 343 (5H)
OS Map 141, 224/234: TL023954

CHICHELE COLLEGE
NORTHAMPTONSHIRE
NN10 8DZ

The gatehouse, chapel and other remains of a communal residence for priests serving the parish church, founded by locally-born Archbishop Chichele before 1425. Regularly used to display works of art. Managed by Higham Ferrers Tourism, Business and Community Partnership.

OPENING TIMES
Quadrangle – any reasonable time. Contact the keykeeper for the chapel: Mrs D Holyoak, 12 Lancaster St, Higham Ferrers NN10 8HY
Tel: 01933 314157

VISIT US
Direction: College Street, Higham Ferrers

Train: Wellingborough 5 miles

Bus: Stagecoach 49, 50, 51, X46, X47; Expresslines 'Rushden Higham Link'

Tel: 01933 314006

ACQ.1949

Dogs on leads (restricted areas only).

MAP Page 343 (6G)
OS Map 153, 224: SP960687

ELEANOR CROSS, GEDDINGTON
NORTHAMPTONSHIRE
NN14 1AD

In 1290 Eleanor of Castile, the beloved wife of Edward I and mother of his 14 children, died at Harby in Nottinghamshire. The places where her body rested on the journey south to its tomb in Westminster Abbey were marked by stone crosses. The stately triangular Geddington cross, with its canopied statues surmounted by a slender hexagonal pinnacle, is the best-preserved of only three intact survivors. Other crosses stand at Hardingstone near Northampton and Waltham Cross, Hertfordshire.

OPENING TIMES
Any reasonable time

VISIT US
Direction: Located in the village of Geddington, off A43 between Kettering and Corby

Train: Kettering 4 miles

Bus: Centrebus 8 to Geddington

Tel: 01604 735464

ACQ.1915

MAP Page 343 (5G)
OS Map 141, 224: SP894830

VISIT US

Direction: 1 mile W of Rushton, on unclassified road; 1 mile from Desborough on A6

Train: Kettering 5 miles

Bus: Stagecoach in Northants service 19, alight Desborough Cemetery, then 1 mile walk

Tel: 01536 710761

NON-MEMBERS

Adult	£3.30
Concession	£3.00
Child	£2.00

OPENING TIMES

29 Mar-3 Nov, Wed-Sun
& Bank Hols   11am-5pm

ACQ.1951 OVP

Dogs on leads (restricted areas only).

Parking in lay-by on opposite side of road to entrance.

MAP Page 343 (5G)
OS Map 141, 224: SP830831

This delightful triangular building was designed by Sir Thomas Tresham (father of one of the Gunpowder Plotters) and constructed between 1593 and 1597. It is a testament to Tresham's Roman Catholicism: the number three, symbolising the Holy Trinity, is apparent everywhere. There are three floors, trefoil windows and three triangular gables on each side. On the entrance front is the inscription 'Tres Testimonium Dant' ('there are three that give witness'), a Biblical quotation from St John's Gospel referring to the Trinity. It is also a pun on Tresham's name: his wife called him 'Good Tres' in her letters.

ST ANDREW'S CHURCH, CRANFORD
NORTHAMPTONSHIRE
NN14 4AD

© CCT

Sumptuous memorials to 300 years of the Robinson family fill medieval St Andrew's, which lies next to the Robinson seat of Cranford Hall. Structural additions, stained glass and furnishings from across the centuries give this church a rich and varied history.

Owned and managed by The Churches Conservation Trust.

OPENING TIMES
Keyholder nearby

VISIT US
Train: Kettering 4 miles

Bus: Centrebus Midlands service 16

10 mins from Eleanor Cross, 30 mins from Kirby Hall

MAP Page 343 (5G)
OS Map 141, 224: SP925773

ST PETER'S CHURCH, DEENE
NORTHAMPTONSHIRE
NN17 3EJ

© Steven Cole

Set in the estate of Deene Park, St Peter's is the family church of the Brudenells, who bought the estate in 1514. The church is a large building of local stone and Collyweston slate, with a tall west tower, a broach spire, and a number of family memorials.

Owned and managed by The Churches Conservation Trust.

OPENING TIMES
Keyholder nearby

VISIT US
Train: Kettering 10½ miles

Bus: Stamford & Welland Vale Call Connect service 4S will serve the village by request. Tel 0845 263 8153 to book

4 mins from Kirby Hall

MAP Page 343 (5G)
OS Map 141, 224: SP952928

ST PETER'S CHURCH, NORTHAMPTON
NORTHAMPTONSHIRE
NN1 1SR

© CCT

One of the most outstanding Norman churches in the county, this 900-year-old church in Northampton city centre is filled with glorious carved treasures. Inside, great stone arches rise and flow with zigzag waves of banded and plain stone, supported by carved capitals overflowing with foliage, scrollwork, birds and beasts.

Owned and managed by The Churches Conservation Trust.

OPENING TIMES
Nov-Feb, Wed-Sat	11am-3pm
Mar-Oct, Wed-Sat	10am-4pm

VISIT US
Train: Northampton ¼ mile

Bus: Multiple bus routes from town centre

30 mins from Chichele College

MAP Page 343 (6G)
OS Map 152, 207/223: SP7497160377

PROPERTY EVENTS NEAR YOU
Check our website for up-to-the-minute information on our year long programme of events.
www.english-heritage.org.uk/events

MATTERSEY PRIORY
NOTTINGHAMSHIRE
DN10 5HN

The remains (mainly the 13th-century refectory and kitchen) of a small monastery for just six Gilbertine canons – the only wholly English monastic order.

OPENING TIMES
Any reasonable time

VISIT US
Direction: ¾ mile down rough drive, 1 mile E of Mattersey off B6045

Train: Retford 7 miles

Bus: Stagecoach East Midlands service 27, 27A; Yourbus 83 to village centre then ½ mile walk

Tel: 01604 735464

ACQ.1913 🐕

MAP Page 343 (1G)
OS Map 112/120, 280: SK703896

MILTON MAUSOLEUM, MARKHAM CLINTON
NOTTINGHAMSHIRE
NG22 0PJ

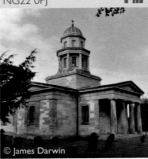

© James Darwin

This lovely Classical building with its domed tower was designed for the 4th Duke of Newcastle as a mausoleum for his wife. Inside there is an elegant Ionic reredos screen and some stunning marble effigies.

Owned and managed by The Churches Conservation Trust.

OPENING TIMES
May-Sep on 2nd and 4th Sun of each month   2.30pm-4.30pm

At other times key holder nearby

VISIT US
Train: Retford 4¼ miles

Bus: Yourbus service 38 to Milton

20 mins from Rufford Abbey

MAP Page 343 (2G)
OS Map 120, 271: SK715730

RUFFORD ABBEY
NOTTINGHAMSHIRE
NG22 9DF

RUFFORD ABBEY

The best-preserved remains of a Cistercian abbey west cloister range in England, dating mainly from c. 1170. Incorporated into part of a 17th-century and later mansion, set in Rufford Country Park. Graphic panels show how the abbey was transformed into a great house.

Managed by Nottinghamshire County Council.

OPENING TIMES
1 Apr-31 Oct, daily	10am-5pm
1 Nov-31 Mar, daily	10am-4.30pm
25 Dec	Closed

See www.nottinghamshire.gov.uk/ruffordcp for full details

VISIT US
Direction: 2 miles S of Ollerton off A614

Train: Mansfield 8 miles

Bus: 'The Sherwood Arrow' (Stagecoach) service Nottingham-Worksop; also Travelwright 227 (Wed and Fri only)

Tel: 01623 821338

ACQ.1959 🦌 🐕 🏠 🛡 ✤ ♠ 🧍 🧍
♣ P 🅿 🏛 🍴 👜 ♿ 💻

Occasional charge for members on event days.

Parking (charge applies – not managed by EH).

Shop – craft centre.

MAP Page 343 (2F)
OS Map 120, 270: SK646648

VISIT US

Direction: In Lyddington, 6 miles N of Corby; 1 mile E of A6003, next to the church

Train: Oakham 7 miles

Bus: Centrebus 'Rutland Flyer' service 1 Corby-Oakham (passes close to ⊞ Oakham)

Tel: 01572 822438

NON-MEMBERS

Adult	£4.40
Concession	£4.00
Child	£2.60
Family	£11.40

OPENING TIMES

29 Mar-3 Nov, Wed-Sun & Bank Hols   10am-5pm

ACQ.1952 ☐ ⚔ ⌂ ⊡ ♿ ⚠ OVP
Disabled access (ground floor only).

MAP Page 343 (5G)
OS Map 141, 234: SP876970

Set beside the church in a picturesque ironstone village, Lyddington Bede House originated as the medieval wing of a palace belonging to the Bishops of Lincoln. By 1600 it had passed to Sir Thomas Cecil, son of Queen Elizabeth I's chief minister, who converted it into an almshouse for twelve poor 'bedesmen' over 30 years old and two women (over 45), all free of lunacy, leprosy or the French pox. It continued to serve as an almshouse until the 1930s. Visitors can wander through the bedesmen's rooms, with their tiny windows and fireplaces, and view the Bishops' Great Chamber with its beautifully carved early Tudor ceiling cornice.

Interpretation includes a case displaying a Bible and prayer book used at the Bedehouse, and audio boxes where you can hear letters read by the 'bedesmen'. One of the bedeswomen's rooms has been recreated as it may have appeared in late Victorian times. There is a small herb garden.

DISCOUNTED ATTRACTIONS:

Use your membership to get exclusive discounts at these independent attractions in the East Midlands. Please remember to show your card as proof of membership.

FREE ENTRY TO THE UPSTAIRS ROOMS

ALTHORP
Northampton NN7 4HQ
Enjoy an insight into the personalities of the people who lived here. A fascinating collection of pictures, ceramics and furniture – reminisces this family's 500 year history.
www.spencerofalthorp.com
T. 01604 770107

FREE ENTRY

ASHBY DE LA ZOUCH MUSEUM
Leicestershire LE65 1HU
2010/2007 County Museum of the year. Model of Ashby Castle. Temporary displays, archives, research/family history facilities, guided walks.
www.ashbydelazouchmuseum.org.uk
T. 01530 560090

20% DISCOUNT ON ENTRY

BOSWORTH BATTLEFIELD
Leicestershire CV13 0AD
Re-live the drama and excitement of the Battle of Bosworth in 1485 at the award-winning Bosworth Heritage Centre.
www.bosworthbattlefield.com
T. 01455 290429

20% OFF ADULT HOUSE AND GARDEN TICKETS

BURGHLEY HOUSE
Lincolnshire PE9 3JY
England's greatest Elizabethan House. Burghley was built and designed by William Cecil, Lord High Treasurer to Queen Elizabeth I.
www.burghley.co.uk
T. 01780 752451

25% OFF ICE AGE TOUR

CRESWELL CRAGS
Nottinghamshire and Derbyshire Border S80 3LH
Home to Britain's oldest cave art and remarkable archeology, Creswell Crags provides a glimpse of life during the Ice Age.
www.creswell-crags.org.uk
T. 01909 720378

GROUP DISCOUNT RATE

CRICH TRAMWAY VILLAGE
Derbyshire DE4 5DP
Travel through time on vintage trams along the period street and out into the open countryside.
www.tramway.co.uk
T. 01773 854321

EAST MIDLANDS

Discount applies to:

Terms and conditions may apply, so make sure you check the individual pages on our website or call the individual property for more details.

⊞

78 DERNGATE: THE CHARLES RENNIE MACKINTOSH HOUSE & GALLERIES
Northampton NN1 1UH
Style. Inspiration. Innovation. The only house in England designed by Charles Rennie Mackintosh.
www.78derngate.org.uk
T. 01604 603407

⊞ OVP

GRIMSTHORPE CASTLE
Lincolnshire PE10 0LY
Grimsthorpe is a historic house, park and garden, open for adults and children to enjoy the countryside, nature and history.
www.grimsthorpe.co.uk
T. 01778 591205

⊞ OVP ??3

KELMARSH HALL & GARDENS
Northampton NN6 9LY
Original James Gibbs house set in renowned gardens with wonderful views and vistas.
www.kelmarsh.com
T. 01604 686543

⊞ OVP ??2

PAPPLEWICK PUMPING STATION
Nottinghamshire NG15 9AJ
Britain's finest working Victorian water pumping station, with woodland play area and miniature railway.
www.papplewickpumpingstation.org.uk
T. 0115 963 2938

⊞ OVP ??2

PEAK RAIL
Derbyshire DE4 3NA
Take a nostalgic journey back in time through the Derbyshire dales. Stations at Matlock, Darley Dale and Rowsley South.
www.peakrail.co.uk
T. 01629 580381

⊞ ??2

ROCKINGHAM CASTLE
Leicestershire LE16 8TH
A royal fortress for 450 years and a much-loved family home. Set in 18 acres of gardens with activities for children.
www.rockinghamcastle.com
T. 01536 770240

WEST MIDLANDS

Kenilworth Castle and Elizabethan Garden

Remember to check opening times before you visit any of our properties **www.english-heritage.org.uk/daysout**

Details of local public transport information in England are available from Traveline **www.traveline.org.uk** or call 0871 200 2233.

Stoke-on-Trent

24

19 Oswestry

Shropshire

18

Staffordshire

Burton upon Trent

Stafford

13

16

Shrewsbury

23   Telford

9

25

11   10   14   22

Tamworth

8

Wolverhampton

17   15   21

Nuneaton

28 Birmingham

Bishop's Castle

27

West Midlands

Coventry

12   20

Kidderminster

Rugby

Ludlow

Worcestershire

26

7   30

Warwick

5

Warwickshire

Leominster

29 Worcester

Stratford-upon-Avon

Herefordshire

Great Malvern

Evesham

1

Hereford   6

4

Ross-on-Wye

3

Make the most of your membership and keep up to date with upcoming events, the latest news and special offers by subscribing to our e-newsletter. Register online now at **www.english-heritage.org.uk/newsletter**

HIGHLIGHTS FOR 2013/14 IN THE **WEST MIDLANDS**

p.218

p.216

p.222

Kenilworth Castle & Elizabethan Garden: one of Britain's most impressive historic sites.

Wroxeter Roman City: glimpse life 2,000 years ago in the recreated Roman Town House.

Witley Court & Gardens: romantic ruins, beautiful fountains & perfect picnic spots.

PROPERTIES

HEREFORDSHIRE

ARTHUR'S STONE
HEREFORDSHIRE

An atmospheric Neolithic burial chamber made of great stone slabs, in the hills above Herefordshire's Golden Valley.

OPENING TIMES
Any reasonable time

VISIT US
Direction: 7 miles E of Hay-on-Wye off B4348 near Dorstone

Bus: Stagecoach in South Wales service 39; Yeomans Canyon service 39A (Sun) ⇌ Hereford – Brecon to within ¾ mile

ACQ.1909 🐾 **P**

MAP Page 342 (7B)
OS Map 148/161, OL13/201: SO319431

CHURCH OF ST JOHN THE BAPTIST, LLANROTHAL
HEREFORDSHIRE
NP25 5QJ

© Nicholas Kaye

CHURCH OF ST JOHN THE BAPTIST, LLANROTHAL

This remote whitewashed church, right on the Welsh border, sits in an idyllic valley by the River Monnow. The church is said to have been founded by a Celtic saint, St Ridol, and has a beautiful medieval interior.

Owned and managed by The Churches Conservation Trust.

OPENING TIMES
Open daily during daylight hours

VISIT US
Train: Abergavenny 10¾ miles

Bus: Stagecoach service 36 to Welsh Newton (2¼ miles walk); Yeomans service 412 to Broad Oak (2¼ miles walk).

20 mins from Goodrich Castle

MAP Page 342 (7B)
OS Map 161, OL14: SO489169

EDVIN LOACH OLD CHURCH
HEREFORDSHIRE

The ruins of an 11th-century and later church built within the earthworks of a Norman motte and bailey castle, with a Victorian church nearby.

OPENING TIMES
Any reasonable time

VISIT US
Direction: Located 4 miles N of Bromyard on an unclassified road off B4203

Bus: The closest town is Bromyard (3½ miles). Bus services operated by Astons 405, First/DRM 420, DRM 469, 476, 482, 672, 673

ACQ.1980 🐾 **P**

MAP Page 342 (6C)
OS Map 149, 202: SO663584

GOODRICH CASTLE
SEE FEATURE – PAGE 206

LONGTOWN CASTLE
HEREFORDSHIRE

Built within an earlier square earthwork, Longtown Castle is a powerful, thick-walled round keep of c. 1200, characteristic of the Welsh Borders, on a large earthen mound within a stone-walled bailey. Set in the beautiful Olchon valley, with magnificent views of the Black Mountains.

OPENING TIMES
Any reasonable time

VISIT US
Direction: Located in the centre of Longtown

Bus: Abbey Cars service 441 (Wed) & 442 (Tue); Roy Brown Coaches (summer service) B17

ACQ.1973 🐾 **P**

MAP Page 342 (7B)
OS Map 161, OL13: SO321291

MORTIMER'S CROSS WATER MILL HEREFORDSHIRE
HR6 9PE

Owned and managed by Mr C Partington, this 18th century water mill is remarkable for being so complete and in such good condition. Milling days are held on Bank Holiday Mondays, and special day and evening tours are available by arrangement with the owner. Please call for details.

MORTIMER'S CROSS WATER MILL

NON-MEMBERS

Adult	£5.00
Concession	£4.00
Child	£3.00

OPENING TIMES

29 Mar-30 Sep, Sun
& Bank Hols   10am-4pm

Other times by arrangement

Access to the mill is by guided
tour only: 11am, 1pm & 3pm

Tours led by the miller on Bank
Holiday Mondays only. See website
for details

VISIT US

Direction: Located 7 miles NW of
Leominster on B4362

Train: Leominster 7½ miles

Bus: Lugg Valley 489 (Tue, Fri only),
491 (1st, 3rd & 5th Wed only), 494
(Sat only), 498 (2nd & 4th Wed only),
802 (Sun only)

Tel: 01568 708820

ACQ.1953 ☒ ⚲ ⚠

Disabled access (exterior and ground
floor only).

Warning: there are steep river banks and
sluice channels which are hazardous at
all times.

Limited parking in lay-by.

MAP Page 342 (6B)
OS Map 137/148/149, 203:
SO426637

ROTHERWAS CHAPEL
HEREFORDSHIRE

The family chapel of the Roman
Catholic Bodenham family.
The originally simple medieval
building has a fine Elizabethan
timber roof, a rebuilt 18th-century
tower, and striking Victorian
interior decoration and
furnishings by the Pugins.

OPENING TIMES

Any reasonable time. Key available
at nearby filling station

ROTHERWAS CHAPEL

VISIT US

Direction: 1½ miles SE of Hereford
on B4399, left into Chapel Road

Train: Hereford 3½ miles

Bus: First service 78, 78A;
Yeoman 82 then ½ mile walk

ACQ.1928 ☒ P ⚲

Disabled access via kissing gate only.

MAP Page 342 (7B)
OS Map 149, 189: SO536383

ST MICHAEL'S CHURCH, MICHAELCHURCH
HEREFORDSHIRE
HR2 8LD

© Nicholas Kaye

Said to have been founded
by Bishop Herwald of Llandaff
in 1056, this lovely church
hugs the side of a remote
valley. A Roman altar is built
into a blocked doorway, and
13th-century paintings decorate
the walls.

**Owned and managed by The
Churches Conservation Trust.**

OPENING TIMES

Open daily during daylight hours

VISIT US

Train: Hereford 9¼ miles

Bus: Stagecoach service 36 to
Sandyway then 2 miles walk;
Stagecoach 32 or 33 to Harewood
End then 2 miles walk

60 mins from Goodrich Castle

MAP Page 342 (7B)
OS Map 162, 189: SO522255

WIGMORE CASTLE
HEREFORDSHIRE

Once the stronghold of the
turbulent Mortimer family,
Wigmore Castle was later
dismantled to prevent its use
during the Civil War. Now it is
among the most remarkable
ruins in England. The site has been
excavated, but is largely buried up
to first floor level by earth and
fallen masonry. Yet many of its
fortifications survive to full height,
including parts of the keep on its
towering mound. Graphic panels
tell the story of this important
medieval castle, now conserved
for its wildlife habitats as well as
its historic interest.

OPENING TIMES

Any reasonable time

VISIT US

Direction: Located 8 miles W of
Ludlow on A4110. Accessible via
footpath ¾ mile from the village
on Mortimer Way

Train: Bucknell 6 miles,
Ludlow 10 miles

Bus: Lugg Valley 489 (Tue, Fri only),
491 (1st, 3rd & 5th Wed only), 498
(2nd & 4th Wed only), 802 (Sun only);
Roy Brown Coaches X11 (Mon only)

ACQ.1995 ☒ P ⚠

Toilets (including disabled) at the
Village Hall.

There are steep steps to the summit,
which are hazardous in icy and wet
conditions. Children must stay under
close control. Do not climb on the walls or
banks. Strong footwear is recommended.

MAP Page 342 (6B)
OS Map 137/148, 203: SO408693

Goodrich stands majestically on a wooded hill commanding the passage of the River Wye into the picturesque valley of Symonds Yat.

VISIT US

Address: Goodrich Castle, Castle Lane, Goodrich, Ross-on-Wye, Herefordshire HR9 6HY

Direction: 5 miles S of Ross-on-Wye off A40

Bus: H&H Coaches service 34 and 411 (Wed) to within ½ mile

Tel: 01600 890538

NON-MEMBERS

Adult	£6.20
Concession	£5.60
Child	£3.70
Family	£16.10

OPENING TIMES

25 Mar-30 Jun, daily	10am-5pm
1 Jul-31 Aug, daily	10am-6pm
1 Sep-3 Nov, daily	10am-5pm
4 Nov-16 Feb, Sat-Sun	10am-4pm
17-21 Feb, daily	10am-4pm
22 Feb-31 Mar, Sat-Sun	10am-4pm
24-26 Dec and 1 Jan	Closed

ACQ.1920

A non-refundable car parking charge of £1 applies.

Dogs on leads.

Disabled access (limited, please call for details or ask the visitor centre on arrival).

The tearoom will close 30 minutes before the site closes.

MAP Page 342 (7C)
OS Map 162, OL14: SO577200

Goodrich's delightful tearoom serves a fine selection of light refreshments made from locally-sourced Herefordshire ingredients.

The castle was begun in the late 11th century by the English landowner Godric, who gave it his name. A generation later the splendidly preserved square keep that still forms its core was added, probably in the time of Richard 'Strongbow' de Clare, Earl of Pembroke and Lord of Goodrich 1148-76.

Under King Richard the Lionheart, Goodrich was granted along with the earldom of Pembroke to the famous William Marshal, a great castle builder who may have initiated work on the inner ward. Each of Marshal's five sons inherited the fortress in turn, the fourth son dying childless at Goodrich in 1245.

Thereafter the fortress and earldom passed to Henry III's half-brother, William de Valence, who rebuilt its defences and living quarters in the most up-to-date style.

Goodrich still boasts one of the most complete sets of medieval domestic buildings surviving in any English castle. William's widow Countess Joan frequently stayed here with an entourage of up to 200, entertaining her relations and friends in the most lavish style.

During the Civil War, Goodrich was held successively by both sides. Sir Henry Lingen's

Royalists eventually surrendered in 1646 under threats of undermining and a deadly Parliamentarian mortar. Visitors can see the famous 'Roaring Meg', the only surviving Civil War mortar, which has returned to the castle after over 350 years, and a cache of Civil War cannonballs, found at Goodrich in the 1920s. The visitor centre features an exhibition exploring life at the castle from its late 11th-century origins until its dramatic fall in 1646, including Civil War artefacts.

SHROPSHIRE

ACTON BURNELL CASTLE
SHROPSHIRE

The impressive red sandstone shell of a battlemented tower house mansion, built c.1283-92 by Bishop Robert Burnell, Edward I's Lord Chancellor. Parliament was held nearby in 1283, when the king ratified a law for the protection of merchants, known as the Statute of Acton Burnell.

OPENING TIMES
Any reasonable time

VISIT US
Direction: Located in Acton Burnell, signposted from A49, 8 miles S of Shrewsbury

Train: Shrewsbury or Church Stretton, both 8 miles

Bus: Boultons (of Cardington) service 540

MAP Page 342 (4B)
OS Map 126, 241: SJ534019

BOSCOBEL HOUSE AND THE ROYAL OAK
SEE FEATURE OPPOSITE

BUILDWAS ABBEY
SHROPSHIRE – TF8 7BW

Impressive ruins of a Cistercian abbey, including its unusually unaltered 12th-century church, beautiful vaulted and tile-floored chapter house and recently re-opened crypt chapel.

In a wooded Severn-side setting, not far from the Iron Bridge (p.211) and Wenlock Priory (p.213) – near the home of Dr William Penny Brookes, originator of the still-continuing Olympian Wenlock Games, a major inspiration for the modern International Olympics.

NON-MEMBERS
Adult	£3.60
Concession	£3.20
Child	£2.20

OPENING TIMES
29 Mar-30 Sep, Wed-Sun & Bank Hols	10am-5pm
24-26 Dec and 1 Jan	Closed

VISIT US
Direction: On S bank of River Severn on A4169, 2 miles W of Ironbridge

Train: Telford Central 6 miles

Bus: Arriva Midlands service 96

Tel: 01952 433274

ACQ.1925 OVP

Disabled access is limited.

Nature trail (not managed by EH) including site of abbey fishponds.

MAP Page 342 (4C)
OS Map 127, 242: SJ643043

CANTLOP BRIDGE
SHROPSHIRE

A single-span, cast-iron road bridge over the Cound Brook. Possibly designed and certainly approved by the great engineer Thomas Telford, who was instrumental in shaping industrial Shropshire and the West Midlands.

OPENING TIMES
Any reasonable time

VISIT US
Direction: ¾ mile SW of Berrington on an unclassified road off A458

Train: Shrewsbury 5 miles

Bus: Boultons (of Cardington) service 540

ACQ.1977

MAP Page 342 (4B)
OS Map 126, 241: SJ517062

VISIT US

Direction: On minor road from A41 to A5, 8 miles NW of Wolverhampton. 5 mins drive from M54 J3

Train: Cosford 3 miles

Bus: Arriva/Midland service 3; Coastal Liner 17 (Wed only); Arriva Midlands services 88/88A to Bishopswood then 1 mile walk

Tel: 01902 850244

NON-MEMBERS

Adult	£6.20
Concession	£5.60
Child	£3.70
Family	£16.10

OPENING TIMES

29 Mar–3 Nov, Wed–Sun & Bank Hols 10am–5pm

House will be closed for 1 hour at 11am and 2pm for guided tours. Guided tours are subject to availability and booking is advisable

4 Nov–31 Mar, Sat–Sun 10am–4pm Guided tours only

24–26 Dec and 1 Jan Closed

Last entry 1 hour before closing

ACQ.1954

Dogs on leads (grounds only).

Parking (coaches welcome).

Disabled access limited. Call for details.

MAP Page 342 (4C)
OS Map 127, 242: SJ838082

A pretty timber-framed house that played a brief but important role in English history, Boscobel was converted into a lodge by John Giffard in about 1630. The Giffards were Roman Catholics, and tradition holds that its real purpose was to serve as a secret refuge for persecuted Catholics at times of need.

Boscobel was destined for greater fame. Following the execution of King Charles I in 1649, his son made a brave though misguided attempt to regain the throne. Defeated in 1651 at Worcester, the final battle of the Civil War, young Charles fled for his life.

Initially Charles intended to cross the River Severn into Wales, but found his way blocked by Cromwell's patrols. He sought refuge instead at Boscobel, hiding first in a tree, known afterwards as 'The Royal Oak', and then in a priest-hole in the house's attic. The future King Charles II then travelled on in disguise via other safe houses before escaping to France.

Boscobel became a much-visited place, although it remained a working farm. Today's visitors can enjoy our audio and visual displays; take a guided tour of the lodge; see the garden and a descendant of the Royal Oak; and find out about Boscobel's past as a working Victorian farm.

There is a permissive path from Boscobel House to White Ladies Priory, another of Charles's hiding places.

CHURCH OF ST MARY THE VIRGIN, SHREWSBURY
SHROPSHIRE – SY1 1EF

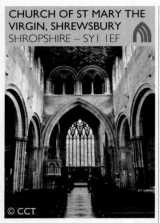

© CCT

St Mary's is a gem on a grand scale. It has the tallest spire in England; glorious stained glass including a world-famous 14th century 'Jesse window' and a Medieval cartoon strip featuring St Bernard; a stunning 15th century carved oak ceiling and a wealth of rich colours and fascinating treasures.

Owned and managed by The Churches Conservation Trust.

OPENING TIMES

1 Apr-31 Oct, Mon-Sat	10am-5pm
1 Nov-31 Mar, Mon-Sat	10am-4pm
Sometimes open on Sundays	

VISIT US

Train: Shrewsbury 15 mins walk

Bus: Shrewsbury is served by many buses

10 mins from Haughmond Abbey

MAP Page 342 (4B)
OS Map 126, 241: SJ494126

CLUN CASTLE
SHROPSHIRE

CLUN CASTLE

The dramatic riverside ruins and extensive earthworks of a Welsh Border castle, its tall 13th-century keep unusually set on the side of its mound.

Information panels tell the story of the castle and the adjacent town.

OPENING TIMES
Any reasonable time

VISIT US
Direction: In Clun, off A488, 18 miles W of Ludlow

Train: Hopton Heath 6½ miles; Knighton 6½ miles

Bus: Minsterley 745 (Mon & Fri only); M&J service 773 & 860 (Tue only)

ACQ. 1991 ⚔ P ⌂ ⚠

MAP Page 342 (5B)
OS Map 137, 201: SO299809

HAUGHMOND ABBEY
SHROPSHIRE – SY4 4RW

The extensive remains of an Augustinian abbey, including its abbots' quarters, refectory and cloister. The substantially surviving chapter house has a frontage richly bedecked with 12th- and 14th-century carving and statuary and a fine timber roof of c. 1500. Pictorial interpretation boards guide the visitor and an introductory exhibition displays archaeological finds. Picnic area and light refreshments available.

NON-MEMBERS

Adult	£3.60
Concession	£3.20
Child	£2.20

HAUGHMOND ABBEY

Members can also get a Passport discount at Ironbridge Gorge Museums. See p.224 for details.

OPENING TIMES

29 Mar-30 Sep, Wed-Sun & Bank Hols	10am-5pm

VISIT US
Direction: Located 3 miles NE of Shrewsbury off B5062

Train: Shrewsbury 3½ miles

Bus: Arriva 519 Shrewsbury – Newport

Tel: 01743 709661

ACQ. 1931 ⚔ ⌂ ▣ P ⌂ ♿ ⚠ OVP
Disabled access (not easy).

MAP Page 342 (4B)
OS Map 126, 241: SJ542152

IRON BRIDGE
SEE FEATURE OPPOSITE

LANGLEY CHAPEL
SHROPSHIRE

A small chapel tranquilly set all alone in charming countryside. Its atmospheric interior contains a perfect set of 17th-century timber furnishings, including a musicians' pew.

OPENING TIMES

29 Mar-3 Nov, daily	10am-6pm
4 Nov-30 Mar, daily	10am-4pm
24-26 Dec and 1 Jan	Closed

VISIT US
Direction: 1½ miles S of Acton Burnell, on an unclassified road off A49; 9½ miles S of Shrewsbury

Train: Shrewsbury 7½ miles

Bus: Boultons (of Cardington) service 540 (then 1¼ mile walk)

ACQ. 1914 ⚔ P

MAP Page 342 (5B)
OS Map 126/127/138, 217/241: SJ538001

VISIT US

Direction: Adjacent to A4169

Bus: Arriva 77, 88, 88A 96, 99, 99A Gorge Connect service WH1 (summer Sat & Sun only)

OPENING TIMES

Any reasonable time

Members can also get a Passport discount at Ironbridge Gorge Museums. See p.224 for details.

ACQ.1975

MAP Page 342 (4C)
OS Map 127, 242: SJ672034

The world's first iron bridge was erected over the River Severn here in 1779. Britain's best-known industrial monument, the bridge gave its name to the spectacular wooded gorge which, though now tranquil, was once an industrial powerhouse and the cradle of the Industrial Revolution. Ironbridge Gorge is now a World Heritage Site.

At the beginning of the 18th century, Abraham Darby I pioneered the process of using coke made from local coal to smelt local iron ore, but industrial expansion was hampered by the lack of a bridge over the Severn, which had to be a single span to allow for barge traffic. An iron bridge was first suggested by the Shrewsbury architect Thomas Pritchard: he designed a single span-bridge 30 metres long, but died as work began. The project was then taken over by Abraham Darby III, who cast the bridge in his Coalbrookdale foundry, using 378 tons of iron. Recent research shows that most parts were individually cast to fit, each being slightly different from the next: and that traditional woodworking-style joints were adapted to assemble them.

Costing over £6000, this proclamation of the achievements of Shropshire ironmasters was formally opened on New Year's Day 1781. It continued in full use by ever-increasing traffic until closed and designated an Ancient Monument in 1934. Massive strengthening works were later undertaken, and in 1999-2000 English Heritage assisted with a full survey of this revolutionary and iconic structure.

The Iron Bridge is the perfect place to begin a tour of the Gorge's many museums and the many other English Heritage sites nearby, including Buildwas Abbey, Wenlock Priory and Wroxeter Roman City.

LILLESHALL ABBEY
SHROPSHIRE

Extensive ruins of an Augustinian abbey, later a Civil War stronghold, in a deeply rural setting. Much of the church survives, unusually viewable from gallery level, along with the lavishly sculpted processional door and other cloister buildings. Graphic panels show how the abbey appeared in medieval times.

OPENING TIMES

29 Mar-3 Nov, daily	10am-6pm
4 Nov-30 Mar, daily	10am-4pm
24-26 Dec and 1 Jan	Closed

VISIT US

Direction: On an unclassified road off A518, 4 miles N of Oakengates

Train: Oakengates 4½ miles

Bus: Arriva service 481 Telford-Stafford (passes close to ⬛ Telford Central and Stafford) or Arriva 115/116 (Sat only passes close to Shinall station) to within 1 mile – alight between Sheriffhales and Heath Hill

[ACQ.1950] 🎫 P ♿

Disabled access via kissing gate only.

MAP Page 342 (4C)
OS Map 127, 242: SJ738142

MITCHELL'S FOLD STONE CIRCLE
SHROPSHIRE

A Bronze Age stone circle, the focus of many legends, set in dramatic moorland on Stapeley Hill. It once consisted of some 30 stones, 15 of which are still visible.

OPENING TIMES
Any reasonable time

VISIT US
Direction: 16 miles SW of Shrewsbury

Train: Welshpool 10 miles

Bus: Minsterley Motors service 553 Shrewsbury – Bishop's Castle (passes close to ⬛ Shrewsbury. Also Minsterley Motors 745 (Mon & Fri only) 775 (Wed only) – all to Pennerley Junction within 1 mile. Also Shropshire Link service Zone 1 area 1 (Wed & Fri only)
Tel: 0845 678 9068

[ACQ.1915] 🎫 P

MAP Page 342 (5B)
OS Map 137, 216: SO304984

MORETON CORBET CASTLE
SHROPSHIRE

The ruins of the medieval castle and Tudor manor house of the Corbets are dominated by the theatrical shell of an ambitious Elizabethan mansion wing in Italianate style, which was devastated during the Civil War. Fine Corbet family monuments fill the adjacent church.

OPENING TIMES
Any reasonable time

VISIT US
Direction: In Moreton Corbet off B5063 (a turning off A49), 7 miles NE of Shrewsbury

Train: Yorton 4 miles

Bus: Arriva service 64 to Shawbury then ¾ mile walk

[ACQ.1939] 🎫 P ♿
Disabled access is limited.

MAP Page 342 (4C)
OS Map 126, 241: SJ561231

OLD OSWESTRY HILL FORT
SHROPSHIRE

Among the most hugely impressive Iron Age hillforts on the Welsh Borders, covering 40 acres, with formidable multiple ramparts.

Information panels tell you about the hillfort and its inhabitants.

OPENING TIMES
Any reasonable time

VISIT US
Direction: 1 mile N of Oswestry, off an unclassified road off A483

Train: Gobowen 2 miles

Bus: Arriva service 2, 2A, 53 to Gobowen Road or Arriva Oswestry town service 404 to Old Fort Way and then short walk

[ACQ.1946] 🎫 P
Sheep grazing on site.

MAP Page 342 (3B)
OS Map 126, 240/258: SJ295310

ST ANDREW'S CHURCH, WROXETER
SHROPSHIRE – SY5 6PH

St Andrew's is built on the site of Viroconium, the fourth largest town of Roman Britain, and evidence of its past can be found in and around the church. Parts of the building date from before the Domesday Book (1086) but the interior mostly dates from the 17th and 18th centuries and contains some wonderful monuments.

Owned and managed by The Churches Conservation Trust.

OPENING TIMES
Open daily during daylight hours

VISIT US
Train: Shrewsbury 4 miles

Bus: Arriva Midlands bus route 96 Shrewsbury-Telford

Next to Wroxeter Roman City

MAP Page 342 (4C)
OS Map 126, 241: SJ564083

STOKESAY CASTLE
SEE FEATURE – PAGE 214

WENLOCK PRIORY
SHROPSHIRE – TF13 6HS

WHITE LADIES PRIORY
SHROPSHIRE

The tranquil ruins of Wenlock Priory stand in a picturesque setting on the fringe of beautiful Much Wenlock. An Anglo-Saxon monastery was founded here in about 680 by King Merewalh of Mercia, whose abbess daughter Milburge was hailed as a saint. Her relics were miraculously re-discovered here in 1101, attracting both pilgrims and prosperity.

By then Wenlock had been re-founded by the Normans as a priory of Cluniac monks. The impressive remains of this medieval priory survive today, everywhere reflecting the Cluniac love of elaborate decoration. Parts of the great 13th-century church still stand high; and in the adjoining cloister garth is an unusual monks' washing fountain with 12th-century carvings. Once enclosed in an octagonal building, 16 monks could wash here at once before eating in the nearby refectory.

Perhaps the greatest glory of the priory is the extravagantly decorated chapter house of about 1140, its walls bedecked with interlocking blind arcading on multiple carved columns.

All this is enhanced by the topiary-filled cloister garden, and set against the backdrop of the complete infirmary wing,

converted into a mansion after the priory's dissolution and still a private residence.

Much Wenlock was the home of Dr William Penny Brookes, originator of the Wenlock Olympian Games first held here in 1850, a major inspiration for the modern International Olympics. July 2013 will see the 127th Wenlock Olympian Games contested in the town.

NON-MEMBERS

Adult	£4.10
Concession	£3.70
Child	£2.50

OPENING TIMES

29 Mar-30 Sep, daily	10am-6pm
1 Oct-3 Nov, daily	10am-5pm
4 Nov-16 Feb, Sat-Sun	10am-4pm
17-21 Feb, daily	10am-4pm
22 Feb-31 Mar, Sat-Sun	10am-4pm
24-26 Dec and 1 Jan	Closed

VISIT US

Direction: In Much Wenlock

Train: Telford Central 9 miles

Bus: Arriva service 88, 88A & 436

Tel: 01952 727466

ACQ.1964 🎧♿🎁❄🖼🚶♂🚻👜 **P**
📷♿ OVP
A non-refundable car parking charge of £1 applies.

MAP Page 342 (5C)
OS Map 127/138, 217/242: SJ625001

Ruins of the late 12th-century church of a small nunnery of 'white ladies' or Augustinian canonesses. Charles II came here in 1651 before seeking refuge at nearby Boscobel House.

Permissive path to White Ladies Priory from Boscobel House, where there is parking when Boscobel is open. Approximately 20 minutes walk.

OPENING TIMES

Any reasonable time

VISIT US

Direction: Located 1 mile SW of Boscobel House off an unclassified road between A41 and A5; 8 miles NW of Wolverhampton

Train: Cosford 2½ miles

Bus: Arriva/Midland service 3; Coastal Liner 17 (Wed only); Arriva Midlands services 88/88A to Bishopswood then 1 mile walk

ACQ.1938 👜

MAP Page 342 (4C)
OS Map 217, 242: SJ826076

WROXETER ROMAN CITY
SEE FEATURE – PAGE 216

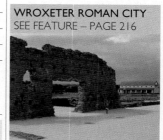

Stokesay Castle is the finest and best preserved fortified medieval manor house in England. Set in peaceful countryside near the Welsh border, the castle, timber-framed gatehouse and parish church form an unforgettably picturesque group.

VISIT US

Address: Stokesay Castle, Nr Craven Arms, Ludlow, Shropshire SY7 9AH

Direction: 7 miles NW of Ludlow off A49

Train: Craven Arms 1 mile

Bus: Minsterley Motors (of Stiperstones) 435 to Stokesay turning on the A49 then ½ mile walk

Tel: 01588 672544

Local Tourist Information
Ludlow: 01584 875053

NON-MEMBERS

Adult	£6.20
Concession	£5.60
Child	£3.70
Family	£16.10

OPENING TIMES

29 Mar–3 Nov, daily	10am–5pm
4 Nov–16 Feb, Sat–Sun	10am–4pm
17–21 Feb, daily	10am–4pm
22 Feb–31 Mar, Sat–Sun	10am–4pm
24–26 Dec and 1 Jan	Closed

ACQ.1986 🎧 🛡 ♿ 🏠 🚶 🔞 ✂ 🅿
🏠 ♿ ☕ ⚠ OVP

A non-refundable car parking charge of £1 applies.

Disabled access (call site for details).

Entrance to the courtyard is through a historic gate. Unsuitable for motorised scooters and unassisted wheelchair users.

Tearoom (seasonal): 29 Mar–3 Nov.

MAP Page 342 (5B)
OS Map 137/148, 203: SO436815

An audio tour will help you to imagine Stokesay as the centre of medieval life. Its grounds include cottage-style gardens, a tearoom open from April to October, and a gift shop.

Lawrence of Ludlow, a wealthy local wool-merchant wishing to set up as a country gentleman, bought the property in 1281, when the long Anglo-Welsh wars were ending. So it was safe to raise here one of the first fortified manor houses in England, 'builded like a castle' for effect but lit by large domestic-style windows.

Extensive recent tree-ring dating confirms that Lawrence had completed virtually the whole of the still-surviving house by 1291, using the same team of carpenters throughout. More remarkably, the dating also revealed that it has scarcely been altered since.

Stokesay's magnificent open-hearthed great hall displays a fine timber roof, shuttered gable windows and a precipitous staircase, its treads cut from whole tree-trunks. It is flanked by the north tower, with an original medieval tiled floor and remains of a wall painting, and a 'solar' or private apartment block and the tall south tower – the most castle-like part of the house, self-contained and reached by a defensible stairway.

The solar block contains one of the few post-medieval alterations to the house, a fine panelled chamber. Its dominating feature is a fireplace with a richly carved overmantel, still bearing clear traces of original painting in five colours. This was added in about 1641, at the same time as the truly delightful gatehouse:

an outstanding and recently-conserved example of the Marches style of lavishly showy timber-framing, bedecked with charming carvings of Adam and Eve.

A few years later, in 1645, Stokesay experienced its only known military encounter, surrendering without fighting to a Parliamentarian force. So the house remained undamaged, and sensitive conservation by Victorian owners and English Heritage have left it the medieval jewel which survives today.

An audio tour helps you to imagine Stokesay as a centre of medieval life. Its attractions include beautiful cottage-style gardens, a moat, a tearoom open from April to October, and a gift shop.

VISIT US

Direction: 5 miles SE of Shrewsbury, on a minor road signposted from the B4380

Train: Shrewsbury 5½ miles; Wellington Telford West 6 miles

Bus: Arriva 96 Telford – Shrewsbury (passes close to ➔ Telford Central)

Tel: 01743 761330

NON-MEMBERS

Adult	£5.20
Concession	£4.70
Child	£3.10
Family	£13.50

OPENING TIMES

29 Mar–3 Nov, daily	10am–5pm
4 Nov–31 Mar, Sat–Sun	10am–4pm
24–26 Dec and 1 Jan	Closed

ACQ. 1947 🎧 🐕 🎦 👓 🚻 ♿ 📷 P
📷 ⚠ OVP

MAP Page 342 (4B)
OS Map 126, 241: SJ565087

Now set among fields, Wroxeter (or 'Viriconium') was once the fourth largest city in Roman Britain, with up to 5000 citizens. It began as a legionary fortress and developed into a thriving civilian city, populated by retired soldiers and traders. Today the most impressive features are the remains of the 2nd-century municipal baths and the huge wall dividing them from the exercise hall, once in the heart of the city.

The audio tour reveals how Wroxeter worked in its heyday, and the fascinating site museum displays an amazing wealth of site finds, from military weapons and equipment to fashion accessories and medical instruments, illustrating the everyday life of the citizens. Vivid interpretation traces the rise, flourishing and eventual abandonment of the city.

An unusual and popular feature of the site is a recreation of a Roman town house, complete with dining-room, bedroom and bath-suite. Inspired by houses excavated here, it was built using traditional methods as interpreted by six modern building-trade workers, for the Channel 4 series 'Rome Wasn't Built in a Day'. It now also features replicas of Roman furniture.

An education room is available for schools.

STAFFORDSHIRE

CROXDEN ABBEY
STAFFORDSHIRE

The impressive remains of an abbey of Cistercian 'white monks', including towering fragments of its 13th-century church, infirmary and 14th-century abbot's lodging. Information panels and a display of decorative stonework tell the story of the abbey's spectacular architecture.

OPENING TIMES
29 Mar-3 Nov, daily	10am-6pm
4 Nov-30 Mar, daily	10am-4pm
24-26 Dec and 1 Jan	Closed

VISIT US
Direction: 5 miles NW of Uttoxeter off A522

Train: Uttoxeter 6 miles

Bus: Closest service is Phil Smith 184 to Hollington (Wed only). Otherwise First 32 to Fole, or First 32A, or Alton Towers Transport 30 to Alton then 2½ miles walk

No climbing on the walls.

MAP Page 342 (3D)
OS Map 128, 259: SK066397

WALL ROMAN SITE (LETOCETUM)
STAFFORDSHIRE
WS14 0AW

Wall was an important staging post on Watling Street, the Roman military road to North Wales. It provided overnight accommodation for travelling Roman officials and imperial messengers. The foundations of an inn and bathhouse can be seen, and many of the excavated finds are displayed in the on-site museum.

Managed by English Heritage on behalf of the National Trust, with thanks to the Friends of Letocetum.

OPENING TIMES
Site
1 Mar-3 Nov, daily	10am-5pm
4 Nov-28 Feb, daily	10am-4pm
24-26 Dec and 1 Jan	Closed

Museum
30-31 Mar, 1, 27-28 Apr, 4-6, 25-27 May, 29-30 Jun, 27-28 Jul, 4, 11, 18, 24-26 Aug, 1, 28-29 Sep, 26-27 Oct   11am-4pm

11am-4pm or dusk, whichever comes sooner

VISIT US
Direction: Off Eastbound A5 at Wall, near Lichfield

Train: Shenstone 1½ miles

Bus: Arriva Midland service 81 or Heartlands Travel 81A (Sat only)

MAP Page 342 (4D)
OS Map 139, 244: SK098066

WARWICKSHIRE

ALL SAINTS' CHURCH, BILLESLEY
WARWICKSHIRE
B49 6NF

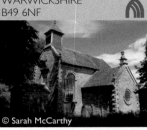

© Sarah McCarthy

Tradition has it that William Shakespeare married Anne Hathaway here. His granddaughter's wedding's also said to have taken place in this church that dates back 1,000 years. Some remains of the early church survive, in particular two spectacular 12th century stone carvings.

Owned and managed by The Churches Conservation Trust.

OPENING TIMES
Open daily during daylight hours

VISIT US
Train: Wilmcote 2½ miles and Stratford-upon-Avon 4 miles

Bus: Stagecoach Warwickshire service 26 Stratford-Redditch. Nearest official stop is Haselhor, but ask driver to drop you off near the Redhill intersection from whence it is c.½ mile walk

30 mins to Kenilworth Castle and Elizabethan Garden

MAP Page 342 (6E)
OS Map 151, 205: SP148568

Don't forget to check opening times online before you visit.

www.english-heritage.org.uk/daysout/properties

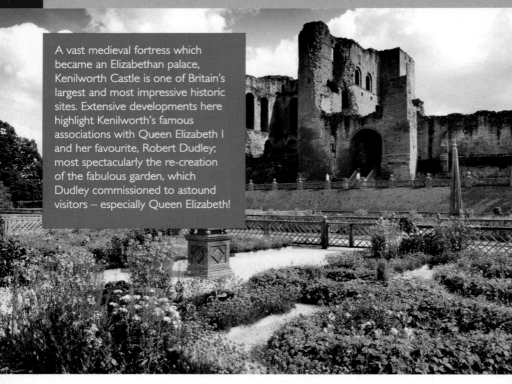

A vast medieval fortress which became an Elizabethan palace, Kenilworth Castle is one of Britain's largest and most impressive historic sites. Extensive developments here highlight Kenilworth's famous associations with Queen Elizabeth I and her favourite, Robert Dudley; most spectacularly the re-creation of the fabulous garden, which Dudley commissioned to astound visitors – especially Queen Elizabeth!

VISIT US

Address: Kenilworth Castle, Castle Green, Off Castle Road, Kenilworth, Warwickshire CV8 1NE

Direction: In Kenilworth off A46. Clearly signposted from the town centre, off B4103

Train: Warwick or Coventry 5 miles

Bus: Johnsons of Henley 539 passes the castle site; Travel West Midlands 11; Stagecoach U2, U12, 16, U17 & X17 all serve Kenilworth from surrounding area

Tel: 01926 852078

Local Tourist Information
Kenilworth: 01926 748900

NON-MEMBERS

Adult	£9.00
Concession	£8.10
Child	£5.40
Family	£23.40

Additional charges for members and non-members may apply on event days

OPENING TIMES

25 Mar-3 Nov, daily	10am-5pm
4 Nov-16 Feb, Sat-Sun	10am-4pm
17-21 Feb, daily	10am-4pm
22 Feb-31 Mar, Sat-Sun	10am-4pm
24-26 Dec and 1 Jan	Closed

Note: the gatehouse may close early for private events, please call or check the website before you visit

ACQ.1938 🎧 🎭 👹 E f 🌺 ❄
📷 🍷 🔔 🚶 🚻 P 🏰 📷 ♿
📖 ⚠ OVP

Audio tours available (English, French, German and a children's version). Audio tours not available on Bank Holiday weekends or special event days.

Tearoom open as per site, finishing 30 minutes before site closes.

A car parking charge applies to ensure that EH members and paying visitors have priority. The charge will be refunded on admission, except on Bank Holiday weekends and at selected special events.

MAP Page 342 (5E)
OS Map 140, 221: SP278723

🍷 Available for corporate and private hire

🔔 Licensed for civil wedding ceremonies

NEW FOR 2013

From summer 2013, new stairs
and viewing platforms in
'Leicester's Building' will – for
the first time since the Civil War
– allow a close-up view of the
remains of the inner apartments
where Queen Elizabeth I stayed
during her famous 1575 visit
to Kenilworth.

Spanning more than five centuries, Kenilworth's
varied buildings and architectural styles reflect
its long connection with successive English
monarchs. Geoffrey de Clinton, Henry I's
treasurer, began the massive Norman keep at
the core of the fortress in the 1120s, and under
Henry II Kenilworth became a royal castle. King
John greatly strengthened it between 1210 and
1215, enlarging the surrounding watery 'mere'
which effectively made it an island stronghold.
Thus it could withstand an epic siege in 1266,
when rebellious barons held out against Henry
III's siege engines for six months, succumbing
only to starvation. In the impressively-timbered
Tudor stables, which now house the castle's
tearoom, trebuchet balls from the siege can be
seen in the fascinating interactive display on the
castle's history.

During the late 14th century John of Gaunt,
Duke of Lancaster, rebuilt the splendid great
hall and staterooms of Kenilworth's inner court,
beginning the castle's transition into a palace and
favourite residence of the Lancastrian and early
Tudor kings. Here Henry V received the insulting
French 'gift' of tennis-balls which sparked off the
Agincourt campaign, and by Henry VIII's time the
castle was already renowned for its 'many fair
chambers'. The scene was set for Kenilworth's
greatest period of fame.

This began when Queen Elizabeth's I favourite,
Robert Dudley, Earl of Leicester, took

possession of the castle in 1563. He then
lavished fortunes on converting it into a great
showpiece mansion, designed to receive the
Queen and her court on their ceremonial
'progresses' around her realm. Striking
evidence of Dudley's transformation can
still be seen everywhere at Kenilworth. Not
content with remodelling its existing structures,
he added the tall, mansion-sized 'Leicester's
Building' – complete with a 'dancing chamber'
on its top floor – specifically for the Queen's
use: as well as an imposing new entrance to
his quasi-royal palace, 'Leicester's Gatehouse'.

As part of a multi-million pound English
Heritage investment in Kenilworth Castle,
Leicester's Gatehouse is displayed with the
chambers on its lower floors re-created as
they might have appeared when the gatehouse
was last inhabited in the 1930s, while the
top floor houses *The Queen and the Castle:
Robert Dudley's Kenilworth*. Featuring items
both from museums and private collections,
this exhibition tells the story of Elizabeth I's
relationship with Dudley and her four visits
to Kenilworth.

On the last and most famous of these visits, in
July 1575, Elizabeth stayed here for 19 days – her
longest sojourn in a courtier's house during any of
her progresses. Dudley not only entertained her
lavishly throughout with music, dancing, hunting
and plays; he also created specially for her visit a

The impressively-timbered Tudor stables now house the castle's tearoom and a fascinating interactive display on the castle's history.

fabulous garden, the re-creation of which opened in May 2009 after five years of intensive archaeological excavations, research and development. A bejewelled Renaissance aviary; magnificent carved arbours; a planting scheme abundant in colour, perfume and fruit and an 18-foot-high fountain carved from dazzling Carrara marble. These are just some of the glories of Robert Dudley's garden at Kenilworth Castle. In an age famous for its extravagance, it was designed to score off rival aristocratic garden-creators, but principally to astound visitors, including Elizabeth I.

This garden, lost for centuries, has been brought back to life by a pioneering team of historians, archaeologists, plantsmen and plantswomen, designers, craftspeople and gardeners. It presents the most complete evocation of an Elizabethan garden anywhere in the world – a garden to seduce and beguile visitors today, just as it did in 1575.

Such an outstandingly comprehensive re-creation of Elizabethan garden architecture, design, statuary and planting has never been attempted on this scale before. It has been made possible by important advances in garden archaeology and the survival of an extraordinary eye-witness description of the Kenilworth garden, written by Robert Langham in 1575.

Thus a garden that was once the 'glory of England' can once again be admired at this most romantic of castles. It opens a window on the period's most enduring love story – that of Elizabeth I and her favourite, Robert Dudley.

Though largely unscathed during the Civil War, Kenilworth was afterwards rendered indefensible and gradually fell into dilapidation. Made famous by Walter Scott's romantic novel, *Kenilworth* (1821), it came into state guardianship in 1938.

Visit the website for details of special events held here throughout the year.

WEST MIDLANDS

HALESOWEN ABBEY
WEST MIDLANDS – B62 8RJ

Remains of an abbey founded by King John in the 13th century.

A free podcast is available on our website **www.english-heritage.org.uk/halesowenabbey**

OPENING TIMES
Open to view from the public footpath only. Check website for open days during 2013

VISIT US
Directions: Off A456, ½ mile W of J3, M5

Train: Old Hill 2½ miles

Bus: Diamond services 002, 007; National Express West Midlands services 9 & 241 (then ½ mile walk)

ACQ.1976

MAP Page 342 (5D)
OS Map 139, 219: SO975828

J. W. EVANS SILVER FACTORY
BIRMINGHAM – B1 3EA

Established in 1881, J. W. Evans is one of the most complete surviving historic factories in Birmingham's Jewellery Quarter. Behind the frontage of four terraced houses, the workshops retain their original drop stamps and fly presses. They are packed with thousands of dies for the manufacture of silverware, as well as the whole of the working equipment, stock and records of the business. English Heritage stepped in to rescue the factory in 2008. The site is now open for pre-booked guided tours only.

www.english-heritage.org.uk/jwevans

J. W. EVANS SILVER FACTORY

OPENING TIMES
Pre-booked tours only, (max 10 persons per tour)

10, 20, 24 Apr

8,11,18 May

1, 12, 22, 26 Jun

6, 10 Jul

10 Aug

4, 14, 28 Sep

2, 12, 23, 26 Oct

VISIT US
Direction: Located ½ mile from Birmingham City Centre.
54-57 Albion Street

Train: Jewellery Quarter 5 minutes, New Street ½ mile

Bus: From surrounding areas

Tel: 0870 333 1181

ACQ.2008

MAP Page 342 (5D)
OS Map 139, 220: SP062870

WORCESTERSHIRE

CHURCH OF ST MARY MAGDALENE, CROOME D'ABITOT
WORCESTERSHIRE
WR8 9DW

© CCT

A masterpiece of architectural fantasy. The original church at Croome was demolished, and replaced by this 'Georgian Gothic' church in Croome Park. Built by some of the finest craftsmen in England, every

CHURCH OF ST MARY MAGDALENE, CROOME D'ABITOT

detail has been considered, from pretty plaster mouldings to handsome carved pews and elegant Gothic windows.

Owned and managed by The Churches Conservation Trust.

OPENING TIMES
Open when Croome Park is open. For further details see National Trust website

VISIT US
Train: Pershore 7 miles

Bus: Astons Summer Sunday service 381 serves Croome Park. Otherwise First service 362 Worcester-Upton On Severn serves the nearby village of Kinnersley (c.2 miles walk).

MAP Page 342 (6D)
OS Map 150, 190: SO886450

LEIGH COURT BARN
WORCESTERSHIRE

An outstanding display of English medieval carpentry, this mighty timber-framed barn is the largest cruck framed structure in Britain. Built for Pershore Abbey in 1344, it is 46 metres (150 feet) long, with 18 cruck blades each made from a single oak tree.

OPENING TIMES
1 Apr-30 Sep,
Thu-Sun & Bank Hols   10am-5pm

VISIT US
Direction: 5 miles W of Worcester on an unclassified road off A4103

Train: Worcester Foregate Street 5 miles

Bus: Astons service 417, LMS Travel 423 & 425 (Fri only) to within 1 mile

ACQ.1990

MAP Page 342 (6C)
OS Map 150, 204: SO783535

WITLEY COURT AND GARDENS
WORCESTERSHIRE – WR6 6JT

A hundred years ago, Witley Court was one of England's great country houses, hosting many extravagant parties. Today it is a spectacular ruin, the result of a disastrous fire in 1937.

VISIT US

Address: Witley Court, Worcester Road, Great Witley, Worcestershire WR6 6JT

Direction: 10 miles NW of Worcester on A443

Train: Droitwich Spa 8½ miles

Bus: Yarranton service 758 Worcester – Tenbury Wells (passes close to Worcester Foregate Street ≥); Worcestershire Fleet transport service 359 (Fri only); R&B service 760 (Thu only)

Tel: 01299 896636

Local Tourist Information Worcester: 01905 726311

NON-MEMBERS

Adult	£6.90
Concession	£6.20
Child	£4.10
Family	£17.90

OPENING TIMES

29 Mar-30 Sep, daily	10am-6pm
1 Oct-3 Nov, daily	10am-5pm
4 Nov-16 Feb, Sat-Sun	10am-4pm
17-21 Feb, daily	10am-4pm
22 Feb-31 Mar, Sat-Sun	10am-4pm
24-26 Dec and 1 Jan	Closed

Last entry 1 hour before site closes

ACQ.1972 🎧♿🐕♿📶f♥📷⌂ 🚶🔥P🏛📷♿💻⚠

Disabled access (exterior and grounds only). A terrain guide is available on the website.

Tearoom (seasonal): 29 Mar-3 Nov (not managed by EH).

MAP Page 342 (6C)
OS Map 138/150, 204: SO769649

NEW FOR 2013

Visitors will be able to enjoy a new children's play area in Witley Court's Wilderness area. Designed to sit within the woodland environment, its centrepiece will be a tree house: there will also be a space for toddlers as well as climbing equipment for older children.

⌂ HOLIDAY COTTAGE AT **WITLEY COURT AND GARDENS**

The substantial **Pool House** holiday cottage can sleep up to 8 people, and has its own well-screened garden with sheltered dining terrace.

The vast and rambling remains of the palatial 19th-century mansion are surrounded by magnificent landscaped gardens, which still contain huge stone fountains. The largest, representing Perseus and Andromeda – now restored – was described in its day as making the 'noise of an express train' when fired.

Before 1846, when William Humble Ward (later first Earl of Dudley) inherited Witley Court, the land surrounding the house was laid out in the 18th-century English landscape style. As part of Ward's transformation of the estate, he called in the leading landscape designer of the time, William Andrews Nesfield, whose skills in designing intricate and elegant parterres were complemented by his great ability as an artist and engineer.

Nesfield started work in 1854, creating the South Parterre with its great Perseus and Andromeda fountain and elegantly designed plantings and parterres of clipped evergreens and shrubs. The East Parterre garden, with its Flora Fountain, was designed in the Parterre de Broderie style, resembling embroidery. Following the disastrous fire in 1937 the

Witley Estate fell into long decline. English Heritage has now restored the south garden, and Wolfson Foundation funding has assisted with major restoration works in the East Parterre garden. A scrollwork pattern of box hedges is interspersed with coloured gravels and colourful bedding plant displays. The Woodland Walks in the North Park pass many different species of tree and shrub from all over the world. Discover some of Witley's wildlife with a stroll around the newly opened lakeside walk.

Close to Witley Court is Great Witley Church (not managed by English Heritage), with its amazing Italianate Baroque interior. There is a tearoom by the church, and Witley Court has a superb gift shop. The restored Perseus and Andromeda fountain, with the original high cascades operating, will be firing between April and October. (Apr-Sep weekdays: 11am, 12pm, 2pm, 3pm, 4pm & 5pm and weekends on the hour every hour from 11am-5pm. Oct weekdays: 11am, 12pm, 2pm, 3pm & 4pm and weekends on the hour every hour from 11am-4pm).

DISCOUNTED ATTRACTIONS:

Use your membership to get exclusive discounts at these independent attractions in the West Midlands. Please remember to show your card as proof of membership.

2 for 1 ENTRY

ANNE HATHAWAY'S COTTAGE & GARDENS
Warwickshire CV37 6QW
Visit Anne Hathaway's Cottage & Gardens, the most romantic of the five Shakespeare Houses, and see the family home of Shakespeare's wife.
www.shakespeare.org.uk
T. 01789 204016

2 for 1 ENTRY

COMPTON VERNEY
Warwickshire CV35 9HZ
Visitors of all ages are warmly welcomed to this award-winning art gallery. Explore art from around the world and relax and play in 'Capability' Brown landscaped parkland.
www.comptonverney.org.uk
T. 01926 645500

50% DISCOUNT ON ENTRY

EASTNOR CASTLE
Herefordshire HR8 1RL
Eastnor is a dramatic, fairytale castle situated in the foothills of the Malvern Hills, within an Area of Outstanding Natural Beauty. Please see website for seasonal opening.
www.eastnorcastle.com
T. 01531 633160

25% DISCOUNT ON ENTRY

HAWKSTONE PARK FOLLIES
Shropshire SY4 5UY
A great day out for all the family. A powerful and timeless landscape, filled with eccentric follies.

www.hawkstone.co.uk
T. 01948 841700

£2 OFF ENTRY

HERITAGE MOTOR CENTRE
Warwickshire CV35 0BJ
The Centre is home to the world's largest collection of historic British cars. Check website for activities and special events.
www.heritage-motor-centre.co.uk
T. 01926 641188

20% PASSPORT DISCOUNT

IRONBRIDGE GORGE MUSEUMS – Ironbridge
Shropshire TF8 7DQ
Explore the ten Ironbridge Gorge Museums in this World Heritage Site with a great value Annual Passport Ticket.
www.ironbridge.org.uk
T. 01952 433424

WEST MIDLANDS

Discount applies to:

| KEY | ⊞ MEMBERS | OVP OVP HOLDERS | ᴨ⸮ NO. OF MEMBER'S CHILDREN |

Terms and conditions may apply, so make sure you check the individual pages on our website or call the individual property for more details.

2 for 1 ENTRY

 ⊞

MARY ARDEN'S FARM
Warwickshire CV37 9UN
Visit the real working Tudor Farm, the home of Shakespeare's mother Mary Arden, and experience life as it would have been when he was a boy. (Closed in winter).
www.shakespeare.org.uk
T. 01789 204016

2 for 1 ENTRY

⊞ OVP ᴨ 2

ROYAL SHAKESPEARE COMPANY
Warwickshire CV37 6BB
Take a trip up the Royal Shakespeare Theatre Tower to experience an alternative view across Stratford-upon-Avon and beyond.
www.rsc.org.uk
T. 0844 800 1110

2 for 1 ENTRY

⊞

SHAKESPEARE'S BIRTHPLACE
Warwickshire CV37 6QW
Explore the fascinating story of William Shakespeare's life. Includes free entry to Hall's Croft and Nash's House & New Place.
www.shakespeare.org.uk
T. 01789 204016

15% DISCOUNT ON ENTRY

⊞ OVP ᴨ 2

STONELEIGH ABBEY
Warwickshire CV8 2LF
A source of inspiration to Jane Austen, Stoneleigh Abbey covers 800 years of history and is situated in beautiful parkland. Viewed by guided tours.

www.stoneleighabbey.org
T. 01926 858535

50% DISCOUNT ON ENTRY

⊞ ᴨ 2

WARWICK CASTLE
Warwickshire CV34 4QU
Immerse yourself in a thousand years of history, come rain or shine. See lavishly decorated state rooms, walk the towers and ramparts, or explore the 60 acres of glorious gardens.
www.warwick-castle.com
T. 0871 265 2000

25% DISCOUNT ON ENTRY

⊞ ᴨ 4

THE WEDGWOOD MUSEUM
Staffordshire ST12 9ER
The story of Josiah Wedgwood, the Company he founded and its craftsmanship throughout Wedgwood's 250 year heritage.
www.wedgwoodmuseum.org.uk
T. 01782 371919

YORKSHIRE
AND THE
HUMBER

York Cold War Bunker

Remember to check opening times before you visit any of our properties www.english-heritage.org.uk/daysout

Details of local public transport information in England are available from Traveline www.traveline.org.uk or call 0871 200 2233.

Brodsworth Hall and Gardens

17
23
18 Richmond
10
15
North Yorkshire
Northallerton
26
14
Whitby 27
Scarborough 20
19 11
13   8
22 Ripon
7
16
12 25
Bridlington 1
Harrogate
Settle
Skipton
28 York
21 9
3
Hornsea
East Riding
West Yorkshire
Beverley
Bradford Leeds
24   Selby
Halifax
2
Kingston upon Hull
Goole   5
Huddersfield
North Lincolnshire
6
Scunthorpe
Grimsby
Barnsley 31   29
South Yorkshire
30   Doncaster
North East Lincolnshire
4
Sheffield
Rotherham
32

Make the most of your membership and keep up to date with upcoming events, the latest news and special offers by subscribing to our e-newsletter. Register online now at www.english-heritage.org.uk/newsletter

Byland Abbey

HIGHLIGHTS FOR 2013/14 IN THE **YORKSHIRE & THE HUMBER**

p.252

p.235

p.248

Brodsworth Hall & Gardens: explore evocative interiors & acres of restored gardens.

Clifford's Tower: fabulous views over the City of York.

Whitby Abbey: discover the abbey's link to Dracula.

PROPERTIES

EAST RIDING OF YORKSHIRE
1 Burton Agnes Manor House
2 Howden Minster
3 Skipsea Castle

NORTH LINCOLNSHIRE
4 Gainsthorpe Medieval Village
5 St Peter's Church, Barton-upon-Humber
6 Thornton Abbey and Gatehouse

NORTH YORKSHIRE
7 Aldborough Roman Site

8 Byland Abbey
9 Clifford's Tower
10 Easby Abbey
11 Helmsley Castle
12 Kirkham Priory
13 Marmion Tower
14 Middleham Castle
15 Mount Grace Priory
16 Pickering Castle
17 Piercebridge Roman Bridge
18 Richmond Castle
19 Rievaulx Abbey
20 St Mary's Church, Studley Royal
21 Scarborough Castle

22 Spofforth Castle
23 Stanwick Iron Age Fortifications
24 Steeton Hall Gateway
25 Wharram Percy Deserted Medieval Village
26 Wheeldale Roman Road
27 Whitby Abbey
28 York Cold War Bunker

SOUTH YORKSHIRE
29 Brodsworth Hall and Gardens
30 Conisbrough Castle
31 Monk Bretton Priory
32 Roche Abbey

BURTON AGNES MANOR HOUSE
EAST RIDING OF YORKSHIRE

A medieval manor house interior, with a rare and well-preserved Norman undercroft and a 15th-century roof, all encased in brick during the 17th and 18th centuries.

OPENING TIMES

29 Mar-3 Nov, daily	11am-5pm
4 Nov-28 Mar	Closed

The nearby Burton Agnes Hall and Gardens are privately owned and are not managed by English Heritage

VISIT US

Direction: In Burton Agnes village, 5 miles SW of Bridlington on A166

Train: Nafferton 5 miles

Bus: East Yorkshire service 121 & 744 (Sun)

Parking (in Hall and Gardens car park, subject to charge).

MAP Page 345 (3J)
OS Map 101, 295: TA102632

HOWDEN MINSTER
EAST RIDING OF YORKSHIRE

The ruins of an elaborately decorated 14th-century chancel and chapter house (viewable only from the outside), attached to the working 'minster' parish church of Howden.

OPENING TIMES

Any reasonable time

24-26 Dec and 1 Jan	Closed

VISIT US

Direction: In Howden; 23 miles W of Kingston Upon Hull, 25 miles SE of York, near the junction of A63 and A614

Train: Howden 1½ miles

Bus: East Yorkshire services X55, X56, 155 (Sun),160 (Wed & Sat only), 162 (Wed), 358 (Tue)

ACQ.1971 ⚡ P

Parking (on-street parking nearby – pay and display).

MAP Page 345 (4H)
OS Map 105/106, 291: SE748283

SKIPSEA CASTLE
EAST RIDING OF YORKSHIRE

The impressive earthwork remains of a big Norman motte and bailey castle, dating from the 1070s and among the first built in Yorkshire.

OPENING TIMES

Any reasonable time

VISIT US

Direction: Located 8 miles S of Bridlington; W of Skipsea village

Train: Bridlington 9 miles

Bus: East Yorkshire services 130

ACQ.1911 ⚡

Dogs on leads (restricted areas only).

Waterproof footwear recommended.

MAP Page 345 (3J)
OS Map 107, 295: TA162551

GAINSTHORPE MEDIEVAL VILLAGE
NORTH LINCOLNSHIRE

A deserted medieval village, one of the best-preserved examples in England, clearly visible as a complex of grassy humps and bumps. According to legend demolished as a den of thieves, the real reason for its abandonment remains uncertain.

OPENING TIMES

Any reasonable time

VISIT US

Direction: Located on minor road W of A15 – towards Cleatham; S of Hibaldstow; 5 miles SW of Brigg

Train: Kirton Lindsey 3 miles

Bus: Hornsby Travel service 94

ACQ.1974 ⚡

Access via grazing field. Farm livestock likely to be present.

MAP Page 345 (5J)
OS Map 112, 281: SE954011

ST PETER'S CHURCH, BARTON-UPON-HUMBER
SEE FEATURE – PAGE 232

VISIT US

Direction: 18 miles NE of Scunthorpe, on a road N of A160; 7 miles SE of the Humber Bridge, on a road E of A1077

Train: Thornton Abbey ¼ mile

Bus: Stagecoach service 150 to nearby village of East Halton (1½ miles)

Tel: 01469 541445

NON-MEMBERS

Adult	£4.50
Concession	£4.10
Child	£2.70

OPENING TIMES

29 Mar-30 Jun, Thu-Mon	10am-5pm
1 Jul-31 Aug, daily	10am-5pm
1 Sep-3 Nov, Fri-Sun	10am-5pm
4 Nov-31 Mar, Sat-Sun	10am-4pm
24-26 Dec and 1 Jan	Closed

Disabled access (except gatehouse interior and part of chapter ruins).

Dogs on leads (restricted areas only).

The enormous and ornate fortified gatehouse of Thornton Abbey is the largest and among the finest of all English monastic gatehouses. An early example of brick building in England, it proclaimed the wool trade-based prosperity of one of the wealthiest English Augustinian monasteries, for centuries a focus of spiritual and economic influence. Begun in the 1360s, the gatehouse stands some 21 metres (69 feet) high, and resembles a castle keep-gatehouse. It may have protected the abbey's treasures as well as providing spacious lodgings for the abbot and his guests.

Within the grounds stand the ruins of the monastic buildings, notably the elegantly decorated octagonal chapter house of 1282-1308. These buildings were plundered for stone to build a 'most stately' Jacobean manor house which, mysteriously, 'fell quite down to the bare ground without any visible cause' (Abraham de la Pryme). Evidence of its formal gardens has recently been discovered.

An oak staircase gives visitors access to the restored gatehouse's atmospheric interior. An exhibition with children's activities offers an insight into the abbey's history, including its role as the meeting place for huge Victorian Temperance rallies.

St Peter's Church, Barton-upon-Humber (see p.232) is nearby.

MAP Page 345 (5J)
OS Map 113, 284: TA118189

ST PETER'S CHURCH, BARTON-UPON-HUMBER
NORTH LINCOLNSHIRE
DN18 5EX

This famous Anglo-Saxon and medieval church is an archaeological as well as an architectural treasure, and one of Britain's largest resources for historic bone analysis. The analysis of over 2800 burials excavated here has brought remarkable insight into medieval disease, diet and burial practice, and informed modern medical understanding.

The *Buried Lives* exhibition investigates the late 11th century origins of the church, tracking its fortunes and those of its people through 1000 years. Thornton Abbey and Gatehouse (see p.231) is nearby.

NON-MEMBERS

Adult	£3.70
Concession	£3.30
Child	£2.20

OPENING TIMES

29 Mar-30 Sep, Sat-Sun & Bank Hols	10am-3pm
1 Oct-28 Mar	Closed

VISIT US

Direction: In Barton-upon-Humber

Train: Barton-upon-Humber ½ mile

Bus: Stagecoach in Lincolnshire services 250, 252, 260, 360, 450 and Humber Flyer 2; Stagecoach/East Yorkshire Humber Fast Cat service 350 also passes close by

Tel: 01652 632516/01302 722598

ACQ.1923 E ♿ ▢ ♿ ♿ ▢ ▢
♿ OVP

MAP Page 345 (5J)
OS Map 107, 112, 281: TA035219

ALDBOROUGH ROMAN SITE
N. YORKSHIRE – YO51 9ES

Among the northernmost urban centres in the Roman Empire, Aldborough was the 'capital' of the Romanised Brigantes, the largest tribe in Britain. One corner of the defences is laid out amid a Victorian arboretum, and two mosaic pavements can be viewed in their original positions. The site museum has an outstanding collection of Roman finds.

NON-MEMBERS

Adult	£3.50
Concession	£3.20
Child	£2.10

OPENING TIMES

29 Mar-30 Sep, Sat-Sun & Bank Hols	10am-6pm
1 Oct-28 Mar	Closed

VISIT US

Direction: Located in Aldborough, ¾ mile SE of Boroughbridge on a minor road off B6265; within 1 mile of junction of A1 and A6055

Train: Cattal 7½ miles

Bus: Local bus services available. Call site for details

Tel: 01423 322768

ACQ.1952 ♿ ▢ ♿ ▢ ♿ ♿ ▢
▢ ▢ OVP

Dogs on leads (restricted areas only).

MAP Page 345 (3G)
OS Map 299, 99: SE405662

BYLAND ABBEY
SEE FEATURE OPPOSITE

CHURCH OF CHRIST THE CONSOLER, SKELTON-CUM-NEWBY
N. YORKSHIRE – HG4 5AE

© CCT

A grieving mother built this impressive church in the grounds of Newby Hall as a memorial for her murdered son. The interior is wonderfully rich, with pattern and colour everywhere, and a little carved stone dog provides a sweetly domestic touch amid the magnificent splendour. The same patroness and architect built St Mary's, Studley Royal (see p.241)

Owned and managed by The Churches Conservation Trust.

OPENING TIMES
Open daily during daylight hours

VISIT US

Train: Knaresborough 6½ miles

Bus: Eddie Brown/Harrogate Coach Travel services 142 & 143

15 mins from Aldborough Roman Site, 40 mins from Rievaulx Abbey

MAP Page 345 (3G)
OS Map 99, 299: SE360679

Don't forget to check opening times online before you visit.
www.english-heritage.org.uk/daysout/properties

VISIT US

Direction: 2 miles S of A170, between Thirsk and Helmsley; near Coxwold village

Train: Thirsk 10 miles

Bus: Hutchinsons 12 (Sun only); Stephensons 31/31X; Moorsbus M11 (summer, Sun, Bank Hols)

Tel: 01347 868614

Local Tourist Information 01751 473791

NON-MEMBERS

Adult	£4.50
Concession	£4.10
Child	£2.70

OPENING TIMES

29 Mar-30 Jun, Thu-Mon	10am-6pm
1 Jul-31 Aug, daily	10am-6pm
1-30 Sep, Thu-Mon	10am-6pm
1 Oct-3 Nov, Thu-Mon	10am-5pm
4 Nov-31 Mar, Sat-Sun	10am-4pm
24-26 Dec and 1 Jan	Closed

ACQ.1921

OVP

Parking (adjacent to Abbey Inn).

Toilets at Abbey Inn.

Byland was one of the great Yorkshire Cistercian abbeys, housing at its zenith well over 200 monks and lay brothers. Much of its huge cathedral-sized church survives, including the whole north side and the greater part of the 13th-century west front. The mixture of rounded Romanesque and pointed Gothic arches shows how architectural styles changed, and reveals that Byland was one of the earliest Gothic buildings in the north. Its great circular rose window, now surviving only in part, was probably the model for the rose window of York Minster.

Archaeological research by English Heritage is beginning to throw light on the abbey's wider landscape setting, revealing how the monks tamed a very boggy and inhospitable site when building work started in the mid-12th century. The compact museum is full of archaeological site finds, intermingled with colourful interpretation panels giving an insight into monastic life.

Rievaulx Abbey and Helmsley Castle are within reasonable travelling distance.

MAP Page 345 (2G)
OS Map 100, OL26/299: SE549789

CHURCH OF ST JOHN THE BAPTIST, STANWICK
N. YORKSHIRE – DL11 7RT

© CCT

Surrounded by the high ramparts and impressive earthworks of Stanwick Camp, an important settlement in pre-Roman Britain, this Early English church is in an area of great natural beauty. St John's has the best collection of Anglo-Saxon grave markers in North Yorkshire. A 9th-century cross-shaft found in the churchyard and carved stones set into the walls suggest an even earlier building than Early English occupied this site.

Owned and managed by The Churches Conservation Trust.

OPENING TIMES
Open daily during daylight hours

VISIT US
Train: Darlington 7 miles

1 mile Stanwick Iron Age Fortification

MAP Page 345 (1F)
OS Map 92, 304: NZ185120

CLIFFORD'S TOWER, YORK
SEE FEATURE OPPOSITE

EASBY ABBEY
N. YORKSHIRE

The impressive ruins of an abbey of Premonstratensian 'white canons', most notable for the lavishly-appointed refectory of c.1300 and extensive monastic buildings. Within the precinct is the still-active parish church, displaying outstanding 13th-century wall-paintings. In a beautiful setting by the River Swale, Easby can also be reached in dry weather via a pleasant walk from Richmond Castle.

A free audio tour of the abbey can be downloaded from our website **www.english-heritage. org.uk/easbyabbey**

OPENING TIMES

29 Mar-29 Sep, daily	10am-6pm
30 Sep-3 Nov, daily	10am-5pm
4 Nov-31 Mar, daily	10am-4pm
24-26 Dec and 1 Jan	Closed

VISIT US
Direction: 1 mile SE of Richmond, off B6271

Bus: Dales & District 32, 32A, X34, 55

ACQ.1930 🐕 ♿ 🚻 🅿 🚹 ⚠

Guidebook (from Richmond Castle).

MAP Page 345 (2F)
OS Map 92, 304: NZ185003

HELMSLEY CASTLE
SEE FEATURE – PAGE 236

HOLY TRINITY CHURCH, WENSLEY
N. YORKSHIRE – DL8 4HX

© Graham Moore

Built on 8th-century Saxon foundations, this church stands on the bank of the River Ure in picturesque Wensleydale. Inside, there are interesting medieval wall paintings and a fine Flemish brass, and visitors can sit and marvel at the sumptuous richness of the local landowners' family pew, said to have come from Easby Abbey.

Owned and managed by The Churches Conservation Trust.

OPENING TIMES
Open daily during daylight hours

VISIT US
Train: Northallerton 17 miles

Bus: Dales & District service 156 serves Wensley

10 mins from Middleham Castle

MAP Page 345 (2F)
OS Map 99, OL30: SE092895

For information on events taking place at **Clifford's Tower**, including the York Residents' Festival.

Check out **www.english-heritage.org.uk/daysout/events**

VISIT US

Direction: Tower St, York

Train: York 1 mile

Bus: From surrounding areas

Tel: 01904 646940

Local Tourist Information
York: 01904 550099

NON-MEMBERS

Adult	£4.20
Concession	£3.80
Child	£2.50
Family	£10.90

OPENING TIMES

29 Mar-30 Sep, daily	10am-6pm
1 Oct-3 Nov, daily	10am-5pm
4 Nov-31 Mar, daily	10am-4pm
24-26 Dec and 1 Jan	Closed

ACQ.1915 🎭 f 🖐 ⬜ ✈ P 📷
⚠ OVP

Parking (local charge).

Access (via steep steps).

MAP Page 345 (3G)
OS Map 105, 290: SE605515

Perched on the summit of the mighty fortress mound raised by William the Conqueror in 1068, Clifford's Tower was the keep and chief strongpoint of York Castle, the greatest royal stronghold in medieval northern England. Built during the 1250s for Henry III, its four-lobed shape – giving it the old local nickname 'the Minced Pie' – is unique in England.

Like the city it once overawed, the tower has a rich history. A timber predecessor was burnt when York's Jews committed mass suicide there to avoid massacre by a mob in 1190. The present tower saw the hanging in chains in 1537 of Robert Aske, tragic leader of the Pilgrimage of Grace. Following plots to sell off its stonework by a crooked Elizabethan custodian, the tower was used as a Civil War gun-platform.

Today it remains the principal surviving remnant of the medieval castle, still commanding amazing 360 degree panoramas from its lofty rampart walk. There are unrivalled views of the Minster; the towers and spires of York's medieval and later churches; and the fine Georgian buildings in the old castle bailey. In the distance the Yorkshire Wolds and – on a clear day – even the North York Moors can be seen.

Family events bring the history of the tower to life during the summer holidays.

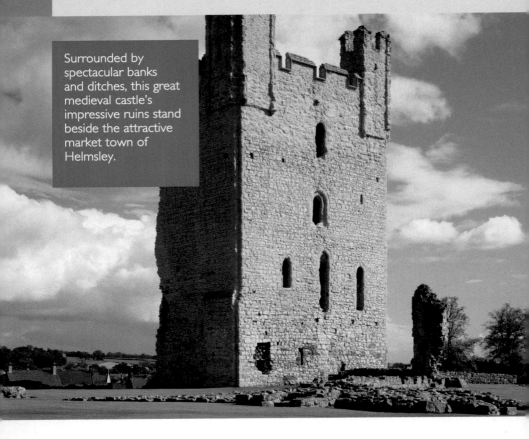

Surrounded by spectacular banks and ditches, this great medieval castle's impressive ruins stand beside the attractive market town of Helmsley.

Rievaulx and Byland Abbeys are both nearby. Rievaulx can be reached on foot via the Cleveland Way National Trail. Approx. 1½ hours (3½ miles/5.6 km) each way. Strong footwear is required.

VISIT US

Address: Helmsley Castle, Castlegate, Helmsley, North Yorkshire YO62 5AB

Direction: Near the town centre

Bus: Stephenson's 31, 31X, 194, 195; Scarborough & District 128; Moorsbus M2, M3, M9, M11 & M13

Tel: 01439 770442

NON-MEMBERS

Adult	£5.00
Concession	£4.50
Child	£3.00
Family	£13.00

OPENING TIMES

29 Mar-30 Sep, daily	10am-6pm
1-27 Oct, Thu-Mon	10am-5pm
28 Oct-3 Nov, daily	10am-5pm
4 Nov-16 Feb, Sat-Sun	10am-4pm
17-23 Feb, daily	10am-4pm
24 Feb-31 Mar, Sat-Sun	10am-4pm
24-26 Dec and 1 Jan	Closed

Helmsley Archaeology store tours
26 Apr, 24 May, 21 Jun, 26 Jul, 27 Sep, 18 Oct   11am & 2pm
Booking essential on 01439 770442.
Tours are free to members and non-members and are led by the Collections Curators

Audio tours.

Parking (large car park adjacent to castle; charge payable).

Toilets (in car park and town centre).

MAP Page 345 (2G)
OS Map 100, OL26: SE611836

The fortress was probably begun after 1120 by Walter Espec – 'Walter the Woodpecker'. Renowned for piety as well as soldiering, this Norman baron of 'gigantic stature' also founded nearby Rievaulx Abbey and Kirkham Priory, both English Heritage properties.

Most of Helmsley's surviving stonework defences were raised during the late 12th and 13th centuries by the crusader Robert de Roos and his descendants. They include a pair of immensely strong 'barbican' entrances and the high, keep-like east tower, unusually D-shaped in plan, which still dominates the town.

But Helmsley is not only a medieval fortress. During the Elizabethan period the Manners family remodelled the castle's chamber block into a luxurious mansion, whose fine plasterwork and panelling still partly survive. The castle's first and last military trial came during the Civil War. Held for King Charles, it endured a three-month siege before being starved into submission in November 1644 by Parliamentarians under Sir Thomas Fairfax, who was seriously wounded in the fighting. Fairfax then dismantled the defences but spared the mansion, subsequently the home of his daughter and her husband, the profligate Duke of Buckingham.

Demoted to a romantic backdrop when later owners moved to nearby Duncombe Park, Helmsley Castle has been revitalised by English Heritage, making it more accessible to a wide range of visitors. This includes a visitor centre building with shop and information point, an audio tour and an imaginative hands-on exhibition in the mansion range. Displaying a fascinating array of finds from Civil War cannon balls to early tableware, this exhibition explores the social and domestic, as well as the military, aspects of the fortress. Facilities for disabled visitors include full ground-level ramping, a virtual tour of less accessible areas, and a tactile model with braille text. Enhanced learning resources include family friendly books and activities.

HOLY TRINITY CHURCH, YORK
N. YORKSHIRE– YO1 7LF

© Graham White

Holy Trinity has the air of a hidden treasure, standing in a secluded churchyard behind York's busiest shopping street. On sunny days, gems of coloured light are scattered on the walls. The box pews and medieval stained glass are exceptionally fine, and monuments paint a picture of city life.

Owned and managed by The Churches Conservation Trust.

OPENING TIMES

Tue-Sat	10am-4pm
Sun-Mon	12-4pm

VISIT US
Train: York ½ mile

Bus: Served by many operators

10 min walk from Clifford's Tower

MAP Page 345 (3G)
OS Map 105, 290: SE605522

KIRKHAM PRIORY
N. YORKSHIRE – YO60 7JS

The riverside ruins of an Augustinian priory, picturesquely set in the beautiful Derwent valley. Features include a gatehouse bedecked with heraldry, including that of the De Roos family, Barons of Helmsley Castle; handsome monastic washbasins; and a small display of monastic artefacts.

NON-MEMBERS

Adult	£3.50
Concession	£3.20
Child	£2.10

OPENING TIMES

29 Mar-31 Jul, Thu-Mon	10am-5pm
1-31 Aug, daily	10am-6pm
1-30 Sep, Thu-Mon	10am-5pm
1 Oct-3 Nov, Sat-Sun	10am-5pm
4 Nov-31 Mar, Sat-Sun	10am-4pm
24-26 Dec and 1 Jan	Closed

VISIT US
Direction: 5 miles SW of Malton, on a minor road off A64

Train: Malton 6 miles

KIRKHAM PRIORY

Bus: Ryecat 184 & 185 to Kirkham Priory village (Tue, Fri, Sat); otherwise Yorkshire Coastliner X40, 840, 843 & 845 (pass York and ✦ Malton) to Whitwell On The Hill then ¾ walk

Tel: 01653 618768

Local Tourist Information
01653 600048

MAP Page 345 (3H)
OS Map 100, 300: SE736658

MARMION TOWER
N. YORKSHIRE

The fine 15th-century gatehouse of a vanished riverside manor house, with a beautiful oriel window. The monuments of the manor's Marmion family owners grace the adjacent church.

OPENING TIMES

29 Mar-29 Sep, daily	10am-6pm
30 Sep-3 Nov, daily	10am-5pm
4 Nov-31 Mar, daily	10am-4pm
24-26 Dec and 1 Jan	Closed

VISIT US
Direction: On A6108 in West Tanfield

Train: Thirsk 10 miles

Bus: Dales & District service 159 also Vintage Omnibus Service 127 (summer only)

MAP Page 345 (3F)
OS Map 99, 298: SE268787

VISIT US

Direction: Located at Middleham; 2 miles S of Leyburn on A6108

Train: Leyburn (Wensleydale Railway) 2 miles

Bus: Dales & District 159 also Vintage Omnibus 127 (summer)

Tel: 01969 623899

Local Tourist Information
Leyburn: 01969 623069

NON-MEMBERS

Adult	£4.50
Concession	£4.10
Child	£2.70

OPENING TIMES

29 Mar-30 Sep, daily	10am-6pm
1 Oct-3 Nov, Thu-Mon	10am-5pm
4 Nov-31 Mar, Sat-Sun	10am-4pm
24-26 Dec and 1 Jan	Closed

ACQ.1926 🐕 E ♿ ▢ ▣ 🅿 ♿
⚠ OVP

Disabled access (except keep).

MAP Page 345 (2F)
OS Map 99, OL30: SE127876

Set in a delightful little Wensleydale market town, Middleham Castle was traditionally the favourite home of Richard III, and was certainly his northern power-base.

The core of the castle is the mighty keep, three storeys high and with twelve foot thick walls, probably built during the 1170s by Robert fitz Randolph. Around this keep the mighty Neville family, Earls of Westmorland and of Warwick, progressively constructed three ranges of luxurious chambers and lodgings, turning the castle into a fortified palace – 'the Windsor of the North' – by the mid 15th century. Though roofless, many of these buildings survive, including a multi-storey latrine tower and a horse-mill, making Middleham a fascinating castle to explore.

Richard III probably spent part of his youth here, in the guardianship of Richard Neville, known as 'Warwick the Kingmaker': the Kingmaker also twice received Edward IV here during the Wars of the Roses, once as an honoured guest and once as a prisoner. After Warwick's death in battle, Richard married his daughter Anne, and took over the castle. Here Richard's son Edward of Middleham was born, and here he died in 1484, aged no more than ten.

There are wonderful views over Wensleydale from the viewing platform on the keep. An exhibition about notable personalities from the castle's past includes a replica of the beautiful Middleham Jewel, a 15th-century pendant decorated with a large sapphire found near the castle. Family friendly books and activities.

⌂ HOLIDAY COTTAGE AT **MOUNT GRACE PRIORY**

Prior's Lodge sleeps four, with views over the mansion's garden in one direction, the monastic ruins in the other.

VISIT US

Direction: 12 miles N of Thirsk; and 6 miles NE of Northallerton, near A19. Warning: take care when turning off the fast dual carriageway. Look out for brown EH direction signs placed approx ½ mile before the turning.

Train: Northallerton 6 miles

Tel: 01609 883494

Local Tourist Information
Thirsk: 01845 522755

NON-MEMBERS

Adult	£5.40
Concession	£4.90
Child	£3.20
Family	£14.00

National Trust members admitted free, except on event days

OPENING TIMES

29 Mar-30 Jun, Thu-Mon	10am-6pm
1 Jul-31 Aug, daily	10am-6pm
1-30 Sep, Thu-Mon	10am-6pm
1 Oct-3 Nov, Thu-Mon	10am-5pm
4 Nov-31 Mar, Sat-Sun	10am-4pm
24-26 Dec and 1 Jan	Closed

Picturesquely set beneath a wooded slope of the Cleveland Hills, Mount Grace Priory is among the most unusual and important of English Heritage's monastic sites, with the bonus of an 'Arts and Crafts' mansion to admire.

Much the best-preserved Carthusian priory in England, Mount Grace differs radically from conventional monasteries. For instead of living together like other monks, Carthusians ('Christ's Poor Men') were communities of hermits. Founded by St Bruno at the Grand Chartreuse in France, the order was revered for piety, humility and intense spirituality. Thomas Holland, Duke of Surrey, founded this last of the great Yorkshire monasteries in 1398.

The furnished reconstruction of one of the monk's cells ranged round the immense great cloister reflects the Carthusian ideal of solitude. The cottage-like building has its own little private cloister, walled garden and outside toilet. The occupant lived in strict isolation, not even seeing the

NEW FOR 2013

The attics of the mansion are open to the public for the first time.

servant who passed his frugal meatless meals through an L-shaped serving hatch.

All this is approached through a mansion adapted in 1654 from the priory's guest range, and much extended in 1901 by Sir Lowthian Bell, wealthy patron of the Arts and Crafts movement. Several of its rooms have been refurbished in this style, using William Morris wallpapers. It also displays a fascinating introductory exhibition and some notable site artefacts.

Owned by the National Trust, maintained and managed by English Heritage.

MAP Page 345 (2G)
OS Map 99, OL26: SE449985

Available for corporate and private hire

PICKERING CASTLE
N. YORKSHIRE – YO18 7AX

A fine early Norman castle set in an attractive moors-edge market town, with spectacular views from the motte-top. Pickering is a classic and well-preserved example of an early earthwork castle refortified in stone during the 13th and 14th centuries. There is an exhibition in the chapel.

NON-MEMBERS

Adult	£4.00
Concession	£3.60
Child	£2.40
Family	£10.40

OPENING TIMES

29 Mar-30 Jun, Thu-Mon	10am-5pm
1 Jul-31 Aug, daily	10am-6pm
1-30 Sep, Thu-Mon	10am-5pm
1 Oct-3 Nov, Sat-Sun	10am-5pm
4 Nov-31 Mar	Closed

VISIT US

Direction: In Pickering; 15 miles SW of Scarborough

Train: Malton (9 miles) or Pickering (North Yorkshire Moors Rly) ¼ mile

Bus: Scarborough & District 128; Ryecate 175; Yorkshire Coastliner 840 & X40 (Sun), Summer Sundays and Bank Hols Moorsbus M3, M5, M6, M8 & M14. Also Coastal & Country 90 (Wed); Hutchinsons 170 & 171; Stephensons 173, 174 (Mon & Fri) & 175 (Mon & Fri)

Tel: 01751 474989

Local Tourist Information
Pickering: 01751 473791

PICKERING CASTLE

ACQ.1926 [icons] P
[icons] OVP
Disabled access (except motte).

MAP Page 345 (2H)
OS Map 100, OL27: SE799845

PIERCEBRIDGE ROMAN BRIDGE
N. YORKSHIRE

Stonework foundations of a bridge, now marooned in a field, which once led to Piercebridge Roman Fort.

OPENING TIMES
Any reasonable time

VISIT US

Direction: At Piercebridge; 4 miles W of Darlington, on B6275

Train: Darlington 5 miles

Bus: Arriva 75, 76

ACQ.1975 [icons]

Parking available at nearby George Hotel. May infrequently be restricted when hosting large functions.
Not managed by English Heritage.

MAP Page 345 (1F)
OS Map 93, 304: NZ214155

RICHMOND CASTLE
SEE FEATURE – PAGE 242

RIEVAULX ABBEY
SEE FEATURE – PAGE 244

SCARBOROUGH CASTLE
SEE FEATURE – PAGE 246

ST MARY'S CHURCH, STUDLEY ROYAL
N. YORKSHIRE – HG4 3DY

This magnificent High Victorian Anglican church was designed in the 1870s by the flamboyant architect William Burges, and has been called his 'ecclesiastical masterpiece'. The extravagantly decorated interior displays coloured marble, stained glass, a splendid organ and painted and gilded figures in all their original glory.

Owned by English Heritage and managed by the National Trust as part of the Fountains Abbey and Studley Royal Estate (see p.256).

OPENING TIMES

29 Mar-29 Sep, daily	12pm-4pm
30 Sep-28 Mar	Closed

VISIT US

Direction: Located 2½ miles W of Ripon, off B6265; in the grounds of the Studley Royal Estate

Bus: Dales & District 139 (operated by The Little Red Bus on Sun & Bank Hols)

Tel: 01765 608888

ACQ.1975 [icons] P
Parking (at visitor centre or Studley Royal).

MAP Page 345 (3F)
OS Map 99, 298/299: SE275693

VISIT US

Direction: In Richmond just off the market place

Bus: Arriva 59 & X59; Dales & District 29, 30, 31, 31A, 31B, 31C, 32, 32A, 54, X54, 55, 159; Hodgsons Coaches 79, 79A (Thu) & 79X; Also Dales Bus 830 & 831 (Sun & Bank Hols)

Tel: 01748 822493

NON-MEMBERS

Adult	£4.80
Concession	£4.30
Child	£2.90

OPENING TIMES

29 Mar-30 Sep, daily	10am-6pm
1-27 Oct, Thu-Mon	10am-5pm
28 Oct-3 Nov, daily	10am-5pm
4 Nov-16 Feb, Sat-Sun	10am-4pm
17-23 Feb, daily	10am-4pm
24 Feb-31 Mar, Sat-Sun	10am-4pm
24-26 Dec and 1 Jan	Closed

ACQ.1916 ♿ ✕ 🚻 🛡 E 🌿 ❀ 🖼
🚹 🚶 🗓 🏠 🚗 ♿ OVP

Parking (2 hours free in market place – not managed by EH).

Disabled parking available at site on request, or in market place.

MAP Page 345 (2F)
OS Map 92, 304: NZ172007

Richmond Castle is impressively sited on a rocky promontory above the River Swale, overlooking a picturesque market town at the foot of beautiful Swaledale. Among the oldest Norman stone fortresses in Britain, it was begun in about 1070 by William the Conqueror's Breton supporter Alan the Red. The towering keep, added about a century later during the reign of Henry II, stands over 100 feet (30m) high, with walls up to 11 feet (3.35m) thick. It is remarkably complete within, and visitors can climb to the top for panoramic views over the castle's great courtyard, the market place of Richmond and the Yorkshire Dales.

According to legend, King Arthur and his knights lie sleeping in a cavern beneath the keep, and the drumbeats of a drummer-boy lost in a secret passage can still be heard. More certainly, two medieval kings of Scotland were confined here after defeat in battle.

A fascinating exhibition traces the building of the castle, its relationship with the town, and the extraordinary story of the 'Richmond Sixteen', the conscientious objectors imprisoned here for refusing to fight in World War I. A touch-screen display allows visitors to view the evocative inscriptions left on their cell walls. Family-friendly books and activities.

SPOFFORTH CASTLE
N. YORKSHIRE

The ruined hall and chamber of a fortified manor house of the powerful Percy family, begun in the 13th and rebuilt in the 15th century. Its undercroft is cut into a rocky outcrop.

Managed by Spofforth-with-Stockeld Parish Council.

OPENING TIMES

29 Mar-29 Sep, daily	10am-6pm
30 Sep-31 Mar, daily (managed by a keykeeper)	10am-4pm
24-26 Dec and 1 Jan	Closed

SPOFFORTH CASTLE

VISIT US

Direction: 3½ miles SE of Harrogate; off A661 at Spofforth

Train: Pannal 4 miles

Bus: Transdev Harrogate & District services 770; Connexions Buses X70

ACQ.1924

Dogs on leads (restricted areas only).

MAP Page 345 (4G)
OS Map 104, 289: SE360511

STANWICK IRON AGE FORTIFICATIONS
N. YORKSHIRE

STANWICK IRON AGE FORTIFICATIONS

A section of the ramparts of the huge Iron Age trading and power-centre of the Brigantes, the most important tribe in pre-Roman northern Britain. This is a short reconstructed portion of a much larger circuit of defences, once some 4 miles (6½ kilometres) long and enclosing an area of 766 acres (310 hectares). Following Roman conquest, the Brigantian centre moved to Aldborough Roman Site (see p.232).

OPENING TIMES
Any reasonable time

VISIT US

Direction: Located on a minor road off A6274, at Forcett Village

Train: Darlington 10 miles

Bus: Dales & District service 29; Hodgsons 79A (Thu)

ACQ.1953

Dogs on leads (restricted areas only).

MAP Page 345 (1F)
OS Map 92, 304: NZ179124

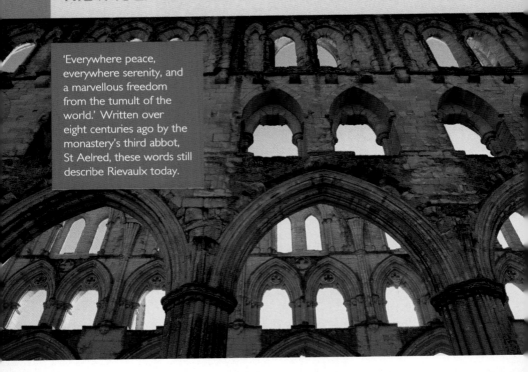

'Everywhere peace, everywhere serenity, and a marvellous freedom from the tumult of the world.' Written over eight centuries ago by the monastery's third abbot, St Aelred, these words still describe Rievaulx today.

VISIT US

Address: Rievaulx Abbey, Rievaulx, Nr Helmsley, North Yorkshire YO62 5LB

Direction: In Rievaulx; 2¼ miles N of Helmsley, on minor road off B1257

Bus: Moorsbus services M9 (Sun & Bank Hols). Also Moorsbus service M2 passes within ¼ mile (Sun & Bank Hols in high summer)

Tel: 01439 798228

Local Tourist Information
Helmsley: 01751 473791

NON-MEMBERS

Adult	£6.00
Concession	£5.40
Child	£3.60

OPENING TIMES

29 Mar-30 Sep, daily	10am-6pm
1 Oct-3 Nov, daily	10am-5pm
4 Nov-16 Feb, Sat-Sun	10am-4pm
17-23 Feb, daily	10am-4pm
24 Feb-31 Mar, Sat-Sun	10am-4pm
24-26 Dec and 1 Jan	Closed

ACQ.1917

Audio tours (also available for the visually impaired, those with learning difficulties and in French and German).

Parking: Limited pay and display parking, refundable to EH members and paying visitors on purchase of admission ticket.

MAP Page 345 (2G)
OS Map 100, OL26: SE577850

Enjoy afternoon tea made from local produce in the cosy on-site café.

🏠 HOLIDAY COTTAGE AT **RIEVAULX ABBEY**

Set in a beautiful valley, Rievaulx is among the most tranquil and atmospheric of all the ruined abbeys of the North. Nestled into its breathtaking surroundings is a stunning detached holiday cottage, which comfortably sleeps four people.

Words are not the only link to Rievaulx's medieval monks. Over the past few years, the site has become something of an archaeological treasure, with unexpected discoveries shedding new light on the lives of the monks and the extensive renewal and rebuilding of their abbey church in the Early English Gothic style. Archaeologists continue to study the landscape around Rievaulx, revealing the remarkable extent of the abbey's influence and industry. Their discoveries are showcased within the on-site museum.

The abbey was established by St Bernard of Clairvaux, as part of the missionary effort to reform Christianity in western Europe. Twelve Clairvaux monks came to Rievaulx in 1132. From these modest beginnings grew one of the wealthiest monasteries of medieval England and the first northern Cistercian monastery. Rievaulx also enjoyed the protection of Walter Espec of nearby Helmsley Castle, who provided much of the abbey's land.

A steady flow of monks came to Rievaulx, attracted by the prestige of Abbot Aelred, author and preacher, who was regarded then and later as a wise and saintly man. Following his death in 1167, the monks of Rievaulx sought canonisation for their former leader,

and in the 1220s they rebuilt the east part of their church in a much more elaborate style to house his tomb. Most of this 13th-century 'presbytery' still stands to virtually its full impressive height, a reminder of Rievaulx's original splendour.

Rievaulx was still a vibrant community when Henry VIII dissolved it in 1538. Its new owner, Thomas Manners, first Earl of Rutland, swiftly instigated the systematic destruction of the buildings, yet the substantial remains constitute one of the most eloquent of all monastic sites, free 'from the tumult of the world'. Schoolchildren from the local area have helped to create a Sensory Garden full of scented and flavoured herbs, amid tile motifs based on medieval designs.

Don't miss the indoor exhibition, *The Work of God and Man*, which explores the agricultural, industrial, spiritual and commercial aspects of Rievaulx's history, employing a variety of lively and interactive displays. A new exhibition also traces the rediscovery of Rievaulx Abbey and its archaeology and conservation. There are family-friendly events, books and activities during school holidays.

SCARBOROUGH CASTLE NORTH YORKSHIRE – YO11 1HY

VISIT US

Direction: Castle Road, E of the town centre

Train: Scarborough 1 mile

Bus: From surrounding areas

Tel: 01723 372451

Local Tourist Information
Scarborough: 01723 383636

NON-MEMBERS

Adult	£5.00
Concession	£4.50
Child	£3.00
Family	£13.00

OPENING TIMES

29 Mar-30 Sep, daily	10am-6pm
1-27 Oct, Thu-Mon	10am-5pm
28 Oct-3 Nov, daily	10am-5pm
4 Nov-16 Feb, Sat-Sun	10am-4pm
17-23 Feb, daily	10am-4pm
24 Feb-31 Mar, Sat-Sun	10am-4pm
24-26 Dec and 1 Jan	Closed

Please note: tearoom closes 30 mins before castle

New guidebook.

Parking (pre-booked parking only for disabled visitors, otherwise located in town centre).

MAP Page 345 (2J)
OS Map 101, 301: TA050892

Scarborough Castle defends a prominent headland between two bays, with sheer drops to the sea and only a narrow landward approach. Specially constructed viewing platforms on the battlements offer panoramic views. Long before the castle was built, this natural fortress was favoured by prehistoric settlers, and later housed a defended Roman signal station.

Henry II's towering 12th-century keep, dominating the approach, is the centrepiece of fortifications developed over later centuries in response to repeated sieges – notably by rebel barons in 1312 and twice during the Civil War. Though again strengthened with barracks and gun-batteries against Jacobite threats in 1745, the castle failed to defend the harbour against the American sea-raider John Paul Jones in 1779, and was itself damaged by German naval bombardment in 1914. During World War II it played the more covert role of hosting a secret listening post.

The site's 3,000 year history is explored in the restored Master Gunner's House, accompanied by artefacts from each period of Scarborough's past. Less mobile visitors can enjoy a ground-floor, touch-screen virtual tour of the displays, as well as virtual views reproducing those from the raised platforms.

Timelined graphic panels around the castle focus on characters from the past and there are free activity sheets, an audio tour, and an investigative story box to help younger visitors visualise and understand the history of the castle.

Complete your day out with afternoon tea made from local produce in the cosy on site café.

STEETON HALL GATEWAY
N. YORKSHIRE – LS25 5PD

A fine example of a small, well-preserved manorial gatehouse dating from the 14th century.

OPENING TIMES
29 Mar-31 Mar, daily
(exterior only)   10am-5pm

VISIT US
Direction: Located 4 miles NE of Castleford, on a minor road off A162 at South Milford

Train: South Milford 1 mile

Bus: Arriva Yorkshire services 492 & 493; Utopia Coaches 404 & 491

ACQ.1948 🐕 ♿

Dogs on leads (restricted areas only).

MAP Page 345 (4G)
OS Map 105, 290: SE484314

ST PETER'S CHURCH, WINTRINGHAM
N. YORKSHIRE
YO17 8HU

© Cameron Newham

This beautiful and peaceful church, with an elegant spire, has Norman origins and is full of interesting furnishings including Jacobean bench pews, medieval carvings and stained glass. If you look carefully, you might even find some mythical beasts and ancient sword markings!

Owned and managed by The Churches Conservation Trust.

OPENING TIMES
Open daily during daylight hours

ST PETER'S CHURCH, WINTRINGHAM

VISIT US
Train: Malton 6 miles

Bus: Yorkshire Coastliner service 843 to Scampston, Wintringham Lane End and then walk (c. 2 mile)

20 mins from Wharram Percy Deserted Medieval Village, 35 mins from Scarborough Castle

MAP Page 345 (3H)
OS Map 101, 300: SE887731

ST STEPHEN'S CHURCH, FYLINGDALES
N. YORKSHIRE
YO22 4PN

© CCT

St Stephen's, a fisherman's church, stands majestically on the hillside overlooking the sea. Resonating with a resilient North Sea fishing community there are memorials to the shipwrecked in both the church and churchyard. Outside, windswept gravestones huddle tightly round the church walls.

Owned and managed by The Churches Conservation Trust.

VISIT US
Train: Whitby 5 miles

Bus: Arriva Bus 93 runs a regular service from Middlesborough bus station to Scarborough rail station going past the church

10 mins from Whitby Abbey

OPENING TIMES
Keyholder nearby

MAP Page 345 (2J)
OS Map 94, OL27: NZ942059

WHARRAM PERCY DESERTED MEDIEVAL VILLAGE
N. YORKSHIRE

The most famous and intensively studied of Britain's 3000 or so deserted medieval villages, Wharram Percy occupies a remote but attractive site in a beautiful Wolds valley. Above the substantial ruins of the church, and a millpond, the outlines of many lost houses are traceable on a grassy plateau. First settled in prehistoric times, Wharram flourished as a village between the 12th and 14th centuries, before final abandonment in about 1500. Graphic interpretation panels tell its story and recreate the original appearance of the buildings.

A free downloadable audio tour is available at **www.english-heritage.org.uk/wharrampercy**

OPENING TIMES
Any reasonable time

VISIT US
Direction: 6 miles SE of Malton, on minor road from B1248; ½ mile S of Wharram-le-Street. Park in car park, then ¾ mile walk via uneven track, steep in places. Site also accessible on foot via Wolds Way ramblers' path. Sturdy and waterproof footwear required. Parts of site slope steeply, and farm livestock likely to be present on site and access path

Train: Malton 8 miles

Bus: Busking Ltd service 133 (Sat, Sun & Bank Hols)

ACQ.1972 🐕 📷 P 🏞 ⚠

Please note: site is hazardous in snowy conditions.

New brief guidebook.

MAP Page 345 (3H)
OS Map 100, 300: SE859644

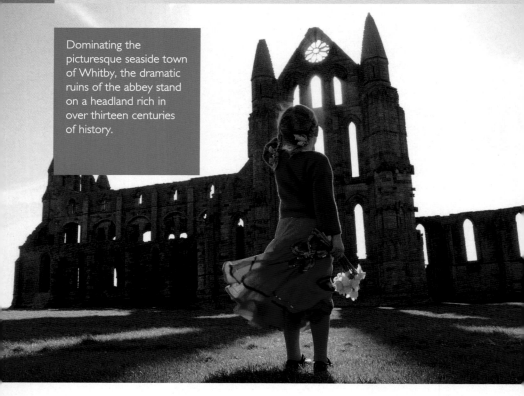

Dominating the picturesque seaside town of Whitby, the dramatic ruins of the abbey stand on a headland rich in over thirteen centuries of history.

VISIT US

Address: Whitby Abbey, Abbey Lane, Whitby, North Yorkshire YO22 4JT

Direction: On cliff top, E of Whitby

Train: Whitby ½ mile

Bus: Esk Valley service 97 & Coastal & Country Whitby Town Tour to Whitby Abbey

Tel: 01947 603568

Local Tourist Information 01723 383636

NON-MEMBERS

Adult	£6.40
Concession	£5.80
Child	£3.80
Family	£16.60

OPENING TIMES

29 Mar-30 Sep, daily	10am-6pm
1-27 Oct, Thu-Mon	10am-5pm
28 Oct-3 Nov, daily	10am-5pm
4 Nov-16 Feb, Sat-Sun	10am-4pm
17-23 Feb, daily	10am-4pm
24 Feb-31 Mar, Sat-Sun	10am-4pm
24-26 Dec and 1 Jan	Closed

ACQ.1920

Disabled access (south entrance parking, charged).

Dogs on leads.

Parking not managed by English Heritage (charge payable).

Toilets situated in the car park are not operated by English Heritage.

Tearoom not managed by English Heritage.

The mansion now houses the highly imaginative and award-winning visitor centre, displaying fascinating finds from the Anglo-Saxon, medieval and Cholmley periods.

MAP Page 345 (1J)
OS Map 94, OL27: NZ903112

The first monastery here was founded in AD 657 by King Oswy of Northumbria. An Anglo-Saxon style 'double monastery' for men and women, its first head was the formidable royal princess Abbess Hild; here Caedmon the cowherd was miraculously transformed into an inspired poet; here the future of the English church was decided in 664; and here the relics of Northumbrian kings and saints were enshrined.

Though many excavated finds from it are displayed in the visitor centre, nothing survives above ground of the Anglo-Saxon monastery. The imposing ruins belong to the church of the Benedictine abbey refounded on its site in 1090 by the Normans. From 1220 onwards, the abbey church was completely rebuilt in the Early English style. The pinnacled east end and north transept still stand high, richly carved with characteristic 'dog's tooth' embellishment. Time, war and nature have left their marks Parts of the church collapsed during storms, its west front was hit by German naval shelling in 1914 and centuries of wind and rain have added their own etched and pitted decoration. These supremely romantic ruins enjoy panoramic views, and literary renown as the backdrop to Bram Stoker's *Dracula*, the Victorian novel which has made Whitby the 'Goth' capital of Britain. More recently the site has inspired *Shadowmancer* and other best-selling children's novels by ex-vicar and ex-policeman GP Taylor.

The ruins share the headland with the Cholmley family mansion, begun after Henry VIII's suppression of the abbey. Its impressive Classical façade of 1672 is fronted by a restoration of the 'hard garden' courtyard rediscovered during English Heritage excavations. The courtyard's centrepiece is a specially-commissioned bronze copy of the famous 'Borghese Gladiator' statue. The Roman marble original of this spectacular life-sized statue, now in the Paris Louvre, dates from the 1st century BC: it was found in 1611 in Italy and bronze casts were made for King Charles I. Copies graced many great English houses and gardens including the Cholmleys' Whitby mansion, recalling the family's Civil War support for the Royalist cause.

The mansion now houses the highly imaginative and award-winning visitor centre. Displaying fascinating finds from the Anglo-Saxon, medieval and Cholmley periods, this is packed with digital displays and entertaining interactives: touch-screens allow visitors to question Whitby personalities, from Abbess Hild via a medieval monk to Bram Stoker.

Please note: from the Whitby harbour area, the abbey can only be directly reached on foot via the 199 'abbey steps'. Alternatively, a well-signposted road leads from the town outskirts to the cliff-top abbey.

WHEELDALE ROMAN ROAD
N. YORKSHIRE

A mile-long stretch of enigmatic ancient road – probably Roman but possibly later or earlier – still with its hard core and drainage ditches. Amid wild and beautiful moorland.

OPENING TIMES
Any reasonable time

VISIT US
Direction: S of Goathland; W of A169; 7 miles S of Whitby

Train: Goathland (North Yorkshire Moors Rly) (4 miles) or Newtondale Halt (then 3 mile forest walk)

Bus: Yorkshire Coastliner service 840 to Goathland then 4 miles walk. Alternatively alight at Ellerbeck bridge and walk 2½ miles over Howl Moor

Local Tourist Information
Pickering: 01751 473791

ACQ.1912

MAP Page 345 (2H)
OS Map 94/100, OL27: SE806977

WHITBY ABBEY
SEE FEATURE – PAGE 248

PROPERTY EVENTS NEAR YOU

Check our website for up-to-the-minute information on our year long programme of events.

www.english-heritage.org.uk/events

YORK COLD WAR BUNKER
N. YORKSHIRE – YO24 2HT

English Heritage's most modern, most unusual and perhaps most spine-chilling site, 'No. 20 Group Royal Observer Corps HQ' is the semi-subterranean bunker which would have monitored nuclear explosions and fallout in the Yorkshire region. In service between 1961 and 1991, the Bunker's control rooms display 'colour-psychology décor' together with original monitoring and communications equipment. Decontamination rooms with air filters and special sewage ejectors were intended to seal off the 60-strong workforce from the devastated outside world. A guided tour, enhanced by a striking 10-minute film (PG rated) and interpretation, tells the story of the Cold War's 'Mutually Assured Destruction.'

NON-MEMBERS
Adult	£6.40
Concession	£5.80
Child	£3.80

OPENING TIMES
29 Mar-3 Nov, Sat-Sun & Bank Hols	10am-5pm
4 Nov-31 Mar, Sun	10am-4pm

By tours only. Tours last approx 1 hour. No need to book. Last tour one hour before closing

Weekdays: Admission for schools and groups only. Booking 14 days in advance, minimum fee applies

VISIT US
Direction: Monument Close, off Acomb Road, near the Carlton Tavern, approx. 2 miles from York city centre

Train: York 2 miles

Bus: First in York service 1; Arriva 412 & 413

Tel: 01904 646940 (Clifford's Tower)

Local Tourist Information
York: 01904 550099

ACQ.2001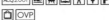
OVP

Parking (limited to 3 spaces).

MAP Page 345 (3G)
OS Map 105, 290: SE580515

SOUTH YORKSHIRE

BRODSWORTH HALL AND GARDENS
SEE FEATURE – PAGE 252

CONISBROUGH CASTLE
S. YORKSHIRE – DN12 3BU

Conisbrough's spectacular magnesian limestone keep, nearly 100 feet high, is cylindrical with wedge-shaped turret-buttresses, a design unique in Britain. Now with reinstated roof and floors, it was built in the late 12th century for Hamelin Plantagenet, illegitimate half-brother of King Henry II, and subsequently reinforced by turreted curtain walls. Conisbrough was among the inspirations for Sir Walter Scott's classic novel, *Ivanhoe*.

Please note: Conisbrough Castle will be closed from September 2013 to spring 2014 while a major HLF-funded project transforms the site into a world class heritage experience.

NON-MEMBERS

Adult	£4.60
Concession	£4.10
Child	£2.80
Family	£12.00

OPENING TIMES
29 Mar-30 Jun, Thu-Mon 10am-6pm

1 Jul-31 Aug, daily 10am-6pm

1 Sep-31 Mar
Closed for redevelopment

CONISBROUGH CASTLE

VISIT US
Direction: Located NE of Conisbrough town centre off A630; 4½ miles SW of Doncaster

Train: Conisbrough ½ mile or Rotherham 6 miles

Bus: Stagecoach services 220, 221 & 222; First X78

Tel: 01709 863329

ACQ.1950 [icons] [OVP]

Dogs on leads (in grounds only).

Parking (visitors with disabilities may be dropped off at the visitor centre).

Access (limited to some areas).

MAP Page 345 (5G)
OS Map 111, 279: SK515989

HOLY TRINITY CHURCH, WENTWORTH
S. YORKSHIRE – S62 7TX

© CCT

Rooted in village history, this atmospheric, partly ruined building started life as a church but was converted to a mausoleum in 1877. Today, only the chancel and north chapel remain intact. Brass and stone memorials and effigies trace the fascinating history of the powerful Wentworth family.

Owned and managed by The Churches Conservation Trust.

HOLY TRINITY CHURCH, WENTWORTH

OPENING TIMES
Open during daylight hours
May-Sep, Sun & Bank Holidays

At other times keyholder nearby

VISIT US
Train: Elsecar 1½ miles

Bus: TM Travel service 44 and Tates/TM Travel service 227 serve the village

20 mins from Conisbrough Castle

MAP Page 345 (5G)
OS Map 110/111, 278: SK384983

MONK BRETTON PRIORY
S. YORKSHIRE

The substantial ruins of a Cluniac monastery, later absorbed into the Benedictine order, with an unusually well-marked ground plan, almost complete west range and 15th-century gatehouse.

NON-MEMBERS
Charge may apply on event days

OPENING TIMES
29-31 Mar, daily 10am-3pm
(managed by a keykeeper)

24-26 Dec and 1 Jan Closed

VISIT US
Direction: Located 1 mile E of Barnsley town centre, off A633

Train: Barnsley 2½ miles

Bus: Stagecoach services 27, 28, 29, 29A, 30, 30A, 32 & X28; Tates 34A; Redline 37, 37A & 38 all to Cundy Cross then a short walk

ACQ.1932 [icons]

MAP Page 345 (5G)
OS Map 110/111, 278: SE373065

BRODSWORTH HALL AND GARDENS
SOUTH YORKSHIRE – DN5 7XJ

NEW FOR 2013

A new exhibition and series of events, 'Duty Calls', funded by the HLF and part of a Yorkshire Country House Partnership initiative, will explore life at Brodsworth during the two World Wars, through the voices of those who lived and worked at the hall.

VISIT US

Address: Brodsworth Hall and Gardens, Brodsworth, Doncaster, South Yorkshire DN5 7XJ

Direction: In Brodsworth, 5 miles NW of Doncaster off A635 Barnsley Road; from junction 37 of A1(M)

Train: South Elmsall 4 miles; Moorthorpe 4½ miles; Doncaster 5½ miles; Adwick Le Street 3 miles

Bus: Tates Travel service 203

Tel: 01302 722598

Local Tourist Information
Doncaster: 01302 734309

NON-MEMBERS

House and gardens

Adult	£9.60
Concession	£8.60
Child	£5.80

Winter (4 Nov-31 Mar)

Adult	£5.90
Concession	£5.30
Child	£3.50

OPENING TIMES

House (Guided tours at 11am and 12 noon, free flow from 1pm)

29 Mar-30 Sep, daily	11am-5pm
1 Oct-3 Nov, daily	11am-5pm
4 Nov-31 Mar	Closed

Gardens

29 Mar-30 Sep, daily	10am-6pm
1 Oct-3 Nov, daily	10am-5pm

Gardens, servants' wing and tearooms

4 Nov-31 Mar, Sat-Sun	10am-4pm
17-21 Feb, daily	10am-4pm
24-26 Dec and 1 Jan	Closed

Last admission is 30 mins before closing

Mobility around the site
Prams and back carriers for babies are not allowed in the hall, small padded pushchairs and slings are available instead. For visitors with mobility needs or young children, an electric buggy operates a shuttle service from the car park. Benches throughout the gardens, although steps and steep slopes limit access to some areas. The hall has ramps and seats, and a lift to the first floor.

MAP Page 345 (5G)
OS Map 111, 279: SE506070

In contrast to the house, the extensive gardens have been wonderfully restored to their original horticultural splendour as 'a collection of grand gardens in miniature'.

Here are our suggestions for enjoying the best of the garden collections:

SPRING

Snowdrops, Bluebells and Daffodils put on a fantastic show.

SUMMER

The Rose Garden with its hundred varieties. Two contrasting herbaceous borders. The fern dell with its architectural foliage. On summer Sunday afternoons, the best of Yorkshire's brass bands play in the gardens.

AUTUMN

Brilliant autumn colours in the acer dell and clipped evergreen foliage in the formal gardens.

WINTER

The collection of Victorian hollies.

Brodsworth Hall is unique. This is no glossily restored showpiece, frozen in manicured grandeur. 'Conserved as found', it is a mansion which grew comfortably old over the years, a country house as it really was: still reflecting its original opulence, but well-worn, gently conserved – and full of surprises.

Built in the 1860s by the fabulously wealthy Charles Thellusson, Brodsworth Hall was occupied by his family for over 120 years. The 'grand rooms' on the ground floor recall the house's Victorian heyday, but elsewhere Brodsworth's gentle decline during the 20th century is much more apparent. The last resident, the indomitable Sylvia Grant-Dalton, fought a losing battle against subsidence and leaking roofs in her latter years. Following her death in 1988, English Heritage took the bold decision to conserve the interiors as they were found, rather than restoring them.

Thus the house appears as she used it, making do and mending with dwindling funds and ever fewer servants. The Library's original wallpaper and carpets are faded, and Charles Thellusson's woodworking room is crowded with delightful clutter. Some bedrooms fell out of use, along with the spartan rooms of the redundant servants' wing. Others were partially modernised over the years, and

include objects from the 1900s to the 1980s which may be startlingly familiar to many visitors.

Downstairs, the cavernous Victorian kitchen with its stupendous cooking range was deserted for a cosier 'Aga kitchen' and scullery. These remain as they were at the end of Brodsworth's active life, with their Tupperware, Formica and Fanny Craddock cookbooks. Beside the Aga rests the once-grand but battered and mended armchair of the house's last cook-housekeeper.

For garden lovers

In contrast to the house, the extensive gardens have been wonderfully restored to their original splendour as 'a collection of grand gardens in miniature', with vistas last enjoyed before World War I.

The flower garden displays a fine selection of period bedding plants, while romantic views from the restored summerhouse take in both the formal gardens and the pleasure grounds. Stroll through the statue walks, the fern dell grotto and the beautiful wild rose dell.

A family-friendly property

Brodsworth Hall and Gardens are outstandingly user-friendly for visitors of all ages. For children, there is a playroom, a hands-on resources room, and an outdoor play area, featuring a real ex-naval training boat. The friendly volunteer room stewards are another unique Brodsworth attraction: many knew the property before English Heritage acquired it.

ROCHE ABBEY
S. YORKSHIRE – S66 8NW

Beautifully set in a valley landscaped by 'Capability' Brown in the 18th century, the most striking feature of this Cistercian abbey is the eastern end of its church, built in the new Gothic style in c. 1170. It has one of the most complete ground plans of any English Cistercian monastery, laid out as excavated foundations. Not far from Conisbrough Castle.

NON-MEMBERS

Adult	£3.50
Concession	£3.20
Child	£2.10

OPENING TIMES

29 Mar–30 Sep, Thu–Sun & Bank Hols	10am–4pm
1 Oct–28 Mar	Closed

VISIT US

Direction: 1½ miles S of Maltby, off A634

Train: Conisbrough 7 miles

Bus: First services 1 to Maltby Muglet Lane then 1½ miles walk. Alternatively TM Travel service 20 to Firbeck Village (then a 2 mile walk)

Tel: 01709 812739

New guidebook.

MAP Page 345 (6G)
OS Map 111/120, 279: SK544898

ALL SAINTS' CHURCH, HAREWOOD
W. YORKSHIRE – LS17 9LG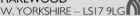

© CCT

All Saints', standing in the grounds of Harewood House, is remarkable for six pairs of alabaster effigies – virtually without rival in England – commemorating the owners of Harewood. They provide a fascinating insight into the armour, robes, jewellery and headdresses of the 15th century.

Owned and managed by The Churches Conservation Trust.

OPENING TIMES

Apr–Oct, daily	10am–6pm
Other times call Harewood House Trust Office on 0113 218 1010 in advance of your visit	

VISIT US

Train: Weeton 3 miles

Bus: Harrogate & District service 36 passes the entrance to Harewood Park

20 mins from Spofforth Castle

MAP Page 345 (4F)
OS Map 104, 289/297: SE314451

CHURCH OF ST JOHN THE EVANGELIST, LEEDS
W. YORKSHIRE – LS2 8JD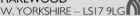

© CCT

The oldest church in Leeds. The glory of the church lies in its magnificent fittings, particularly the fabulously detailed wooden screen. Monuments commemorate the citizens of Leeds, while brightly painted angels play instruments in the roof, looking down to the wonderfully carved pews below.

Owned and managed by The Churches Conservation Trust.

OPENING TIMES

Tue–Sat	11am–3pm

VISIT US

Train: Leeds 1 mile

Bus: Many bus services pass close to the church

30 mins from Steeton Hall Gateway

MAP Page 345 (4F)
OS Map 104, 289: SE302338

DISCOUNTED ATTRACTIONS:

Use your membership to get exclusive discounts at these independent attractions in Yorkshire. Please remember to show your card as proof of membership.

15% DISCOUNT ON ENTRY

⊞ OVP ⭍ 6

BARLEY HALL
North Yorkshire YO1 8AR
Discover the town house of a medieval Lord Mayor of York. Rediscovered under a relatively modern façade, this stunning building has beautiful exposed timber frames and high roofs.
www.barleyhall.org.uk
T. 01904 615505

DISCOUNTED HOUSE & GARDEN TICKET

⊞ ⭍ 6

CASTLE HOWARD
North Yorkshire YO60 7DA
Magnificent 18th-century house built by Sir John Vanbrugh for the 3rd Earl of Carlisle, set within spectacular parkland. With exhibitions, events, adventure playground, shops and cafés.
www.castlehoward.co.uk
T. 01653 648333

15% DISCOUNT ON ENTRY

⊞ OVP ⭍ 6

DIG
AN ARCHAEOLOGICAL ADVENTURE
North Yorkshire YO1 8NN
DIG offers you a unique adventure to get you on your way to becoming a real archaeologist.
www.digyork.com
T. 01904 615505

10% OFF GARDEN TICKET

⊞

DUNCOMBE PARK
North Yorkshire YO62 5EB
A masterpiece of landscape gardening with long sweeping terraces, towering veteran trees, classical temples and breathtaking views over the Rye valley.
www.duncombepark.com
T. 01439 770213

FREE ADMISSION

⊞ ⭍ 6

FOUNTAINS ABBEY & STUDLEY ROYAL WATER GARDEN
North Yorkshire HG4 3DY
Spectacular World Heritage Site including 12th-century abbey ruins and stunning Georgian water garden.
www.nationaltrust.org.uk/fountainsabbey
T. 01765 608888

20% OFF FREEDOM TICKETS

⊞ OVP ⭍ 6

HAREWOOD HOUSE
North/West Yorkshire Border LS17 9LG
Come to Harewood for a day of discovery; exquisite collections in the House, award-winning gardens, adventure playground and exotic bird garden.
www.harewood.org
T. 0113 218 1010

YORKSHIRE

Discount applies to:

| KEY | ▦ MEMBERS | OVP OVP HOLDERS | ▮▮? NO. OF MEMBER'S CHILDREN |

Terms and conditions may apply, so make sure you check the individual pages on our website or call the individual property for more details.

15% DISCOUNT ON ENTRY

▦ OVP ▮▮ 6

JORVIK VIKING CENTRE
North Yorkshire YO1 9WT
Experience life as it was 1000 years ago as you explore the Viking-age city of York at the world-famous Jorvik Viking Centre.

www.jorvik-viking-centre.co.uk
T. 01904 615505

£1 OFF ADULT ENTRY

▦ OVP ▮▮ 6

KELHAM ISLAND MUSEUM
South Yorkshire S3 8RY
Discover the story of life and work in Sheffield. Learn how steelmaking forged the city of today and its impact on the world!

www.simt.co.uk
T. 0114 272 2106

50% DISCOUNT ON ENTRY

▦ OVP ▮▮ 6

MERCHANT ADVENTURERS' HALL
North Yorkshire YO1 9XD
The Merchant Adventurers' Hall is one of York's medieval marvels, constructed in 1357. Discover this stunning building and its unique collections.

www.theyorkcompany.co.uk
T. 01904 654818

15% DISCOUNT ON ENTRY

▦ OVP ▮▮ 6

MICKLEGATE BAR MUSEUM
North Yorkshire YO1 6JX
Visit the ancient Micklegate Bar to explore the pageantry and barbaric history that has unfolded within York's historic walls.

www.micklegatebar.com
T. 01904 615505

ADULT TRAVEL AT CONCESSIONARY RATE

▦ OVP

NORTH YORKSHIRE MOORS RAILWAY
North Yorkshire YO18 7JF
Climb aboard a steam train and ride like Harry Potter for the ultimate trip through Heartbeat Country. Trains run between Pickering and Whitby.

www.nymr.co.uk
T. 01751 472508

£1 OFF ADULT ENTRY

▦ ▮▮ 6

YORK MINSTER
North Yorkshire YO1 7HH
York Minster is one of the great cathedrals of the world. Enjoy its vast spaces and music and witness the human imagination at work on glass, stone and other fabrics.

www.yorkminster.org
T. 0844 939 0016

NORTH WEST

Remember to check opening times before you visit any of our properties **www.english-heritage.org.uk/daysout**

Details of local public transport information in England are available from Traveline **www.traveline.org.uk** or call 0871 200 2233.

Beeston Castle & Woodland Park

Make the most of your membership and keep up to date with upcoming events, the latest news and special offers by subscribing to our e-newsletter. Register online now at **www.english-heritage.org.uk/newsletter**

Hadrian's Wall

16
9 · · 23
Carlisle

Cumbria

15
Workington 18 · Penrith
Keswick · 10 17 · 12
11
8 · 21
· 7

14 · 5
20 · Windermere

22

Ulverston

13
Barrow- 6
in-Furness · 26
19
Lancaster

Lancashire · 25

Blackpool 27 · Burnley
Preston · Blackburn · 24

Southport

Wigan · Bolton
Oldham
Greater Manchester
Merseyside St Helens
Liverpool · Manchester
Birkenhead
Warrington

Cheshire Macclesfield
Chester
2 · · 4
3 · 1
Crewe

Stott Park Bobbin Mill

HIGHLIGHTS FOR 2013/14 IN THE **NORTH WEST**

p.262

p.266

p.275

Beeston Castle & Woodland Park: spectacular location enjoying stunning views over eight counties.

Carlisle Castle: unlock the stories of this fortress in a new exhibition.

Hadrian's Wall: this celebrated World Heritage Site was the north-west frontier of the whole Roman Empire.

PROPERTIES

Spectacularly crowning a sandstone crag towering above the Cheshire Plain, Beeston Castle is among the most dramatically-sited fortresses in England.

VISIT US

Address: Beeston Castle, Chapel Lane, Beeston, Cheshire CW6 9TX

Direction: Located 11 miles SE of Chester, on minor road off A49

Train: Chester 14 miles

Bus: GHA service 83 (Tue) to Beeston; Otherwise Arriva service 84 to Tarporley (2½ miles)

Tel: 01829 260464

Local Tourist Information
Chester: 01244 402111

NON-MEMBERS

Adult	£5.90
Concession	£5.30
Child	£3.50

OPENING TIMES

25 Mar-30 Sep, daily	10am-6pm
1 Oct-3 Nov, daily	10am-5pm
4 Nov-16 Feb, Sat-Sun	10am-4pm
17-21 Feb, daily	10am-4pm
22 Feb-31 Mar, Sat-Sun	10am-4pm
24-26 Dec and 1 Jan	Closed

ACQ.1959

Please note: Steep climb (no disabled access to the top of the hill). Boots or stout footwear recommended.

Parking: charges apply, may vary on event days. Car park not managed by English Heritage.

MAP Page 344 (7D)
OS Map 117, 257/258: SJ537593

The extensive wooded surroundings, rich in wildlife, are fascinating to explore. Visitors can experience some of the best views in Cheshire from within the castle.

Naturally defended by steep cliffs on three sides, Beeston's crag attracted prehistoric settlers. It became an important Bronze Age metal-working site and later an immense Iron Age hillfort, whose earthwork defences were adapted by medieval castle-builders.

The 'Castle of the Rock' – its medieval title – was begun in the 1220s by Ranulf, Earl of Chester, one of the greatest barons of Henry III's England. A defence against aristocratic rivals and a proclamation of Ranulf's power, his fortress is approached via a ruined gatehouse in a multi-towered outer wall, defining a huge outer bailey climbing steadily up the hill.

At its summit is the crowning glory of Beeston, the inner bailey, defended by a deep rock-cut ditch and a mighty double-towered gatehouse. The best-preserved part of the castle, the inner bailey commands astounding views across eight counties, from the Welsh Mountains to the west, to the Pennines in the east. It also contains the famous castle well, over 100 metres deep and traditionally the hiding place of Richard II's treasure.

Beeston Castle experienced a final blaze of glory as an important English Civil War stronghold, which finally surrendered to Parliament in November 1645 after a long and eventful siege. Thereafter it became the romantic ruin which caught the attention of wealthy Victorian John Tollemache, who promoted Beeston as a tourist attraction, even stocking its grounds with kangaroos.

English Heritage's management of the Castle's wooded slopes make the site a paradise for walkers, nature-lovers and adventurous children. A circular Woodland Walk leads fairly gently downhill from near the outer bailey gate. Winding around the base of the crag through wildlife-thronged woods, the path provides glimpses of the castle above, before reaching another of Beeston's attractions, the sandstone caves, one of which appeared as 'Robin Hood's Cave' in a 1992 film. The caves can also be reached via a shorter walk from the Visitor Centre, where the *Castle of the Rock* display vividly recounts Beeston's 4,000 years of history.

Visit the website for details of special events.

CHESTER CASTLE: AGRICOLA TOWER AND CASTLE WALLS
CHESHIRE

The original gateway to Chester Castle, this 12th-century tower houses a chapel with exceptionally fine wall-paintings of c. 1220, rediscovered in the 1980s. An access stair to the castle's wall-walk is nearby.

OPENING TIMES
Castle open for guided tours only. Please contact the Grosvenor Museum on 01244 972197, giving at least three days notice.

VISIT US
Direction: Access via Assizes Court car park on Grosvenor St

Train: Chester 1 mile

Bus: Arriva 1, 3, 3A,4, 4A, 4S, X11, 12; GHA services X1 & 11A pass the site

Tel: 01829 260464

Local Tourist Information: 01244 402111

ACQ.1912 🐕

MAP Page 344 (7C)
OS Map 117, 266: SJ405657

CHESTER ROMAN AMPHITHEATRE
CHESHIRE

The largest Roman amphitheatre in Britain, used for entertainment and military training by the 20th Legion, based at the fortress of 'Deva' (Chester). Excavations by English Heritage and Chester City Council in 2004-5 revealed two successive stone-built amphitheatres with wooden seating. The first included access to the upper tiers of seats via stairs on the rear wall, as at Pompeii, and had a small shrine next to its north entrance. The second provided seat access via vaulted stairways. The two buildings differed both from each

CHESTER ROMAN AMPHITHEATRE

other and from all other British amphitheatres, underlining the importance of Roman Chester.

Managed by Cheshire West and Chester Council.

OPENING TIMES
Any reasonable time

VISIT US
Direction: On Vicars Lane, beyond Newgate, Chester

Train: Chester ¾ mile

Bus: From surrounding areas

Local Tourist Information: 01244 402111

ACQ.1964 🐕 ♿

Disabled access (no access to amphitheatre floor).

MAP Page 344 (7C)
OS Map 117, 266: SJ408662

SANDBACH CROSSES
CHESHIRE

The two massive Saxon stone crosses, elaborately carved with animals and Biblical scenes including the Nativity of Christ and the Crucifixion, dominate the cobbled market square of Sandbach. Probably dating from the 9th century and originally painted as well as carved, they are among the finest surviving examples of Anglo-Saxon high crosses.

OPENING TIMES
Any reasonable time

VISIT US
Direction: Market Sq, Sandbach

Train: Sandbach 1½ miles

Bus: From surrounding areas

ACQ.1937 🐕 ♿

MAP Page 344 (7D)
OS Map 118, 268: SJ759608

CUMBRIA

AMBLESIDE ROMAN FORT
CUMBRIA

The well-marked remains of a 2nd-century fort with large granaries, probably built under Hadrian's rule to guard the Roman road from Brougham to Ravenglass and act as a supply base.

Managed by the National Trust.

OPENING TIMES
Any reasonable time

VISIT US
Direction: 182 metres W of Waterhead car park, Ambleside

Train: Windermere 5 miles

Bus: Stagecoach Cumbria 505, 516, 555, 599, 800 & X33; Reay's services 555R & 559R then ½ mile walk

ACQ.1978 🐕

MAP Page 346 (6D)
OS Map 90, OL7: NY372034

BOW BRIDGE
CUMBRIA

This narrow 15th-century stone bridge across Mill Beck carried an old packhorse route to nearby Furness Abbey (see p.268).

OPENING TIMES
Any reasonable time

VISIT US
Direction: Located ½ mile N of Barrow-in-Furness, on minor road off A590; near Furness Abbey

Train: Barrow-in-Furness 1½ miles

Bus: Stagecoach in Cumbria service 6 & X6 to within ¾ mile

ACQ.1950 🐕

MAP Page 346 (7D)
OS Map 96, OL6: SD224715

BROUGH CASTLE
CUMBRIA

Starkly impressive Brough Castle stands on a ridge commanding strategic Stainmore Pass, on the site of a Roman fort. Frequently the target of Scots raids, its towering keep dates from c. 1200. More comfortable living quarters were later added by the Clifford family, only to be accidentally burnt following a 'great Christmas' party in 1521. Like so many other castles hereabouts, Brough was restored in the 17th century by Lady Anne Clifford, traces of whose additions can still be seen.

St Michael's Parish Church, in pretty Church Brough near the castle, displays an exhibition about the region. This living church is open 10am-4pm daily (not English Heritage).

OPENING TIMES

29 Mar-29 Sep, daily	10am-5pm
30 Sep-31 Mar, daily	10am-4pm
24-26 Dec and 1 Jan	Closed

VISIT US
Direction: 8 miles SE of Appleby S of A66

Train: Kirkby Stephen 10 miles

Bus: Classic service 352; Grand Prix service 563; Cumbria Classic Bus 572 (Wed); Kirby Lonsdale Coaches/Woofs 564; Compass Royston X30 (Summer)

ACQ.1919 🐾 🏠 P ⚠

Please note: approach may be muddy, stout footwear recommended.

Guidebook available at Brougham Castle.

MAP Page 347 (6F)
OS Map 91, OL19: NY791141

BROUGHAM CASTLE
CUMBRIA – CA10 2AA

In a picturesque setting beside the crossing of the River Eamont, Brougham Castle was founded in the early 13th century by King John's agent Robert de Vieuxpont. His great keep largely survives amid many later buildings – including the unusual double gatehouse and impressive 'Tower of League' – added by the powerful Clifford family, Wardens of the Marches. Both a formidable barrier against Scots invaders and a prestigious residence, their castle welcomed Edward I in 1300.

A complex of passages and spiral stairways makes Brougham a fascinating castle to explore, as well as an ideal picnic setting: the keep top provides panoramic views over the Eden Valley and the earthworks of the adjacent Roman fort of Brocavum. Having fallen into decay after James I's visit in 1617, the castle was restored by the indomitable Lady Anne Clifford (see also Brough Castle and Countess Pillar). She often visited with her travelling 'court', and died here in 1676. An exhibition highlights her remarkable life and includes carvings from the Roman fort. There is good wheelchair access to most of the site (excluding the keep).

NON-MEMBERS

Adult	£4.00
Concession	£3.60
Child	£2.40
Family	£10.40

OPENING TIMES

29 Mar-30 Sep, daily	10am-5pm
1 Oct-3 Nov, daily	10am-4pm
4 Nov-31 Mar, Sat-Sun	10am-4pm

BROUGHAM CASTLE

24-26 Dec and 1 Jan	Closed

VISIT US
Direction: 1½ miles SE of Penrith, off A66

Train: Penrith 2 miles

Bus: Stagecoach service 104 and Grand Prix service 563 pass the castle on the A66, but the nearest official stop is at Whinfell Park (about 1 mile east). Fellrunner 132 (Fri) & 562 (Tue) serve Brougham village

Local Tourist information
Penrith: 01768 867466;
Rheged: 01768 860034

Tel: 01768 862488

ACQ.1920 🐾 🏠 🚶 ♿ 📷 📷 P ⛱
🏠 ♿ OVP

Please note: Car parking limited, in 'no through road' opposite castle entrance.

MAP Page 346 (5E)
OS Map 90, OL5: NY537290

CARLISLE CASTLE
SEE FEATURE – PAGE 266

CASTLERIGG STONE CIRCLE
CUMBRIA

Dramatically sited with the mountains of Helvellyn and High Seat as a backdrop, Castlerigg is among the most dramatic stone circles in Britain, probably built in the later Neolithic period.

Managed by the National Trust.

OPENING TIMES
Any reasonable time

VISIT US
Direction: 1½ miles E of Keswick

Train: Penrith 16 miles

Bus: Stagecoach Caldbeck Rambler services 73/73A pass the site. Otherwise Stagecoach 555 and Reay's 555R & 559R to Castle Lane then a 1 mile walk

ACQ.1883 🐾

MAP Page 346 (5D)
OS Map 89/90, OL4: NY291236

A mighty presence in the city it has dominated for nine centuries, Carlisle Castle was a constantly updated working fortress until well within living memory. Now its rich and varied visitor attractions reflect its long and eventful history, vividly retold in a recently-installed exhibition celebrating Carlisle's fame as the most besieged town in Britain.

VISIT US

Address: Carlisle Castle, Castle Way, Carlisle, Cumbria CA3 8UR

Direction: In Carlisle city centre

Train: Carlisle ½ mile

Bus: Stagecoach 38, 60, 60A, 61, 61A, 67, 68, 93, 300, 554, 600. Also Reay's Coaches service 39, 63, 63A, 64, 39 (Tue & Fri only) and Stacey's/Carr's 71

Tel: 01228 591922

Local Tourist Information: 01228 625600

NON-MEMBERS

Adult	£5.70
Concession	£5.10
Child	£3.40

OPENING TIMES

29 Mar-30 Sep, daily	10am-6pm
1 Oct-3 Nov, daily	10am-5pm
4 Nov-16 Feb, Sat-Sun	10am-4pm
17-21 Feb, daily	10am-4pm
22 Feb-31 Mar, Sat-Sun	10am-4pm
24-26 Dec and 1 Jan	Closed

ACQ.1963

Disabled access (limited).

Dogs on leads (restricted areas only).

Guided tours (available at peak times at a small extra charge; groups please pre-book).

Parking (disabled only, but signposted city centre car parks nearby).

MAP Page 346 (4D)
OS Map 85, 315: NY396562

18th CENTURY PISTOL

Even before the medieval castle was begun, this site was an important Roman fortress. The commanding keep, begun during the 12th century by King Henry I of England and completed by King David I of Scotland, is both the oldest part of the castle and a reminder that Carlisle was for centuries a disputed frontier fortress, commanding the especially turbulent western end of the Anglo-Scottish border.

The castle's violent history included medieval assaults, skirmishes with Elizabethan Border Reivers, a Civil War siege – the longest siege of a town in English history – and Bonnie Prince Charlie's Jacobite Rising of 1745-6. Carlisle was then the very last English fortress ever to suffer a siege: overwhelmed by the Duke of Cumberland's Hanoverian army, its Jacobite garrison were imprisoned in the keep's dank basement, where visitors can see the legendary 'licking stones', which they supposedly licked for life-giving moisture. Equally famous are the strange and fantastic carvings on the keep's second floor, probably cut in the 1460-70s. All this and more is highlighted in 'Besieged', a striking new interactive display which includes examples of the weapons used during Carlisle's many sieges; a reconstruction graphic of the interior of the keep; and a retelling of the daring rescue from the castle of the Border

Reiver Kinmont Willie Armstrong. There are also children's dressing-up clothes, and the opportunity to take a 360 degree virtual tour of the castle.

By the time Mary Queen of Scots was imprisoned here in 1568, Henry VIII's updating for heavy artillery had left its mark on Carlisle, including the keep's rounded 'shot-deflecting' battlements and the Half Moon Battery defending the Captain's Tower gatehouse. The interior rooms of this gatehouse, begun in the 12th century and one of the best-preserved in England, are now open to the public for the first time.

The castle's military career did not end after the Jacobite Rising: fear of a radical revolution made it a permanently occupied garrison from the 1820s, when the barrack blocks lining the outer ward were begun. Indeed, the castle remained the headquarters of the Border Regiment until 1959, and the 300-year history of this famous local infantry regiment is vividly told here in Cumbria's Military Museum (entry included in the castle admission charge, tel 01228 532774).

The castle remained the headquarters of the Border Regiment until 1959.

FURNESS ABBEY CUMBRIA – LA13 0PJ

Much the grandest monastic ruins in the North West, set in a lovely wooded valley. Furness Abbey was founded by Stephen, later King of England, and became (after Fountains Abbey) the second richest Cistercian abbey in all England. Dating principally from the 12th and 13th centuries, its very extensive red sandstone ruins reflect this prosperity. They include the imposing east end of the great church with its soaring pillars, and its western tower; the chapter house with its fine carved decoration; almost the entire east range of the cloister; the infirmary chapel; and many of the watercourses which drained the kitchens and latrines.

The visitor centre houses an exhibition about the abbey's history, and a large collection of sculpture from the ruins, including striking and distinctive effigies of knights.

English Heritage is currently addressing severe structural problems at the east end of the church, at present supported by a spectacular steel frame – a sight worth seeing in itself.

NON-MEMBERS

Adult	£4.00
Concession	£3.60
Child	£2.40

OPENING TIMES

29 Mar-31 Jul, Thu-Mon	10am-5pm
1-31 Aug, daily	10am-5pm
1 Sep-3 Nov, Thu-Mon	10am-5pm
4 Nov-31 Mar, Sat-Sun	10am-4pm
24-26 Dec and 1 Jan	Closed

VISIT US

Direction: Located 1½ miles N of Barrow-in-Furness, off A590

Train: Dalton and Roose 2 miles, Barrow-in-Furness 2 miles

Bus: Stagecoach in Cumbria service 6 & X6 to within within ¾ mile

Tel: 01229 823420

ACQ.1923

Dogs on leads (restricted areas only).

MAP Page 346 (7D)
OS Map 96, OL6: SD218717

CLIFTON HALL CUMBRIA

This fortified tower, built in about 1500, is the sole surviving and most important part of the manor house of the Wybergh family. It displays fascinating clues about the changing appearance of the house in the late medieval period.

OPENING TIMES

Any reasonable time	
24-26 Dec and 1 Jan	Closed

VISIT US

Direction: Next to Clifton Hall Farm; 2 miles S of Penrith, on A6

Train: Penrith 2½ miles

Bus: Reay's/Grand Prix/Kirby Lonsdale Coach Hire services 106 & Alba service 111

ACQ.1973

MAP Page 346 (5E)
OS Map 90, OL5: NY530271

COUNTESS PILLAR, BROUGHAM CUMBRIA

A monument erected in 1656 by Lady Anne Clifford of nearby Brougham Castle, to commemorate her final parting here from her mother. On the low stone beside it, money was given to the poor each anniversary of their parting.

OPENING TIMES

Any reasonable time

VISIT US

Direction: ¼ mile E of Brougham. A new access route has also been created which runs from the B6262 (to Brougham) and starts near the junction with the A66

Train: Penrith 2½ miles

Bus: Stagecoach service 104 and Grand Prix service 563 pass the castle on the A66, but the nearest official stop is at Whinfell Park (about 1 mile east). Fellrunner 132 (Fri only) & 562 (Tue only) serve Brougham village

COUNTESS PILLAR, BROUGHAM

 ACQ.1977

Warning: site on a very busy main road. Parking on B6262, close to the junction with A66. Safe access by footpath.

MAP Page 346 (5E)
OS Map 90, OL5: NY546289

FURNESS ABBEY
SEE OPPOSITE

HADRIAN'S WALL
SEE PAGE 275

HARDKNOTT ROMAN FORT
CUMBRIA

This remote and dramatically-sited fort was founded under Hadrian's rule in the 2nd century. Well-marked remains include the headquarters building, commandant's house and bath house. The site of the parade ground survives beside the fort, and the road which Hardknott guarded can be traced for some distance as an earthwork.

Managed by the National Trust.

OPENING TIMES
Any reasonable time

VISIT US
Direction: 9 miles NE of Ravenglass; at W end of Hardknott Pass

Train: Dalegarth (Ravenglass & Eskdale) 3 miles or Ravenglass 10 miles

Bus: Closest by bus is 3D Travel service 6 (Mon-Sat) or AA Travel service X6 (Sun only) to Ravenglass or Muncaster Mill then R&ER Dalegarth and then 3½ mile walk

 ACQ.1949

Warning: access may be hazardous during the winter months.

MAP Page 346 (6C)
OS Map 89/90, OL6: NY218015

KING ARTHUR'S ROUND TABLE CUMBRIA

A Neolithic earthwork henge, dating from c. 2500 BC, but much later believed to be King Arthur's jousting arena. Mayburgh Henge is adjacent.

OPENING TIMES
Any reasonable time

VISIT US
Direction: Located at Eamont Bridge, 1 mile S of Penrith. Mayburgh Henge is nearby

Train: Penrith 1½ miles

Bus: Stagecoach service 108; Reay's Grand Prix/Kirby Lonsdale Coach Hire services 106; Alba service 111 (Tue only) and Fellrunner services 132 (Fri only) & 562 (Tue only)

 ACQ.1884

MAP Page 346 (5E)
OS Map 90, OL5: NY523284

LANERCOST PRIORY
SEE FEATURE – PAGE 270

MAYBURGH HENGE
CUMBRIA

A large and impressive Neolithic henge, much better preserved than neighbouring King Arthur's Round Table. Its banks stand up to 3 metres (10 feet) high and unusually are constructed of pebbles collected from the nearby river. Near the centre is a single standing stone: old drawings suggest that it was one of a group of four here, four more having been removed from the entranceway.

OPENING TIMES
Any reasonable time

VISIT US
Direction: 1 mile S of Penrith off A6

Train: Penrith 1½ miles

MAYBURGH HENGE

Bus: Stagecoach service 108; Reay's/Grand Prix/Kirby Lonsdale Coach Hire services 106; Alba service 111 (Tue only) and Fellrunner services 132 (Fri only) & 562 (Tue only) then very short walk

 ACQ.1884

MAP Page 346 (5E)
OS Map 90, OL5: NY519284

PENRITH CASTLE CUMBRIA

Penrith Castle was begun at the end of the 14th century by William Strickland, Bishop of Carlisle. Later acquired by Ralph Neville, who played a key role in defending this area against the Scots. It was then transformed into a luxurious residence by Richard, Duke of Gloucester (subsequently Richard III). Surviving in places to their full height, the castle walls stand in a public park. Graphic panels tell the story of the castle.

OPENING TIMES

Park:	
Summer	7.30am-9pm
Winter	7.30am-4.30pm

VISIT US
Direction: Opposite Penrith railway station

Train: Penrith (adjacent)

Bus: From surrounding areas

ACQ.1913

MAP Page 346 (5E)
OS Map 90, OL5: NY513299

VISIT US

Direction: Off a minor road S of Lanercost; 2 miles NE of Brampton

Train: Brampton 3 miles

Bus: Alba/Classic Hadrian's Wall Bus AD122 Apr–Nov. Otherwise Stagecoach/Arriva service 685 to within 2½ miles

Tel: 01697 73030

NON-MEMBERS

Adult	£3.50
Concession	£3.20
Child	£2.10

OPENING TIMES

29 Mar–30 Sep, daily	10am–6pm
1 Oct–3 Nov, daily	10am–5pm
4 Nov–16 Feb, Sat–Sun	10am–4pm
17–21 Feb, daily	10am–4pm
22 Feb–31 Mar, Sat–Sun	10am–4pm
24–26 Dec and 1 Jan	Closed

ACQ.1930 🐾 🏪 f P 📷 📷 💬
⚠ OVP

Lanercost tearoom and farm shop is open every day except 25 and 26 Dec. www.lanercost.co.uk Tel: 016977 41267 (not managed by English Heritage).

MAP Page 346 (4E)
OS Map 86, 315: NY556637

The beautiful and now tranquil setting of Augustinian Lanercost Priory belies an often troubled history. Standing less than half a mile from Hadrian's Wall, it suffered frequent attacks during the long Anglo-Scottish wars, once by Robert Bruce in person. The mortally sick King Edward I rested here for five months in 1306-7, shortly before his death on his final campaign.

Yet there is still much to see in this best–preserved of Cumbrian monasteries. The east end of the noble 13th-century church survives to its full height, housing within its dramatic triple tier of arches some fine monuments. The nave, with its lofty west front, is still in full use as the parish church.

Lanercost's cloisters include a beautiful vaulted 13th-century refectory undercroft. They partly owe their preservation to their conversion, after the priory's suppression, into the Tudor mansion of the Dacre family. The west range includes the four-storey Dacre Tower, a pele tower adapted from the monastic kitchen, and the Dacre Hall (used as the village hall so not always open to the public). This displays fragments of 16th-century wall-painting and a splendidly carved Jacobean chimneypiece, recently returned here from its travels.

Set beside an ancient vicarage, and 'vicar's pele tower' (viewable only from outside), Lanercost Priory's extensive remains make an unforgettable ensemble. The English Heritage ticket office and gift shop is next to the church.

Nearby farm buildings have been converted into a visitor centre, with a restaurant/tearoom and display about Hadrian's Wall. The parish church, Dacre Hall and visitor centre are not managed by English Heritage.

PIEL CASTLE CUMBRIA

The impressive ruins of a 14th-century castle with a massive keep, inner and outer baileys and towered curtain walls still standing. It was built by the Abbot of Furness on the south-eastern point of Piel Island, to guard the deep-water harbour of Barrow-in-Furness against pirates and Scots raiders.

OPENING TIMES

Any reasonable time. Access by ferry boat not managed by EH

VISIT US

Direction: Piel Island, 3¼ miles SE of Barrow-in-Furness

By small boat: Two ferries operate services to Piel Island (subject to tides and weather). Call Steve Chattaway on 07516 453784 or Alan Cleasby on 07798 794550. There is a small charge for this service

Train: Barrow-in-Furness 4 miles

Bus: Blueworks Taxis service 11 Barrow-in Furness – Ulverston Roa Island and then ferry to Piel Castle

ACQ.1973 🐕

MAP Page 346 (7D)
OS Map 96, OL6: SD233636

RAVENGLASS ROMAN BATH HOUSE CUMBRIA

The remains of the bath house of Ravenglass Roman fort, established in AD 130, are among the tallest Roman structures surviving in northern Britain: the walls stand almost

RAVENGLASS ROMAN BATH HOUSE

4 metres (13 feet) high. The fort at Ravenglass (whose earthworks can be seen near the bath house) guarded what was probably a useful harbour, and there is evidence that soldiers stationed here served in Hadrian's fleet.

OPENING TIMES

Any reasonable time

VISIT US

Direction: ¼ mile E of Ravenglass, off minor road leading to A595

Train: Ravenglass (adjacent)

Bus: 3D Travel service 6 (Mon-Sat) or AA Travel service X6 (Sun only)

ACQ.1980 🐕

MAP Page 346 (6C)
OS Map 96, OL6: SD088959

SHAP ABBEY CUMBRIA

The impressive full-height 15th-century tower and other remains of a remote abbey of Premonstratensian 'white canons'.

Information panels guide you round the abbey and illustrate daily monastic life.

OPENING TIMES

Any reasonable time

VISIT US

Direction: 1½ miles W of Shap, on the bank of the River Lowther

SHAP ABBEY

Train: Penrith 10 miles

Bus: Alba service 111 (Tue only) passes the approach road; Reay's/ Grand Prix/Kirby Lonsdale service 106 Penrith-Kendal passes within 1½ miles

ACQ.1948 🐕 P ♿

Disabled access (limited views from outside the site).

Steep access road is unsuitable in wintry weather.

MAP Page 346 (6E)
OS Map 90, OL5: NY548152

ST NINIAN'S, BROUGHAM
CUMBRIA – CA10 2AD

© CCT

The originally Norman St Ninian's Church was rebuilt in the 17th century by Lady Anne Clifford, who inherited Brougham Castle. The simple interior is whitewashed, with clear glass windows, stone flagged floor, box pews, an elegant screen, and a three-decker pulpit.

Owned and managed by The Churches Conservation Trust.

OPENING TIMES

Open daily during daylight hours

VISIT US

Train: Penrith 3 miles

Bus: Stagecoach service 104 and Grand Prix service 563 pass the site on the A66, but the nearest official stop is at Whinfell Park (about 1 mile east)

Nr Brougham Castle

MAP Page 346 (5E)
OS Map 90, OL05: NY557289

STOTT PARK BOBBIN MILL
CUMBRIA – LA12 8AX

NEW FOR 2013

From late March 2013, there will be much more to see outside the mill. New displays and interpretation panels will allow visitors to take self-guided tours of the mill's surroundings. Working steam displays will be held during the first weekend of every month, Apr-Oct. Call site for details.

In a lovely setting near Lake Windermere, this unique survival of a working bobbin mill operated commercially from 1835 until 1971. It used timber coppiced from the surrounding woodlands to turn bobbins for the Lancashire cotton industry, later diversifying into products from cotton reels to toggles for Word War II duffel coats. Powered first by water and later by steam and then electricity, it retains much of its belt-operated machinery, and the whole fascinating process of bobbin-making is demonstrated during guided tours. Guided tours are included in the admission charge: the last tour begins ½ hour before closing.

NON-MEMBERS

Adult	£6.40
Concession	£5.80
Child	£3.80
Family	£16.60

OPENING TIMES

29 Mar-31 Jul, Thu-Mon	10am-5pm
1-31 Aug, daily	10am-5pm
1 Sep-3 Nov, Thu-Mon	10am-5pm
4 Nov-31 Mar	Closed
Please call for details of steam days	

VISIT US

Direction: Located 1½ miles N of Newby Bridge, off A590

Train: Grange-over-Sands 8 miles; Lakeside Station (Lakeside & Haverthwaite railway) ¾ mile

Bus: Lecks 538 (Thu only) passes the site. Alternatively Stagecoach service X6 & Lecks 518 or Blueworks summer service X32 to Newby Bridge and then 1½ mile walk. Lakeside and Haverthwaite Railway's Lakeside terminus is ¾ mile walk

Ferry: Windermere ferry from Ambleside or Bowness to Lakeside, then 1 mile

Tel: 01539 531087

Local Tourist Information
Hawkshead: 01539 436946

ACQ.1974 🏠 E P 🚶 ♿ 🔊 📷 📷 📷 ⚠ OVP

Disabled access (ground floor only. Specific interpretation for visually impaired visitors).

Lower car park for disabled parking. Upper car park for general parking.

Dogs welcome on leads.

MAP Page 346 (6D)
OS Map 96/97, OL7: SD372881

WETHERAL PRIORY GATEHOUSE CUMBRIA

Well-preserved 15th-century gatehouse, the sole survivor of a small Benedictine priory. A miniature 'pele-tower' containing two storeys of comfortable rooms, it later became a fortified vicarage, a defence against border raiders.

OPENING TIMES

29 Mar-29 Sep, daily	10am-6pm
30 Sep-31 Mar, daily	10am-4pm
24-26 Dec and 1 Jan	Closed

VISIT US

Direction: Near Wetheral village; 6 miles E of Carlisle, on B6263

Train: Wetheral ½ mile

Bus: Reay's/Stagecoach in Cumbria services 75 to Wetheral then short walk

ACQ. 1978

MAP Page 346 (4E)
OS Map 86, 315: NY468541

LANCASHIRE

GOODSHAW CHAPEL
LANCASHIRE

English Heritage's only Nonconformist place of worship, this atmospheric Baptist chapel displays a complete set of box-pews, galleries and pulpit dating from c.1742 to 1809. A festival of hymns and sermons is held on the first Sunday in July.

OPENING TIMES
Please call the keykeeper for details. Tel: 01706 227333

VISIT US
Direction: In Crawshawbooth, 2 miles N of Rawtenstall via A682 (in Goodshaw Ave – turning off A682 opp. Jester public house). Chapel approx. 1½ miles from main road

Train: Burnley Manchester Road 4½ miles

Bus: Transdev Burnley & Pendle 'Witch Way' services X43/4

ACQ. 1976

MAP Page 344 (4E)
OS Map 103, OL21: SD814261

SAWLEY ABBEY
LANCASHIRE

SAWLEY ABBEY

The remains of a Cistercian abbey founded in 1148, set on the banks of the Ribble against a backdrop of dramatic hills. After its dissolution in 1536, the monks were briefly returned to the abbey during the Pilgrimage of Grace. They remained in possession until the insurrection's collapse and the execution of their abbot.

Managed by the Heritage Trust for the North West.

OPENING TIMES

29 Mar–31 Oct, daily	10am–5pm
1 Nov–31 Mar, daily	10am–4pm
24-26 Dec and 1 Jan	Closed

VISIT US
Direction: Located at Sawley; 3½ miles N of Clitheroe, off A59

Train: Clitheroe 4 miles

Bus: Tyrerbus of Nelson service C2. Alternatively Transdev Lancashire United (of Blackburn) services 280 & X80 stop nearby

ACQ. 1951

MAP Page 344 (4D)
OS Map 103, OL41: SD777464

WARTON OLD RECTORY
LANCASHIRE

A rare survival of a large 14th-century stone house with great hall and chambers. It served as a residence and courthouse for the wealthy and powerful rectors of Warton.

WARTON OLD RECTORY

Managed by the Heritage Trust for the North West.

OPENING TIMES

29 Mar–29 Sep, daily	10am–6pm
30 Sep–31 Mar, daily	10am–4pm
24-26 Dec and 1 Jan	Closed

VISIT US
Direction: At Warton; 1 mile N of Carnforth, on minor road off A6

Train: Carnforth 1 mile

Bus: Stagecoach in Lancashire service 51 & 55

ACQ.1969

MAP Page 344 (3D)
OS Map 97, OL7: SD499723

WHALLEY ABBEY
GATEHOUSE LANCASHIRE

The 14th-century gatehouse of the nearby Cistercian abbey, the second wealthiest monastery in Lancashire, beside the River Calder. The first floor was probably a chapel.

OPENING TIMES
Any reasonable time

VISIT US
Direction: In Whalley; 6 miles NE of Blackburn, on minor road off A59

Train: Whalley ¼ mile

Bus: From surrounding area

ACQ. 1971

MAP Page 344 (4D)
OS Map 103, 287: SD729362

DISCOUNTED ATTRACTIONS: **NORTH WEST**

Use your membership to get exclusive discounts at these independent attractions in the North West. Please remember to show your card as proof of membership.

Discount applies to:

| KEY | ⊞ MEMBERS | OVP OVP HOLDERS | 👪? NO. OF MEMBER'S CHILDREN |

Terms and conditions may apply, so make sure you check the individual pages on our website or call the individual property for more details.

20% DISCOUNT ON ENTRY

⊞ OVP

LOWTHER CASTLE
Cumbria CA10 2HH
The gardens at Lowther are really unique. Ruined gardens lie in the grounds of a ruined castle in an idyllic pastoral landscape unchanged for hundreds of years.
www.lowthercastle.org
Tel. 01931 712192

£2 OFF TICKET PRICE

⊞ OVP 👪 6

NORTON PRIORY MUSEUM & GARDENS
Cheshire
Explore medieval priory remains, woodlands and beautiful Georgian walled garden. Museum offers tea room and shop.
www.nortonpriory.org
Tel. 01928 569895

50% DISCOUNT ON ENTRY

⊞ 👪 2

PENDLE HERITAGE CENTRE
Lancashire BB9 6JQ
Historic farmhouse, restored using traditional building skills. Exhibitions, 18th-century walled garden, shop and café.
www.htnw.co.uk
Tel. 01282 677151

20% DISCOUNT ON ENTRY

⊞ 👪 6

SMITHILLS HALL
Lancashire BL1 7NP
Set in over 2200 acres of woodland, on the edge of the West Pennine Moors, Smithills Hall is one of the oldest and best preserved manor houses in the North West.
www.boltonmuseums.org.uk
Tel. 01204 332377

2 for 1 ENTRY

⊞ OVP 👪 1

STRETTON WATERMILL
Cheshire SY14 7JA
Step back in time and visit a working mill in beautiful rural Cheshire. See one of the country's best preserved demonstration water-powered corn mills.
www.strettonwatermill.blogspot.com
Tel. 01606 271640

2 for 1 ENTRY

⊞ OVP 👪 1

WEAVER HALL MUSEUM AND WORKHOUSE
Cheshire CW9 8AB
Discover the hidden history of Cheshire from the salt industry to archaeological treasures, all housed in a former Victorian workhouse.
www.weaverhallmuseum.org.uk
Tel. 01606 271640

HADRIAN'S WALL

Marching 73 miles from sea to sea across some of the wildest and most dramatic country in England, this celebrated World Heritage Site was the north-west frontier of the whole Roman Empire. Walk along the Wall to discover 2000 years of history at our many forts, museums, and even the High Street of a once-thriving Roman town.

CARING FOR THE HADRIAN'S WALL WORLD HERITAGE SITE AND NATIONAL TRAIL

Whilst planning your holiday or visit, please remember to observe 'Every Footstep Counts' – the World Heritage Site's own country code. As you will appreciate, Hadrian's Wall is a fragile environment and the archaeology is easily damaged. You can help protect this great Wonder of the World by following the general advice:

- Always keep to the signed paths
- Visit the organised paying sites, which are more robust and can accommodate visitors, but please avoid walking alongside the Wall when the ground is very wet. The buried archaeology underfoot is particularly vulnerable to damage in the wet winter months between November and April. Ask about the winter walking passport.
- Avoid walking on the Wall as this may cause it to collapse
- Respect livestock and land
- Keep dogs on a lead and under close control
- Use public transport whenever you can
- Please note, Hadrian's Wall Path National Trail is a footpath only. Please cycle on legal routes only ie: bridgeways, byways, roads and cyclepaths.

English Heritage cares for 24 sites all along the Wall, from large forts with museums to lonely turrets and milecastles amid spectacular hill-country. The following section divides our frontier sites into three sections, beginning near Carlisle – whose mighty medieval castle stands on a Roman site.

f **𝕏** For updates on Hadrian's Wall, don't forget to follow on Facebook and Twitter.

HARE HILL ①

A short length of Wall still stands 2.7 metres (8.8 feet) high.

VISIT US
Direction: ¾ mile NE of Lanercost

ACQ.1972

OS Map 86, 43: NY564646

BANKS EAST TURRET ②

Imposing and well-preserved turret with adjoining stretches of Hadrian's Wall.

VISIT US
Direction: On minor road E of Banks village; 3½ miles NE of Brampton

ACQ.1934 **P** ♿ ⚠

OS Map 86, 315: NY575647

Lanercost Priory
See feature on page 270

Carlisle Castle
See feature on page 266

Scotland

Birdoswald Roman Fort
See feature on page 282

Brampton

Carlisle

Cumbria

Haltwhistle

Hexham

Corbridge

Northumberland

① ② ③ ④ ⑤ ⑥ ⑦ ⑧ ⑨ ⑩ ⑪ ⑫ ⑬ ⑭ ⑮ ⑯ ⑰ ⑱ ⑲ ⑳ ㉑

BIRDOSWALD ROMAN FORT ⑤

See feature on page 282

HARROWS SCAR MILECASTLE AND WALL

A mile-long section of the Wall, rebuilt in stone later in Hadrian's reign. It is linked to Birdoswald Roman Fort (see p.282).

VISIT US ⑥
Direction: ¼ mile E of Birdoswald, on minor road off B6318

ACQ.1946 **P**

Parking at Birdoswald

OS Map 86, OL43: NY620664

WILLOWFORD WALL, TURRETS AND BRIDGE

A fine 914 metre (2999 feet) stretch of Wall, including two turrets and impressive bridge remains beside the River Irthing. Linked by a bridge to Birdoswald Roman Fort (see p.282).

 ⑦

VISIT US
Direction: W of minor road, ¾ mile W of Gilsland

ACQ.1946

OS Map 86, OL43: NY627664

FROM HARE HILL TO WALLTOWN CRAGS

The western section of the Wall – which began at Bowness on the Solway Firth – passes near Carlisle and Lanercost Priory before climbing onto the Whin Sill crags east of Birdoswald Roman Fort, with its 2,000-year history.

3

PIKE HILL SIGNAL TOWER

The remains of one of a network of signal towers predating Hadrian's Wall, Pike Hill was later joined to the Wall at an angle of 45 degrees.

VISIT US

Direction: On minor road E of Banks village

ACQ.1971 P

OS Map 86, 315: NY577648

4

LEAHILL TURRET AND PIPER SIKE TURRET

Turrets west of Birdoswald: Piper Sike has a cooking-hearth.

VISIT US

Direction: On minor road 2 miles W of Birdoswald Fort

ACQ.1952

OS Map 86, OL43/315: NY586652

Newcastle-upon-Tyne

22

23 24

Gateshead

Tyne and Wear

Durham

8

POLTROSS BURN MILECASTLE

One of the best-preserved milecastles on Hadrian's Wall, Poltross includes an oven, a stair to the rampart walk, and the remains of its north gateway. Known locally as 'the King's Stables.'

VISIT US

Direction: On minor road E of Banks village. Immediately SW of Gilsland village, by old railway station

ACQ.1938 P

Parking (near the Station Hotel).

OS Map 86, OL43: NY634662

9

WALLTOWN CRAGS

One of the best places of all to see the Wall, dramatically snaking and diving along the crags of the Whin Sill.

VISIT US

Direction: 1 mile NE of Greenhead, off B6318

ACQ.1939

OS Map 86/87, 43: NY674663

Brampton

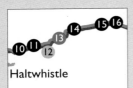

Haltwhistle

FROM CAWFIELDS ROMAN WALL TO BLACK CARTS TURRET

This central section of the Wall climbs and dives across often wild and rugged country, attaining its highest point at Winshields Wall before reaching the famous forts of Vindolanda and windswept Housesteads, with its new Visitor Centre opening this year.

CAWFIELDS ROMAN WALL

A fine stretch of Hadrian's Wall on a steep slope, with turrets and an impressive milecastle, probably built by the Second Legion.

VISIT US

Direction: 1¼ miles N of Haltwhistle, off B6318

ACQ.1960

Parking not operated by EH. Parking charge applies (payable to Northumberland National Park).

OS Map 86/87, OL43: NY716667

WINSHIELDS WALL

The highest point on the Wall, in rugged country with spectacular views.

VISIT US

Direction: W of Steel Rigg car park; on minor road off B6318

ACQ.1937

OS Map 86/87, 43: NY742676

Roman Vindolanda
See Associated Attractions on page 287

Housesteads Roman Fort
See feature on page 285

Carlisle Castle
See feature on page 266

Scotland

Brampton

Haltwhistle

Hexham

Corbridge

Carlisle

Cumbria

Northumberland

Near Carrawburgh fort stands a fascinating temple to the eastern god Mithras, with facsimiles of altars found during excavation. Sited like many Mithraic temples near a military base, it was founded in the 3rd century and eventually desecrated, probably by Christians. Nearby, but no longer visible, was the shrine of the water nymph Coventina.

VISIT US

Direction: 3¾ miles W of Chollerford, on B6318

ACQ.1953   Parking charge payable to Northumberland National Park.

OS Map 87, 43: NY859711

TEMPLE OF MITHRAS, CARRAWBURGH

The Hadrian's Wall Bus (AD122) runs throughout the spring and summer months between Newcastle, Hexham and Carlisle, and is an excellent way to see the stunning scenery in this part of England. It stops at Corbridge, Chesters, Housesteads, Vindolanda and Birdoswald Roman Sites – as well as main railway stations, market places, towns and villages along the way.

ROMAN VINDOLANDA

See Associated Attractions on page 287

HOUSESTEADS ROMAN FORT

See feature on page 285

SEWINGSHIELDS WALL

A length of Wall with milecastle remains, impressively sited along the Whin Sill, commanding fine views of many prehistoric and later earthworks to the north.

VISIT US

Direction: N of B6318; 1½ miles E of Housesteads Fort

ACQ.1946

OS Map 86/87, OL43: NY805702

Newcastle-upon-Tyne

Gateshead

Tyne and Wear

Durham

BLACK CARTS TURRET

A 460-metre (1509 feet) length of Hadrian's Wall including one turret. **Please note:** It is not possible for visitors to park here.

VISIT US

Direction: On minor road E of Banks village; 3½ miles NE of Brampton

ACQ.1970

OS Map 86, 315: NY575647

FROM CHESTERS ROMAN FORT TO BENWELL

Passing into gentler country, the Wall marches through Chesters Roman Fort in its beautiful riverside setting and north of amazingly-preserved Corbridge Roman Town, then on to Benwell – whence it once continued to its North Sea terminus at Wallsend.

17

CHESTERS ROMAN FORT AND MUSEUM

See feature on page 283

18

CHESTERS BRIDGE ABUTMENT

Close to Chesters Roman Fort are the remains of a bridge which carried Hadrian's Wall across the North Tyne. Visible on both river banks, they are most impressive on the eastern side.

VISIT US

Direction: ½ mile S of Low Brunton, on A6079

ACQ.1946

OS Map 87, 43: NY914701

Scotland

Chesters Roman Fort and Museum
See feature on page 283

Carlisle Castle
See feature on page 266

1 2 3 7 8 9 10 11 12 13 14 15 16 17 18 19 20

Brampton

Carlisle

4 5 6

Cumbria

Haltwhistle

Hexham

Corbridge

Corbridge Roman Town
See feature on page 284

Northumberland

20

PLANETREES ROMAN WALL

A 15-metre (49 feet) length of narrow Wall on broad foundations, reflecting a change of policy concerning the thickness of the Wall during construction.

VISIT US

Direction: 1 mile SE of Chollerford on B6318

ACQ.1945

OS Map 87, OL43: NY929696

21

CORBRIDGE ROMAN TOWN

See feature on page 284

22

HEDDON-ON-THE-WALL

A consolidated stretch of Wall, up to 2 metres (6½ feet) thick in places.

VISIT US

Direction: Immediately E of Heddon village; S of A69

ACQ.1935

OS Map 88, 316: NZ137669

BRUNTON TURRET **19**

Wall section and a surviving piece of turret 2½ metres (8.2 feet) high, built by men of the Twentieth Legion.

VISIT US

Direction: ¼ mile S of Low Brunton, off A6079

ACQ.1947

OS Map 87, OL43: NY922698

Newcastle-upon-Tyne

22

23 24

Gateshead

Tyne and Wear

Durham

DENTON HALL TURRET **23**

The foundations of a turret and a 65-metre (213 feet) length of Wall.

VISIT US

Direction: 4 miles W of Newcastle-upon-Tyne city centre, located immediately SE of A69

ACQ.1934

OS Map 88, 316: NZ198655

BENWELL ROMAN TEMPLE

The remains of a small temple to the native god 'Antenociticus', in the 'vicus' (civilian settlement) which stood outside Benwell fort.

VISIT US

Direction: Temple located immediately SE of A69, at Benwell in Broomridge Ave; Vallum Crossing in Denhill Park

ACQ.1936

OS Map 88, 316: NZ217647

BENWELL VALLUM CROSSING **24**

A stone-built causeway, where the road from the south crossed the Vallum earthwork on its way to Benwell fort.

ACQ.1934

OS Map 88, 136: NZ216646

BIRDOSWALD ROMAN FORT
NORTHUMBERLAND – CA8 7DD

NEW FOR 2013

New panels will be displayed around the site to help you interpret the Fort.

VISIT US

Direction: 4 miles west of Greenhead off B6318. Signposted from A69 Carlisle-Hexham road at Brampton roundabout

Train: Brampton 8 miles, Haltwhistle 7 miles

Bus: Alba/Classic service AD122 Carlisle – Hexham 🚆 (Apr-Oct)

Tel: 01697 747602

Haltwhistle Tourist Information 01434 322022

NON-MEMBERS

Adult	£5.40
Concession	£4.90
Child	£3.20

OPENING TIMES

29 Mar-30 Sep, daily	10am-6pm
1 Oct-3 Nov, daily	10am-5pm
4 Nov-16 Feb, Sat-Sun	10am-4pm
17-21 Feb, daily	10am-4pm
22 Feb-31 Mar, Sat-Sun	10am-4pm
24-26 Dec and 1 Jan	Closed

Parking: Pay and display parking refunded to all visitors and members who visit the site.

Disabled access (to visitor centre, toilets, shop, tearoom and part of site. Disabled parking on site).

MAP Page 346 (4E)
OS Map 86, OL43: NY615663

Birdoswald is one of the best places to gain an overview of Hadrian's Wall at one single site. A Roman fort, turret and milecastle can all be seen here, with nearby the longest continuous stretch of Wall visible today. The Visitor Centre illustrates the history of the Wall, and tells the story of Birdoswald and its people over the past 2000 years.

Known as 'Banna', Birdoswald likewise has the best preserved defences of any of the major Hadrian's Wall forts. Three main gates, perimeter walls, angle towers, granaries and drill hall are all still traceable.

Another distinctive feature is the traces of the buildings successively raised here after the Roman withdrawal: including a large 5th-century timber hall, perhaps for a local British chieftain; a medieval fortified tower; an Elizabethan 'bastle house', a defence against 'Border Reivers'; and finally the present turreted farmhouse. Adjacent buildings now house a tearoom, a shop and a small exhibition.

The fort stands on the Hadrian's Wall Path National Trail. Guided tours for groups are available at a small additional fee. Please contact the site for details and bookings.

Accommodation

If you would like to stay within the walls of the fort, a 36-bed farmhouse can be booked for groups. Please call 01697 747602 or email birdoswald.accommodation@ english-heritage.org.uk

VISIT US

Direction: ¼ mile W of Chollerford, on B6318

Train: Hexham 5½ miles

Bus: Alba/Classic service AD122 Carlisle – Hexham (Apr-Oct); also Tyne Valley/Snaith service 880 from Hexham

Tel: 01434 681379

Local Tourist Information
Hexham: 01434 652220

NON-MEMBERS

Adult	£5.40
Concession	£4.90
Child	£3.20

OPENING TIMES

29 Mar-30 Sep, daily	10am-6pm
1 Oct-3 Nov, daily	10am-5pm
4 Nov-16 Feb, Sat-Sun	10am-4pm
17-21 Feb, daily	10am-4pm
22 Feb-31 Mar, Sat-Sun	10am-4pm
24-26 Dec and 1 Jan	Closed

ACQ.1954

Disabled access (companion recommended). Disabled parking and toilets.

Dogs on leads (restricted areas only).

Tearoom (summer only; not managed by English Heritage).

Parking (pay and display. Charge refundable upon admission).

Picturesquely set in the beautiful valley of the River North Tyne, Chesters is the best-preserved example of a Roman cavalry fort in Britain. The site also features a museum containing an amazing collection of archaeological discoveries.

Known as 'Cilurnum', Chesters was one of the series of permanent forts added during the construction of the Wall. It housed a garrison of some 500 troops, by the 3rd century a cavalry regiment originating from Asturias in northern Spain. There is much still to see, including remains of all four principal gates; the headquarters building with courtyard, hall and regimental shrine; and the elaborate and luxurious commandant's house.

Even better preserved, between the fort and the river, is the garrison's bath house. This still displays the complex of rooms which offered soldiers hot, cold or steam baths, as well as a changing-room-cum-clubhouse.

Hundreds of Roman finds from the central section of the Wall – retrieved by the Victorian antiquarian, John Clayton – are crowded into Chesters' highly distinctive museum, which has been restored to its Victorian glory with its original colour-scheme and 'traditional' museum layout. Recent additions include a portrait of John Clayton: and outside, a tactile model of the site, ramped access to the museum, and a viewing platform overlooking the river.

MAP Page 347 (4F)
OS Map 87, OL43: NY912702

VISIT US

Direction: ½ mile NW of Corbridge, on minor road, then signposted

Train: Corbridge 1¼ miles

Bus: Alba/Classic AD122 (Apr-Oct); Go North East 10, 684; Arriva/ Stagecoach in Cumbria services 685; Wrights service 888

Tel: 01434 632349

Local Tourist Information
01434 652220

NON-MEMBERS

Adult	£5.40
Concession	£4.90
Child	£3.20

OPENING TIMES

29 Mar-30 Sep, daily	10am-6pm
1 Oct-3 Nov, daily	10am-5pm
4 Nov-16 Feb, Sat-Sun	10am-4pm
17-21 Feb, daily	10am-4pm
22 Feb-31 Mar, Sat-Sun	10am-4pm
24-26 Dec and 1 Jan	Closed

Dogs on leads (restricted areas only).

Disabled access (parking, toilet, audio tour, access to the museum and perimeter of site).

MAP Page 347 (4F)
OS Map 87, OL43: NY982648

Corbridge Roman Town is the only place in Britain where visitors can walk along the original surface of a Roman 'high street', flanked by the excavated remains of granaries, a fountain house, markets, workshops and temples.

Astride the intersection of the Roman Dere Street and Stanegate roads, Corbridge was initially the site of a series of important forts: but after Hadrian's Wall was fully commissioned it developed into a prosperous garrison town, a tempting leave-centre for off-duty Wall soldiers. Abandoned after the collapse of Roman rule in Britain, the site of the settlement moved to the present Corbridge town, the Saxon tower of whose church– partly built with recycled Roman masonry – can clearly be seen from here.

The Roman town centre has been systematically excavated, producing the array of finds now most attractively displayed in the site museum. Covering every aspect of Roman life, artefacts include the tombstone of little Ertola, who 'lived most happily four years and sixty days', shown still playing with her ball; and the famous Corbridge lion carving. His modern counterpart, Grricola the Roman lion, takes younger visitors on a trail around the museum.

A recently-installed display showcases the Corbridge Hoard, one of the most significant finds from Roman Britain. Buried in the early 2nd century and rediscovered in 1964, this chest contained an extraordinary collection of weapons, tools, and personal possessions, including a soldier's iron bowl and a huge wooden tankard. Most importantly, it also included sections of 'lorica segmentata', articulated Roman armour. These allowed archaeologists to reconstruct how this complex armour – previously known only from depictions – actually worked. A touch-screen display allows visitors to explore the Hoard at many levels of detail.

Among the most popular sites on Hadrian's Wall, Housesteads is also the most complete example of a Roman fort anywhere in Britain. It stands high on the wild Whin Sill escarpment, flanked by dramatic stretches of the Wall. Now 'the Grandest Station' on the Wall – as a Georgian visitor called it – boasts an outstanding exhibition, vividly interpreting life here on the northern edge of the Roman Empire.

VISIT US

Address: Housesteads Roman Fort, Haydon Bridge, Hexham, Northumberland NE47 6NN

Direction: Bardon Mill 4 miles

Bus: Alba/Classic service AD122 (Apr-Oct)

Tel: 01434 344363

Local Tourist Information Hexham: 01434 652220

Disabled access to the museum (companion recommended). Limited access to site. 750-metre walk up a steep gradient. Disabled parking available at the top of the hill. Please enquire at the information centre in the bottom car park to arrange disabled parking. Guide dogs only in the museum.

Car park not operated by English Heritage (charge payable to Northumberland National Park).

NON-MEMBERS

Adult	£6.20
Concession	£5.60
Child	£3.70
Free to National Trust members	

OPENING TIMES

29 Mar-30 Sep, daily	10am-6pm
1 Oct-3 Nov, daily	10am-5pm
4 Nov-16 Feb, Sat-Sun	10am-4pm
17-21 Feb, daily	10am-4pm
22 Feb-31 Mar, Sat-Sun	10am-4pm
24-26 Dec and 1 Jan	Closed

MAP Page 347 (4F)
OS Map 86/87, OL43: NY790688

Begun in about AD 124 as one of twelve permanent forts supporting Hadrian's frontier system, Housesteads was known as 'Vercovicium'. It was garrisoned by around 800 infantry (for most of its existence Tungrians from what is now eastern Belgium) later reinforced by a warband of Frisian cavalry. The big five-acre fort displays the remains of four gateways and a turreted curtain wall: within are a host of clearly traceable buildings, including the headquarters, commandant's house, baths, hospital – and the renowned multi-seater communal latrines. Served by an ingenious drainage system, these even retain the water channel used for washing hands.

The Roman south gate nearby was much later adapted into a 'bastle' farmhouse, fortified against the 'rank robbers hereabouts', the Border Reivers who scared off Elizabethan travellers. Beyond it, outside the fort wall, are the excavated foundations of the Roman 'vicus' or civilian settlement, one of whose houses produced in the 1930s evidence of a gruesome Roman double murder.

The story of Housesteads and its people is now clearly and fascinatingly retold in a new multi-media display in the site museum.

A short film, narrated from the point of view of a local Brigantian British tribesman, traces the history of the fort and recreates its original appearance, also demonstrated by a fine model. Every aspect of Roman life here – what the soldiers wore; the tools and weapons they used; how they were cared for when sick; and gods they worshipped, including trios of 'Hooded Gods' and 'Mother Goddesses' – is illuminated by interpretative displays. These feature many locally excavated artefacts returning to the fort for the first time for centuries, most strikingly a winged Victory statue from a fort gateway. Ingeniously child-friendly, the exhibition includes a dressing-up 'Discovery Box', and incorporates touchable replicas of Roman objects set at child-height, and explained by Felix the Roman soldier. Felix can also be followed on the new interpretation panels which guide visitors round the fort itself.

The fort stands uphill from the car park (via a fairly strenuous 10-minute walk, which also gives access to Hadrian's Wall Path National Trail). Owned by the National Trust, Housesteads is managed by English Heritage. The National Trust will open a new visitor centre by the car park in spring 2013.

DISCOUNTED ATTRACTIONS: **HADRIAN'S WALL**

Use your membership to get exclusive discounts at these independent attractions across Hadrian's Wall. Please remember to show your card as proof of membership.

Discount applies to:

| KEY | ⊞ MEMBERS | OVP OVP HOLDERS | ⛦? NO. OF MEMBER'S CHILDREN |

Terms and conditions may apply, so make sure you check the individual pages on our website or call the individual property for more details.

50% DISCOUNT ON ENTRY

⊞ OVP ⛦6

HEXHAM OLD GAOL
Northumberland NE46 1XD
Built 1330-33, this is the earliest recorded purpose-built prison in England. This fully-accessible building introduces you to the history of the gaol, inmates and the Border Reivers of the 1500s.
www.experiencewoodhorn.com
Tel. 01670 624523

10% DISCOUNT ON ENTRY

⊞

ROMAN VINDOLANDA
Northumberland NE47 7JN
Extensive Roman fort and settlement in the central section of Hadrian's Wall. Active archaeological programme and superb museum.
www.vindolanda.com
Tel. 01434 344277

10% DISCOUNT ON ENTRY

⊞ OVP ⛦6

SEGEDUNUM ROMAN FORT, BATH HOUSE AND MUSEUM
Wallsend NE28 6HR
Segedunum is the gateway to Hadrian's Wall, providing outstanding views across this World Heritage Site.
www.twmuseums.org.uk/segedunum
Tel. 0191 236 9347

2 for 1 ENTRY

⊞ OVP ⛦6

SENHOUSE ROMAN MUSEUM
Cumbria CA15 6JD
Discover the unique and intriguing collection recovered from the adjacent Roman fort and civilian settlement.
www.senhousemuseum.co.uk
Tel. 01900 816168

THE HADRIAN'S WALL BUS (AD122)
runs throughout spring and summer between Newcastle, Hexham and Carlisle.
For timetable details visit **www.hadrians-wall.org/bus**

*Information correct at time of going to press

NORTH EAST

Belsay Hall, Castle and Gardens

Remember to check opening times before you visit any of our properties www.english-heritage.org.uk/daysout

Details of local public transport information in England are available from Traveline www.traveline.org.uk or call 0871 200 2233.

Belsay Hall, Castle and Gardens

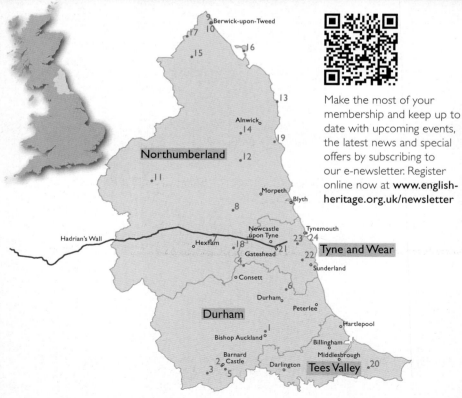

Make the most of your membership and keep up to date with upcoming events, the latest news and special offers by subscribing to our e-newsletter. Register online now at www.english-heritage.org.uk/newsletter

Lindisfarne Priory

HIGHLIGHTS FOR 2013/14 IN THE **NORTH EAST**

p.294

p.304

p.275

Belsay Hall, Castle & Gardens: Medieval castle, Greek Revival villa and extensive gardens.

Tynemouth Priory: set on a headland overlooking the North Sea.

Hadrian's Wall: visit the new Visitor Centre at Housesteads Roman Fort.

PROPERTIES

DURHAM

AUCKLAND CASTLE DEER HOUSE DURHAM

A charming Gothic Revival 'eyecatcher' built in 1760 in the park of the Bishops of Durham. It provided deer with shelter and food, and had grounds for picnics and rooms for enjoying the view.

Managed by the Church Commissioners for England.

OPENING TIMES

Park

29 Mar-29 Sep, daily	10am-6pm
30 Sep-31 Mar, daily	10am-4pm
24-26 Dec and 1 Jan	Closed

VISIT US

Direction: Located in Auckland Park, Bishop Auckland; N of town centre on A68

Train: Bishop Auckland 1 mile

Bus: Aabat Taxis, Aavacra, Arriva, Go-Ahead, JSB Travel, SB Travel and Scarlet Band. Arriva service 56, Go Ahead 18, X21, Aabat Taxis 104, Scarlet Band 113 and Aavacra service 120 pass closest to the castle gates

ACQ.1952 🐕

MAP Page 347 (5G)
OS Map 93, 305: NZ216304

BARNARD CASTLE
DURHAM – DL12 8PR

Barnard Castle is spectacularly set on a high rock above the River Tees, on the fringe of an attractive market town. Taking its name from its 12th-century founder, Bernard de Balliol, this huge and imposing fortress was later developed by the Beauchamp family and Richard III. Richard's boar emblem is carved above a window in the inner ward, the castle's chief strength: here loyalist forces were besieged during the 1569 Northern Rising against Queen Elizabeth I, before surrendering to 5000 rebels. There are fine views over the Tees Gorge, and a 'sensory garden' of scented plants and tactile objects.

NON-MEMBERS

Adult	£4.50
Concession	£4.10
Child	£2.70

OPENING TIMES

29 Mar-30 Sep, daily	10am-6pm
1 Oct-3 Nov, daily	10am-4pm
4 Nov-31 Mar, Sat-Sun	10am-4pm
24-26 Dec and 1 Jan	Closed

VISIT US

Direction: In Barnard Castle town

Bus: Arriva services 75 & 76; Classic service 352; Hodgson services 70, 71, 72, 73, 79 & 79X; Cumbria

BARNARD CASTLE

Classic 572; Scarlet Band services 83, 84, 85, 95 & 9

Tel: 01833 638212

ACQ.1952 🐕 🖵 ♿ 🧍 👤 🎁 📷
♿ ⚠ OVP

Parking (pay and display in town centre).

MAP Page 347 (6G)
OS Map 92, OL31: NZ049165

BOWES CASTLE DURHAM

The impressive ruins of Henry II's 12th-century keep, on the site of a Roman fort guarding the approach to strategic Stainmore Pass over the Pennines.

OPENING TIMES

Any reasonable time

VISIT US

Direction: In Bowes Village off A66; 4 miles W of Barnard Castle town

Bus: Hodgsons 72, 79X; Cumbria Classic 572; Classic services 352

ACQ.1931 🐕

MAP Page 347 (6F)
OS Map 92, OL30/31: NY992135

DERWENTCOTE STEEL FURNACE DURHAM

DERWENTCOTE STEEL FURNACE

Built in the 1730s, Derwentcote is the last surviving cementation steel-making furnace in Britain. It produced high-grade steel for springs and cutting tools.

OPENING TIMES
Any reasonable time (Grounds only – no access to Furnace)

24-26 Dec and 1 Jan	Closed

VISIT US
Direction: 10 miles SW of Newcastle, on A694; between Rowland's Gill and Hamsterley

Train: Metro Centre, Gateshead, 7 miles

Bus: Go North East Red Kite services 45/6 Newcastle-upon-Tyne – Consett

Tel: 01661 881636 (Sat-Sun)

Dogs on leads (restricted areas only).

Parking across main road from site.

MAP Page 347 (4G)
OS Map 88, 307: NZ130566

EGGLESTONE ABBEY
DURHAM

The charming ruins of a small monastery of Premonstratensian 'white canons', picturesquely set above a bend in the River Tees near Barnard Castle (see p.292). Remains include much of the 13th-century church and a range of living quarters, with traces of their ingenious toilet drainage system.

OPENING TIMES
29 Mar-31 Mar, daily	10am-6pm
24-26 Dec and 1 Jan	Closed

EGGLESTONE ABBEY

VISIT US
Direction: 1 mile S of Barnard Castle, on a minor road off B6277

Bus: Hodgsons service 79 & 79X then ½ mile walk

Parking (pay and display).

MAP Page 347 (6G)
OS Map 92, OL31: NZ062151

FINCHALE PRIORY
DURHAM – DH1 5SH

The very extensive remains of a 13th-century priory, founded on the site of the retired pirate St Godric's hermitage. Part of it later served as a holiday retreat for the monks of Durham Cathedral. Beautifully sited by the River Wear, with delightful riverside walks nearby.

OPENING TIMES
29 Mar-31 Mar, daily	10am-5pm
24-26 Dec and 1 Jan	Closed

VISIT US
Direction: 3 miles NE of Durham; on minor road off A167

Train: Durham 5 miles

Bus: Arriva service 42 from Durham to HMP Frankland and then a short walk

Parking (fee applies; not managed by EH).

Tearoom (not managed by EH).

MAP Page 347 (4G)
OS Map 88, 308: NZ296471

NORTHUMBERLAND

AYDON CASTLE
NORTHUMBERLAND
NE45 5PJ

One of the finest and most unaltered examples of a 13th-century English manor house, Aydon Castle stands in a secluded woodland setting. It was originally built as an undefended residence, but almost immediately fortified on the outbreak of Anglo-Scottish warfare. Nevertheless it was pillaged and burnt by the Scots in 1315, seized by English rebels two years later and again occupied by Scots in 1346. In the 18th century Aydon became a farmhouse, remaining so until 1966. Today the castle is a fantastic place to explore with the family, and you can take advantage of the beautiful walks in the surrounding area.

NON-MEMBERS
Adult	£4.00
Concession	£3.60
Child	£2.40

OPENING TIMES
29 Mar-30 Sep, Thu-Mon	10am-5pm
1 Oct-3 Nov, Thu-Mon	10am-4pm
4 Nov-31 Mar	Closed

VISIT US
Direction: 1 mile NE of Corbridge, on minor road off B6321 or A68

Train: Corbridge 4 miles – approach via bridle path from W side of Aydon Road, immediately N of Corbridge bypass

Bus: Classic service AD122 April – November. Otherwise closest is Corbridge served by Go North East 10, 684; Arriva X85; Stagecoach/Arriva 685 and Wrights 888

Tel: 01434 632450

Disabled access (ground floor only).

Dogs on leads (restricted areas only).

MAP Page 347 (4F)
OS Map 87, 316: NZ001663

BELSAY HALL, CASTLE AND GARDENS
NORTHUMBERLAND – NE20 0DX

Belsay has something for everyone. A fine medieval castle, enlarged into a Jacobean mansion; the imposing Greek Revival villa that succeeded it; and the outstanding plant-rich gardens linking the two buildings.

VISIT US

Address: Belsay Hall, Castle & Gardens, Belsay, Northumberland NE20 0DX

Direction: In Belsay; 14 miles NW of Newcastle, on A696

Train: Morpeth 10 miles

Bus: Arriva 508 from Newcastle 🚆 Sun and Bank Hols only, (May-Oct); Arriva Sun and Bank Hol service 714 Belsay village; Snaith's 808 from Newcastle and Munro's 131 Newcastle – Jedburgh

Tel: 01661 881636

Local Tourist Information
Morpeth: 01670 500700

NON-MEMBERS

Adult	£7.90
Concession	£7.10
Child	£4.70
Family	£20.50

OPENING TIMES

29 Mar-30 Sep, daily	10am-6pm
1 Oct-3 Nov, daily	10am-4pm
4 Nov-16 Feb, Sat-Sun	10am-4pm
17-21 Feb, daily	10am-4pm
22 Feb-31 Mar, Sat-Sun	10am-4pm
24-26 Dec and 1 Jan	Closed

Disabled access (grounds, tearoom and ground floor only; toilets).

Dogs on leads (grounds only not halls).

Tearoom (Apr-Oct, open daily; Nov, Dec & Mar, Sat-Sun).

MAP Page 347 (3G)
OS Map 88, 316: NZ086785

Level paths and short grass make the gardens suitable for wheelchairs and there are plenty of seats. The tearoom, in the original Victorian kitchens, provides a perfect setting for a break during your visit.

The whole ensemble is the creation of the Middleton family over more than seven centuries. First came the castle, still dominated by its massive 14th-century defensive 'pele tower'. Built as a refuge at a time of Anglo-Scottish warfare, it was also designed to impress: it still displays rare traces of elaborate medieval wall-paintings. In more peaceful times a Jacobean mansion wing was added: here the family lived until Christmas Day 1817, when they moved into Belsay Hall.

Belsay Hall is an elegant Classical Greek Revival villa, now displayed without furnishings to reveal the fine craftsmanship of its construction. Begun in 1807, it was designed by Sir Charles Monck (formerly Middleton), a man inspired by Ancient Greece and the buildings he had seen on his honeymoon in Athens. Despite its austere façade, it had a comfortable interior, arranged round its amazing central 'Pillar Hall.'

The vast gardens which provide a magnificent setting for the castle and hall are also largely Sir Charles's work. His romantic Quarry Garden, created where stone was cut for his hall, has ravines and sheer rock faces inspired by Sicilian quarries. His grandson Sir Arthur Middleton, likewise a pioneering plantsman, further embellished the Quarry with the exotic species which thrive in its micro-climate and added the Winter Garden, Yew Garden, and Magnolia Terrace. Pre-booked tours of the garden are now available, led by the Head Gardener. At whatever time of the year you visit, there is always something in flower.

SPRING

A white carpet of thousands of Snowdrops, followed by a riot of colour from Daffodils, Spring Snowflakes and Dog's Tooth Violets. Rhododendrons and large Magnolias.

SUMMER

Rhododendrons (May & June). Giant Himalayan Lilies up to nine feet tall, and other species of lilies. A NCCPG National Collection of Iris can be seen, as well as the Pocket Handkerchief Tree.

AUTUMN

Amazing autumn colours of red, yellow and orange foliage. The fallen leaves of Cercidiphyllum Japonicum smell of burnt sugar!

WINTER

Spectacular Rhododendrons flower, and frosted spiders' webs frame the topiary in the Yew Garden. Scented Viburnums and Jasmines and the appropriately titled Christmas Box (Sarcococca) can be found in the Winter Garden.

BERWICK-UPON-TWEED BARRACKS AND MAIN GUARD
NORTHUMBERLAND
TD15 1DF

Berwick Barracks, among the first in England to be purpose-built, were begun in 1717, adapting a design by the distinguished architect Nicholas Hawksmoor. Today the barracks host a number of attractions, including *By Beat of Drum* – an exhibition on the life of the British infantryman. While there, visit the King's Own Scottish Borderers Museum and the Berwick Borough Museum.

The Main Guard is a Georgian Guard House near the quay: it displays *The Story of a Border Garrison Town* exhibition.

The Main Guard is managed by Berwick Civic Society.

NON-MEMBERS
Barracks

Barracks	
Adult	£4.00
Concession	£3.60
Child	£2.40

OPENING TIMES
Barracks

Barracks	
29 Mar-30 Sep, Mon-Fri	10am-5pm
1 Oct-3 Nov, Mon-Fri	10am-4pm
4 Nov-31 Mar	Closed

Main Guard
Please call for details

BERWICK-UPON-TWEED BARRACKS AND MAIN GUARD

VISIT US
Direction: On the Parade, off Church St in town centre

Train: Berwick-upon-Tweed ¼ mile

Bus: From surrounding areas

Tel: 01289 304493

ACQ.1981

OVP

Disabled access (Main Guard).

Dogs on leads (restricted areas only).

Parking: pay and display (in town).

MAP Page 347 (1F) OS Map 75, 346
Barracks: NU001531
Main Guard: NU000525

BERWICK-UPON-TWEED CASTLE AND TOWN DEFENCES
NORTHUMBERLAND
TD15 1DF

The remains of a medieval castle crucial to Anglo-Scottish warfare, superseded by the most complete and breathtakingly impressive bastioned town defences in England, mainly Elizabethan but updated in the 17th and 18th centuries. Surrounding the whole historic town, their entire circuit can be walked, guided by interpretation panels.

OPENING TIMES
Any reasonable time

VISIT US
Direction: The castle is adjacent to Berwick-upon-Tweed railway station. The ramparts surround the town (accessed at various points)

Train: Berwick-upon-Tweed, adjacent

Bus: From surrounding areas

ACQ.1931 P

Disabled access (Ramparts).

Parking: pay and display (in town).

Note: Steep hidden drops. Dangerous after dark.

BERWICK-UPON-TWEED CASTLE AND TOWN DEFENCES

MAP Page 347 (1F)
OS Map 75, 346 Castle: NT993534
Ramparts: NU003530

BLACK MIDDENS BASTLE HOUSE NORTHUMBERLAND

A fortified farmhouse with thick stone walls, of a type distinctive to the troubled 16th-century Anglo-Scottish borders. The living quarters were only accessible at first floor level. Set in splendid walking country, on the Reivers Route cycle trail.

OPENING TIMES
Any reasonable time

VISIT US
Direction: 180 metres N of minor road, 7 miles NW of Bellingham; or along a minor road from A68

Bus: Arriva service 714 (summer Sun only) serves Lanehead (3 miles). Otherwise nearest bus service is Snaith's/Tyne Valley service 880 which links Hexham and Bellingham (7 miles)

ACQ.1978

MAP Page 347 (3F)
OS Map 80, OL42: NY773900

BRINKBURN PRIORY
NORTHUMBERLAND
NE65 8AR

The beautiful 12th-century church of the Augustinian priory of Brinkburn survives completely roofed and restored. Picturesquely set by a bend in the River Coquet, it is

BRINKBURN PRIORY

reached by a scenic 10-minute walk from the car park. Parts of the monastic buildings are incorporated into the elegant adjacent manor house.

NON-MEMBERS

Adult	£3.50
Concession	£3.20
Child	£2.10

OPENING TIMES

29 Mar-30 Sep, Thu-Mon	10am-5pm
1-27 Oct, Sat-Sun	10am-4pm
28 Oct-3 Nov, daily	10am-4pm
4 Nov-31 Mar	Closed

VISIT US

Direction: 4½ miles SE of Rothbury, off B6344

Train: Acklington 10 miles

Bus: Arriva service 14 Morpeth – Thropton (passing ⬛ Morpeth). Nearest stop Brinkburn New Houses then about 1½ mile walk

Tel: 01665 570628

Picnic area (½ mile).

MAP Page 347 (3G)
OS Map 92, 325: NZ116983

DUNSTANBURGH CASTLE
NORTHUMBERLAND
NE66 3TT

Dramatic Dunstanburgh Castle was built at a time when relations between King Edward II and his most powerful baron, Earl Thomas of Lancaster, had become openly hostile. Lancaster began the fortress in 1313, and

DUNSTANBURGH CASTLE

the latest archaeological research carried out by English Heritage indicates that he built it on a far grander scale than was hitherto recognised, perhaps more as a symbol of his opposition to the king than as a military stronghold. The innovative gatehouse, for instance, competed with the new royal castles in Wales.

The earl failed to reach Dunstanburgh when his rebellion was defeated, and was taken and executed in 1322. Thereafter the castle passed eventually to John of Gaunt, who strengthened it against the Scots by converting the great twin towered gatehouse into a keep. The focus of fierce fighting during the Wars of the Roses, it was twice besieged and captured by Yorkist forces, but subsequently fell into decay. Its impressive ruins now watch over a headland famous for seabirds.

Owned by the National Trust, maintained and managed by English Heritage.

NON-MEMBERS

Adult	£4.20
Concession	£3.80
Child	£2.50

Free to National Trust members

OPENING TIMES

29 Mar-30 Sep, daily	10am-6pm
1 Oct-3 Nov, daily	10am-4pm
4 Nov-16 Feb, Sat-Sun	10am-4pm
17-21 Feb, daily	10am-4pm
22 Feb-31 Mar, Sat-Sun	10am-4pm
24-26 Dec and 1 Jan	Closed

VISIT US

Direction: 8 miles NE of Alnwick; on footpaths from Craster or Embleton – 1½ miles rugged coastal walk

Train: Chathill, not Sun, 5 miles from Embleton, 7 miles from Castle;

DUNSTANBURGH CASTLE

Alnmouth, 7 miles from Craster, 8¼ miles from Castle

Bus: Arriva service X18 Travelsure 418. Alight Craster and take coast walk, 1½ miles

Tel: 01665 576231

Local Tourist Information
Craster: 01665 576007

Parking (in Craster village; approx 1½ miles walk. A charge is payable).

Nearest toilets located at car park in Craster Village.

MAP Page 347 (2G)
OS Map 75, 332: NU257219

EDLINGHAM CASTLE
NORTHUMBERLAND

The riverside ruins, principally the solar tower, of a manor house progressively fortified against the Scots during the 14th century.

Managed by the Parochial Church Council of St John the Baptist, Edlingham, with Bolton Chapel.

OPENING TIMES

Any reasonable time

VISIT US

Direction: At E end of Edlingham village, on minor road off B6341; 6 miles SW of Alnwick

Train: Alnmouth 9 miles

Bus: Closest bus is Glen Valley 473 service to Banktop (2 miles)

Note: waterproof footwear is recommended.

MAP Page 347 (2G)
OS Map 81, 332: NU116092

ETAL CASTLE NORTHUMBERLAND – TD12 4TN

Etal Castle was begun in the early 14th century by Robert Manners as a tower house, in a strategic position by a ford over the River Till on the Anglo-Scottish border. Thus intensely vulnerable to attack by raiders, it was soon provided with a curtain wall with corner towers and a large gatehouse.

In 1513 the castle was suddenly thrust into the forefront of history when captured by James IV of Scotland, shortly before his catastrophic defeat at the nearby Battle of Flodden.

An award-winning exhibition tells the story of Flodden and the long border warfare between the two nations.

NON-MEMBERS

Adult	£4.00
Concession	£3.60
Child	£2.40
Family	£10.40

OPENING TIMES

29 Mar-30 Sep, daily	10am-5pm
1 Oct-3 Nov, daily	10am-4pm
4 Nov-31 Mar, Sat-Sun	10am-4pm
24-26 Dec and 1 Jan	Closed

VISIT US

Direction: In Etal village, 10 miles SW of Berwick

Train: Berwick-upon-Tweed 10½ miles

Bus: Glen Valley 267 Berwick-upon-Tweed – Wooler

Tel: 01890 820332

ACQ.1975

Dogs on leads (restricted areas only).

Toilets (in car park).

MAP Page 347 (1F)
OS Map 74/75, 339: NT925393

NORHAM CASTLE
NORTHUMBERLAND
TD15 2JY

Commanding a strategic ford over the River Tweed, Norham was a crucial border stronghold, besieged at least thirteen times by the Scots. But even its powerful great tower and massive walls could not resist James IV's cannon, and it fell to him in 1513, shortly before his defeat at Flodden. Quickly recaptured, it was extensively rebuilt as a powerful artillery fortress.

A free audio tour can be downloaded from our website **www.english-heritage.org.uk/ norhamcastle**

NEW FOR 2013
New graphic panels.

OPENING TIMES

29 Mar-30 Sep, daily	10am-5pm
1 Oct-31 Mar	Closed

VISIT US

Direction: In Norham village; 6 miles SW of Berwick-upon-Tweed, on minor road off B6470 (from A698)

Train: Berwick-upon-Tweed 7½ miles

Bus: Perryman's 67 ⇌ Berwick-upon-Tweed – Galashiels

ACQ.1923

Disabled access (excluding keep).

MAP Page 347 (1F)
OS Map 74/75, 339: NT906476

FLODDEN

2013 marks the 500th anniversary of the Battle of Flodden, fought on 9 September 1513. While Henry VIII was campaigning in France, the flamboyant King James IV of Scotland invaded Northumberland with the largest Scots army ever to attack England. He quickly captured Norham and Etal castles, but was outmanoeuvred by the wily English veteran the Earl of Surrey, and lured from his strong position on Branxton Hill near Etal. Encumbered by their long pikes, the Scots were cut to pieces by English billmen: in the most disastrous defeat ever inflicted by the English on the Scots, King James was killed along with nine Scots earls, fourteen lords, and thousands of his men.

LINDISFARNE PRIORY
SEE FEATURE – PAGE 300

ST ANDREW'S CHURCH, BYWELL
NORTHUMBERLAND
NE43 7AD

© CCT

The tall Saxon tower of St Andrew's dates from about 850, and its massive walls are 5m thick. The body of the church is 13th century, but the mosaic sanctuary floor, glittering reredos and fine stained glass were restored in 1871. There are also some boldly carved medieval grave slabs.

Owned and managed by The Churches Conservation Trust.

OPENING TIMES
Open daily during daylight hours

VISIT US
Train: Stocksfield 1 mile

Bus: Go Ahead service 10, then 1 mile walk

10 mins from Prudhoe Castle (or 15 mins from Corbridge Roman Town)

MAP Page 347 (4G)
OS Map 87, 316: NZ048614

Don't forget to check opening times online before you visit.

www.english-heritage. org.uk/daysout/ properties

PRUDHOE CASTLE NORTHUMBERLAND – NE42 6NA

Begun between 1100 and 1120 to defend a strategic crossing of the River Tyne against Scottish invaders, Prudhoe Castle has been continuously occupied for over nine centuries. After two sieges during the 1170s – the Scots attackers reportedly declaring 'as long as Prudhoe stands, we shall never have peace' – the mighty stone keep and a great hall were added, followed in about 1300 by two strong towers. Passing from its original Umfraville owners to the powerful Percy family in 1398, it was again updated with a fashionable new great hall.

Even after its last military action against the Scots in 1640, Prudhoe's importance as the centre of a great landed estate continued. Early in the 19th century the Percys restored it, building a fine new manor house within its walls. All these developments are now vividly interpreted in a family-friendly exhibition including site finds, helping visitors to explore and understand the extensive remains of this formidable and long-lived fortress.

NON-MEMBERS
Adult	£4.50
Concession	£4.10
Child	£2.70

OPENING TIMES
29 Mar-30 Sep, Thu-Mon	10am-5pm
1 Oct-3 Nov, Thu-Mon	10am-4pm
4 Nov-31 Mar	Closed

VISIT US
Direction: In Prudhoe, on minor road off A695

Train: Prudhoe ¼ mile

Bus: Go North East 10, 11, 686

Tel: 01661 833459

ACQ.1966

Dogs on leads (restricted areas only).
Toilets with disabled access on site.

MAP Page 347 (4G)
OS Map 88, 316: NZ091634

Founded in AD 635 and still a place of pilgrimage today, Lindisfarne Priory on Holy Island was one of the most important centres of early Christianity in Anglo-Saxon England. The dramatic approach to the island across the causeway only emphasises the serene appeal of this atmospheric site.

VISIT US

Address: Lindisfarne Priory, Holy Island, Berwick Upon Tweed, Northumberland TD15 2RX

Direction: On Holy Island, only reached at low tide across causeway; tide tables at each end, or from Tourist Information Centre

Train: Berwick-upon-Tweed 14 miles, via causeway

Bus: Perrymans service 477 from Berwick-upon-Tweed (passes close Berwick-upon-Tweed ⟨≋⟩). Times vary with tides

Tel: 01289 389200

Tourist Information Centre
01289 330733

NON-MEMBERS

Adult	£5.20
Concession	£4.70
Child	£3.10

OPENING TIMES

29 Mar-30 Sep, daily	10am-6pm
1 Oct-3 Nov, daily	10am-4pm
4 Nov-16 Feb, Sat-Sun	10am-4pm
17-21 Feb, daily	10am-4pm
22 Feb-31 Mar, Sat-Sun	10am-4pm
24-26 Dec and 1 Jan	Closed

The causeway floods at high tide, so it is very important to check the tide times before crossing.

Dogs on leads (restricted areas only).

Parking and toilets in the village. Parking pay and display operated by Northumberland County Council.

Access (limited in some areas of priory grounds).

MAP Page 347 (1G)
OS Map 75, 340: NU126417

St Cuthbert, Prior of Lindisfarne, is the most celebrated of the priory's many holy men. After ten years seeking peace as a hermit on lonely Inner Farne Island, he reluctantly became Bishop before retiring to die on Inner Farne in 687. Buried in the priory, his remains were transferred to a pilgrim shrine. After eleven years his coffin was opened and his body found to be undecayed – a sure sign of sanctity.

From the end of the 8th century, the rich monastery was easy prey for Viking raiders. In 875 the monks left, carrying Cuthbert's remains, which after long wanderings were enshrined in Durham Cathedral in 1104, where they still rest. Only after that time did Durham monks re-establish a priory on Lindisfarne. The evocative ruins of the richly decorated priory church they built in c. 1150 still stand, with their famous 'rainbow arch' – a vault-rib of the now-vanished crossing tower. The fascinating museum offers a clear interpretation of the story of St Cuthbert and the 1300 year history of Lindisfarne Priory.

The priory is likewise renowned for the Lindisfarne Gospels, among England's greatest artistic and religious treasures. They were produced here in the late 7th or early 8th century by Bishop Eadfrith, possibly in honour of St Cuthbert's transference to his pilgrim shrine.

The Gospels accompanied the saint's body on its travels to Durham, whence they were removed during Henry VIII's Dissolution of the Monasteries.

NEW FOR 2013

The famous Lindisfarne Gospels will return from London to Durham University Library in Jul-Sep 2013. Combine a trip to see them there with a visit to Holy Island, and see our new exhibition and events programme at the priory in celebration of the Gospels.

VISIT US

Direction: In Warkworth; 7½ miles
S of Alnwick, on A1068

Train: Alnmouth 3½ miles

Bus: Arriva X18 Newcastle –
Alnwick & Travelsure 472

Tel: 01665 711423

Local Tourist Information
Amble: 01665 712313

NON-MEMBERS

Castle:

Adult	£5.00
Concession	£4.50
Child	£3.00
Family	£13.00

Hermitage:

Adult	£3.40
Concession	£3.10
Child	£2.00

OPENING TIMES

Castle:

29 Mar-30 Sep, daily	10am-6pm
1 Oct-3 Nov, daily	10am-4pm
4 Nov-16 Feb, Sat-Sun	10am-4pm
17-21 Feb, daily	10am-4pm
22 Feb-31 Mar, Sat-Sun	10am-4pm
24-26 Dec and 1 Jan	Closed

Hermitage:

29 Mar-30 Sep, Sun, Mon & Bank Hols	11am-4pm
1 Oct-31 Mar	Closed

Audio tours (also available for the
visually impaired and those with learning
difficulties).

Disabled access (limited access).

Dogs on leads (restricted areas only).

Parking (Charge payable, which is
refundable on admission).

The magnificent cross-shaped keep of Warkworth, crowning a hilltop rising steeply above the River Coquet, dominates one of the largest, strongest and most impressive fortresses in northern England. The castle's most famous owners were the Percy family, whose lion badge can be seen carved on many parts of their stronghold. Wielding almost kingly power in the North, their influence reached its apogee under the first Percy Earl of Northumberland and his son 'Harry Hotspur', hero of many Border ballads as the bane of Scots raiders and a dominant character in Shakespeare's *Henry IV*. Having helped to depose Richard II, these turbulent 'kingmakers' both fell victim to Henry IV: the next three Percy earls likewise died violent deaths.

Still roofed and almost complete, the uniquely-planned keep dates mainly from the end of the 14th century. It presides over the extensive remains of a great hall, chapel, fine gatehouse and a virtually intact circuit of towered walls.

Half a mile from the castle, tucked away by the Coquet and accessible only by boat, stands a much more peaceful building: the late medieval cave Hermitage and chapel of a solitary holy man.

The Duke's Rooms and the Hermitage are open on Sun, Mon and Bank Holidays from 29 March to 30 September.

MAP Page 347 (2G)
OS Map 81, 332: NU247058

REDCAR AND CLEVELAND

GISBOROUGH PRIORY
REDCAR AND CLEVELAND

The ruins of an Augustinian priory founded by the Bruce family, afterwards Kings of Scotland. They are dominated by the dramatic skeleton of the 14th-century church's east end.

Managed by Redcar and Cleveland Borough Council.

NON-MEMBERS

Adult	£1.80
Concession	90p
Child	90p
Family	£3.60

OPENING TIMES

29 Mar-29 Sep, Wed-Sun & Bank Hols	10am-4pm
30 Sep-31 Mar, Wed-Sun	10am-3pm
24 Dec-1 Jan	Closed

VISIT US

Direction: In Guisborough town, next to the parish church

Train: Marske 4½ miles

Bus: Arriva services 5, 5A, 5B, 28, 81. Moorsbus M1, M2, M4, M12 (service 28 actually passes by)

Tel: 01287 633801

ACQ.1932 ⬛⬛⬛ P ⬛ ⬛

Toilets and parking (in town).

MAP Page 347 (6H)
OS Map 94, OL26/306: NZ617160

TYNE AND WEAR

BESSIE SURTEES HOUSE
TYNE AND WEAR – NE1 3JF

These two five-storey, 16th- and 17th-century merchants' houses – which now also house English Heritage's local office – are fine examples of Jacobean domestic architecture, with some splendid period interiors. The Surtees house is best known as the scene of the elopement of Bessie with John Scott, later Lord Chancellor of England. An exhibition illustrating the history of the houses is on the first floor.

OPENING TIMES

All year round, Mon-Fri	10am-4pm
Bank Hols & 24 Dec-2 Jan	Closed

VISIT US

Direction: 41-44 Sandhill, Newcastle-upon-Tyne

Train: Newcastle ½ mile

Metro: Central ½ mile

Bus: From surrounding areas

Tel: 0191 269 1200

ACQ.1989 ⬛ E ⬛ ⬛ ⬛

MAP Page 347 (4G)
OS Map 88, 316: NZ256338

HYLTON CASTLE
TYNE AND WEAR

The distinctive and highly decorative gatehouse-tower of a castle built by the wealthy Sir William Hylton shortly before 1400. Originally containing four floors of self-contained family accommodation, its entrance front displays royal and family heraldry, including Richard II's white hart badge.

OPENING TIMES

29-31 Mar, daily	10am-4pm

HYLTON CASTLE

Grounds only – no access to Castle

24-26 Dec and 1 Jan	Closed

VISIT US

Direction: 3¾ miles W of Sunderland

Train: Seaburn Metro (2½ miles) then bus 99; Pallion Metro then bus 29, 29A, 39 or 39A

Bus: Stagecoach services 3, 13; Go North East services 26, 56, X88

ACQ.1950 ⬛ P ⬛

Dogs on leads.

Disabled access (grounds only).

MAP Page 347 (4H)
OS Map 88, 308: NZ358588

ST PAUL'S MONASTERY, JARROW
TYNE AND WEAR

The home of the Venerable Bede, chronicler of the beginnings of English Christianity, Jarrow has become one of the best-understood Anglo-Saxon monastic sites. The Anglo-Saxon church – with the oldest dedication stone in the country, dated AD 685 – partly survives as the chancel of the parish church. A free downloadable audio tour is available from the English Heritage website.

OPENING TIMES

Monastery ruins any reasonable time

VISIT US

Direction: In Jarrow, on minor road N of A185; follow signs for Bede's World

Metro: Bede ¾ miles

Bus: Go North East The Crusader services 27

Tel: 0191 489 7052

ACQ.1956

MAP Page 347 (4H)
OS Map 88, 316: NZ339652

VISIT US

Direction: In Tynemouth, near North Pier

Metro: Tynemouth ½ mile

Bus: Arriva services 306

Tel: 0191 257 1090

NON-MEMBERS

Adult	£4.70
Concession	£4.20
Child	£2.80
Family	£12.20

OPENING TIMES

29 Mar–30 Sep, daily	10am–6pm
1 Oct–3 Nov, daily	10am–4pm
4 Nov–31 Mar, Sat–Sun	10am–4pm
24–26 Dec and 1 Jan	Closed

Gun Battery: Access limited, please ask site staff for details

ACQ.1969

Dogs on leads.

Disabled access (priory only).

Toilets with disabled access on site.

Limited disabled parking avaiable.

Set in an almost impregnable position on a steep headland between the river and the North Sea, Tynemouth has always been as much a fortress as a religious site.

Here stood a 7th-century Anglian monastery, burial place of Oswin, sainted King of Northumbria. After its destruction by Danish raiders, the present Benedictine priory was founded on its site in c. 1090.

The towering east end of the priory church, built in c. 1200 with slender lancet windows and soaring arches, still survives almost to its full height, dominating the headland. Beyond it stands a small but complete and exceptionally well-preserved chapel, with a rose window and an ornately sculpted roof vault. This was built in the mid-15th century as a chantry for the souls of the powerful Percy family, Earls of Northumberland.

Enclosing both headland and monastery, and still surviving in part, were the strong medieval walls which once made Tynemouth among the largest fortified areas in England, and an important bastion against the Scots.

When the priory's 19 monks surrendered Tynemouth to

Henry VIII in 1539, it was immediately adopted as a royal castle. Thereafter the fortress headland continued to play an important role in coastal defence from Elizabethan times until the end of the Second World War.

The interactive *Life in the Stronghold* exhibition takes visitors on a journey from Tynemouth's beginnings as an Anglo-Saxon settlement, via its medieval monastery and Tudor fortification, right up to its importance as a Second World War coastal gun battery.

Conservation works have been carried out on the coastal gun battery and magazine, restored to look as they did during World War I. Replica uniforms hang on the walls, alongside the special magazine clothes which soldiers changed into before handling explosive material. Visitors can explore the space in which soldiers worked underground to prepare ammunition for the guns.

MAP Page 347 (4H)
OS Map 88, 316: NZ373694

DISCOUNTED ATTRACTIONS **NORTH EAST**

Use your membership to get exclusive discounts at these independent attractions in the North East. Please remember to show your card as proof of membership.

Discount applies to:

KEY	⊞ MEMBERS	OVP OVP HOLDERS	♛? NO. OF MEMBER'S CHILDREN

Terms and conditions may apply, so make sure you check the individual pages on our website or call the individual property for more details.

20% OFF ADULT ENTRY

⊞

ALNWICK CASTLE AND THE ALNWICK GARDEN
Northumberland NE66 1NQ
From poisonous plants to Potter-inspired magic, experience a day out full of the unexpected.
www.alnwickcastle.com or www.alnwickgarden.com
Tel. 01665 511350

20% DISCOUNT ON ENTRY

⊞ ♛2

BAMBURGH CASTLE
Northumberland NE69 7DF
The King of Castles, Bamburgh has 14 rooms and over 3000 artefacts, including weapons, porcelain, paintings and furniture. Separate aviation artefacts museum, café and battlements.
www.bamburghcastle.com
Tel. 01668 214515

£1 OFF ADMISSION

⊞ ♛4

THE BOWES MUSEUM
County Durham DL12 8NP
An inspirational day out for all the family, with fascinating collections, stunning galleries, a romantic history and acclaimed Café Bowes and shop, all set in beautiful parkland and gardens.
www.thebowesmuseum.org.uk
Tel. 01833 690606

25% OFF TICKET

⊞ OVP ♛6

KILLHOPE – THE NORTH OF ENGLAND LEAD MINING MUSEUM
Durham DL13 1AR
A multi-award winning Victorian Museum and a grand day out. Accompany a guide on an unforgettable mine tour.
www.killhope.org.uk
Tel. 01388 537 505

2 for 1 TRAIN TICKET

⊞ ♛2

TANFIELD RAILWAY
County Durham NE16 5ET
The world's oldest railway. Six mile round trip behind locally built steam engines in vintage coaches. Stop and see historic Causey Arch. We run Sundays etc. Timetable and details at
www.tanfield-railway.co.uk
Tel. 0845 463 4938

GIVE THE GIFT OF MEMBERSHIP

Give friends and family the opportunity to enjoy these fantastic discounts too!

- Free entry to over 400 historic properties
- Kids go free (up to six per adult in a family group)
- Free or discounted entry to hundreds of events, activities and other attractions
- Free handbook worth £10.95
- Exclusive members' magazine

ASSOCIATED ATTRACTIONS

As well as free, unlimited entry to the hundreds of sites in our care, one of the great benefits of English Heritage membership is free or discounted access to our many Associated Attractions.

Throughout this handbook you will find over 300 Associated Attractions, ranging from other historic attractions in England such as Alnwick Castle and Gardens in Northumberland and the Churchill War Rooms in London to many wonderful castles and heritage sites dotted across Wales, Scotland and the Isle of Man. Plus, for the first time this year, historic sites looked after by OPW Heritage Ireland.

We are in the second year of our collaboration with the Churches Conservation Trust, and maintain our relationships with the Friends of Friendless Churches and the Historic Chapels Trust. Travelling further afield, English Heritage members can also get free entry to properties in the care of the New Zealand Historic Places Trust.

Find out more details, including places to visit, on the following pages and at the back of each regional section of this handbook. Full details can also be found on our website **www.english-heritage.org.uk**

SCOTLAND, WALES AND ISLE OF MAN

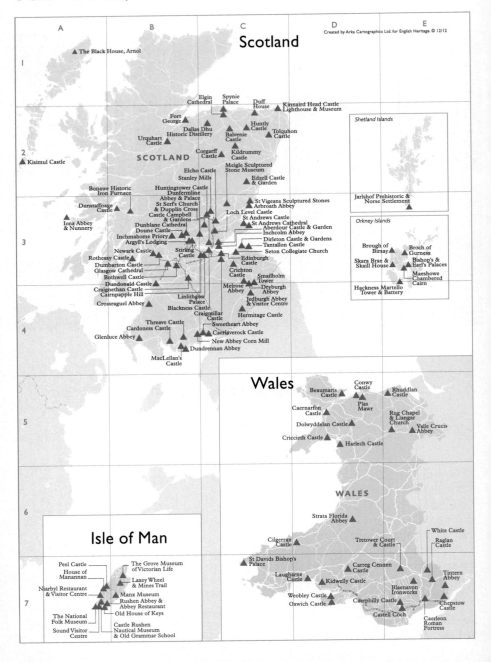

Created by Arka Cartographics Ltd. for English Heritage. © 12/12

Scotland

A • The Black House, Arnol

Kisimul Castle

Elgin Cathedral
Spynie Palace
Duff House
Kinnaird Head Castle Lighthouse & Museum

Fort George
Dallas Dhu Historic Distillery
Huntly Castle
Balvenie Castle
Tolquhon Castle

Urquhart Castle
SCOTLAND
Corgarff Castle
Kildrummy Castle

Meigle Sculptured Stone Museum

Elcho Castle
Stanley Mills
Edzell Castle & Garden

Bonawe Historic Iron Furnace
Huntingtower Castle
Dunfermline Abbey & Palace
St Serf's Church & Dupplin Cross
Castle Campbell & Gardens
St Vigeans Sculptured Stones
Arbroath Abbey

Dunstaffnage Castle
Dunblane Cathedral
Loch Level Castle
St Andrews Castle
St Andrews Cathedral
Aberdour Castle & Garden
Inchcolm Abbey

Iona Abbey & Nunnery
Doune Castle
Inchmahome Priory
Argyll's Lodging
Dirleton Castle & Gardens
Tantallon Castle
Seton Collegiate Church

Newark Castle
Stirling Castle
Edinburgh Castle

Rothesay Castle
Dumbarton Castle
Glasgow Cathedral
Bothwell Castle
Dundonald Castle
Crichton Castle
Smailholm Tower

Craignethan Castle
Cairnpapple Hill
Melrose Abbey
Dryburgh Abbey

Crossraguel Abbey
Linlithgow Palace
Blackness Castle
Craigmillar Castle
Jedburgh Abbey & Visitor Centre

Threave Castle
Cardoness Castle
Hermitage Castle

Glenluce Abbey
Sweetheart Abbey
Caerlaverock Castle
New Abbey Corn Mill

Dundrennan Abbey

MacLellan's Castle

Shetland Islands

Jarlshof Prehistoric & Norse Settlement

Orkney Islands

Brough of Birsay
Broch of Gurness

Skara Brae & Skaill House
Bishop's & Earl's Palaces
Maeshowe Chambered Cairn

Hackness Martello Tower & Battery

Wales

Beaumaris Castle
Conwy Castle
Rhuddlan Castle

Caernarfon Castle
Plas Mawr
Rug Chapel & Llangar Church

Dolwyddelan Castle
Valle Crucis Abbey

Criccieth Castle
Harlech Castle

WALES

Strata Florida Abbey

White Castle

Cilgerran Castle
Tretower Court & Castle
Raglan Castle

St Davids Bishop's Palace

Carreg Cennen Castle

Laugharne Castle
Kidwelly Castle
Tintern Abbey

Weobley Castle
Oxwich Castle
Blaenavon Ironworks
Caerphilly Castle
Caerleon Roman Fortress
Castell Coch
Chepstow Castle

Isle of Man

Peel Castle
House of Mananan
The Grove Museum of Victorian Life

Niarbyl Restaurant & Visitor Centre
Laxey Wheel & Mines Trail

Manx Museum
Rushen Abbey & Abbey Restaurant
Old House of Keys

The National Folk Museum

Sound Visitor Centre
Castle Rushen
Nautical Museum & Old Grammar School

IRELAND

	A	B	C	D	E
1					
2			Glebe House & Gallery		
3					
4					
5					
6					
7					

Glebe House & Gallery

Newmills Corn & Flax Mills

DONEGAL

Donegal Castle

COLERAINE

LONDONDERRY LONDONDERRY

ANTRIM

BALLYMENA M2

LARNE

NORTHERN IRELAND

TYRONE

BELFAST

BANGOR

DOWN

Ceide Fields

Carrowmore Megalithic Cemetery

Sligo Abbey

Parke's Castle

FERMANAGH

PORTADOWN

ARMAGH

M1

NEWRY

MAYO

SLIGO

Boyle Abbey

LEITRIM

MONAGHAN

CAVAN

DUNDALK

ROSCOMMON

LOUTH

DROGHEDA

Old Mellifont Abbey

Loughcrew

Battle of the Boyne Visitor Centre

Teach an Phiarsaigh (Pearse's Cottage)

Aughnanure Castle

Corlea Trackway Visitor Centre

LONGFORD

Hill of Tara

MEATH

St Audoen's Church

Dun Aonghasa

Athenry Castle

GALWAY

WESTMEATH

M6

Clonmacnoise

Trim Castle

Farmleigh

Phoenix Park

National Botanic Gardens

Maynooth Castle

St Mary's Abbey

DUBLIN

Casino

Dublin Castle

OFFALY

Castletown

Kilmainham Gaol

Pearse Museum & St Enda's Park

Portumna Castle & Gardens

REPUBLIC OF IRELAND

Emo Court

KILDARE

Rathfarnham Castle

GREYSTONES

Aras an Uachtarain

Phoenix Park

Ennis Friary

CLARE

Roscrea Heritage (Castle & Damer House)

LAOIS

M7

Glendalough Visitor Centre

WICKLOW

Kilmacurragh Arboretum

Scattery Island

TIPPERARY

Dunmore Cave

CARLOW

Listowel Castle

LIMERICK

Desmond Hall

Rock of Cashel

Kilkenny Castle

St Mary's Church Gowran

M11

Ferns Castle

Ardfert Cathedral

Cahir Castle

KILKENNY

Jerpoint Abbey

WEXFORD

Gallarus Oratory

Swiss Cottage

Ormond Castle

JFK Arboretum

The Blasket Centre

KERRY

The Main Guard

WATERFORD

Reginald's Tower

Tintern Abbey

Ross Castle

CORK

Dungarvan Castle

WATERFORD

Ballyhack Castle

Derrynane House National Historic Park

Barryscourt Castle

CORK

Ilnacullin (Garinish Island)

Desmond Castle

Charles Fort

Skellig Michael

OPW HERITAGE IRELAND

English Heritage members get **free** entry from first year of membership.

The Blasket Centrel, an Bhlascaoid Mhóir, Dún Chaoin, Baile an Fheirtéaraigh, Trá Lí, Co Chiarraí
T. +353 (066) 915 6444/ (066) 915 6371

Ardfert Cathedral, Ardfert, Tralee, Co Kerry
T. +353 (066) 713 4711

Athenry Castle, Athenry, Co Galway
T. +353 (091) 844797

Aughnanure Castle, Oughterard, Co Galway
T. +353 (091) 552214

Battle of the Boyne Visitor Centre, Oldbridge, Co Meath
T. + 353 (041) 980 9950

Boyle Abbey, Boyle, Co Roscommon
T. +353 (071) 966 2604

Brú na Bóinne Visitor Centre, (Newgrange and Knowth), Donore, Co Meath
T. +353 (041) 988 0300

Cahir Castle, Castle Street, Cahir, Co Tipperary
T. +353 (52) 7441011

Carrowmore Megalithic Cemetery, Carrowmore, Co Sligo
T. +353 (071) 916 1534

Castletown, Celbridge, Co Kildare
T. +353 (01) 628 8252

Céide Fields, Ballycastle, Co Mayo
T. +353 (096) 43325

Charles Fort, Summer Cove, Kinsale, Co Cork
T. +353 (021) 477 2263

Clonmacnoise, Shannonbridge, Co Offaly
T. +353 (090) 967 4195

Derrynane House, National Historic Park, Caherdaniel, Co Kerry
T. +353 (066) 947 5113

Desmond Castle (French Prison), Cork Street, Kinsale, Co Cork
T. +353 (021) 477 4855

Donegal Castle, Donegal Town, Co Donegal
T. +353 (074) 972 2405

Dublin Castle, Dame Street, Dublin 2 **T.** +353 (01) 645 8813

Dún Aonghasa, Kilmurvey, Inishmore, Aran Islands, Co Galway
T. +353 (099) 61008

Dunmore Cave, Castlecomer
Road, Co Kilkenny
T. +353 (056) 776 7726

Emo Court, Emo, Co Laois
T. +353 (057) 862 6573

Ennis Friary, Abbey Street,
Ennis, Co Clare
T. +353 (065) 682 9100

Farmleigh, Phoenix Park,
Castleknock, Dublin 15
T. +353 (01) 815 5900/815 5981

Ilnacullin (Garinish Island),
Glengarriff, Bantry, Co Cork
T. +353 (027) 63040

Glebe House and Gallery,
Churchill, Letterkenny,
Co Donegal
T. +353 (074) 913 7071

Glendalough Visitor Centre,
Glendalough, Co Wicklow
T. +353 404 45352/25

Hill of Tara, Navan, Co Meath
T./F. +353 (046) 902 5903

JFK Arboretum, New Ross,
Co Wexford
T. +353 (051) 388171

Jerpoint Abbey, Thomastown,
Co Kilkenny
T. +353 (056) 772 4623

Kilkenny Castle, Kilkenny City,
Co Kilkenny
T. +353 (056) 770 4100

Kilmainham Gaol, Inchicore
Road, Kilmainham, D 8
T. +353 (01) 453 5984

Old Mellifont Abbey, Tullyallen,
Drogheda, Co Louth
T. +353 (41) 982 6459

Parke's Castle, Fivemile Bourne,
Co Leitrim
T. +353 (071) 916 4149

Portumna Castle and Gardens,
Portumna, Co Galway
T. +353 (090) 974 1658

Reginald's Tower, The Quay,
Waterford
T./F. +353 (051) 304220

Rock of Cashel, Cashel,
Co Tipperary
T. +353 (062) 61437

Roscrea Heritage (Castle &
Damer House), Roscrea,
Co Tipperary
T. +353 (0505) 21850

Ross Castle, Killarney,
Co Kerry
T. +353 64 6635851

Sligo Abbey, Abbey Street,
Sligo, Co Sligo
T. +353 (071) 914 6406

Swiss Cottage, Kilcommon,
Cahir, Co Tipperary
T. +353 (052) 7441144

Teach an Phiarsaigh (Pearse's
Cottage), Inbhear, Ros Muc,
Co Galway
T. +353 (091) 574292

The Casino, Cherrymount
Crescent, off the Malahide Road,
Marino, D 3
T. +353 (01) 833 1618

Trim Castle, Trim, Co Meath
T. +353 (046) 943 8619

We welcome visitors
from near and far and we
are particularly delighted
to welcome Members of
English Heritage and holders
of the Overseas Visitor
Pass – we look forward to
meeting you.

For more information about
our sites (including those
where admission is free)
please visit our website
www.heritageireland.ie

HISTORIC SCOTLAND

English Heritage members can gain **half-price** admission to Historic Scotland attractions during the first year of membership and **free** entry in subsequent years.

Aberdour Castle and Garden, Aberdour, Fife **T.** 01383 860519

Arbroath Abbey, Angus **T.** 01241 878756

Argyll's Lodging, Stirling **T.** 01786 450000

Balvenie Castle, Dufftown, Grampian **T.** 01340 820121

Bishop's and Earl's Palaces, Kirkwall, Orkney **T.** 01856 871918

The Black House, Arnol, Lewis, Western Isles **T.** 01851 710395

Blackness Castle, Firth of Forth, Edinburgh and Lothians Tel: 01506 834807

Bonawe Historic Iron Furnace, Taynuilt, Argyll **T.** 01866 822432

Bothwell Castle, Bothwell, Greater Glasgow **T.** 01698 816894

Broch of Gurness, Aikerness, Orkney **T.** 01856 751414

Brough of Birsay, NW of Kirkwall, Orkney **T.** 01856 841 815

Caerlaverock Castle, Nr Dumfries, Dumfries and Galloway **T.** 01387 770244

Cairnpapple Hill, Torphichen, Edinburgh and Lothians **T.** 0782 690 2191

Cardoness Castle, Nr Gatehouse of Fleet, Dumfries and Galloway **T.** 01557 814427

Castle Campbell and Gardens, Dollar Glen **T.** 01259 742408

Corgarff Castle, Nr Strathdon, Grampian **T.** 01975 651460

Craigmillar Castle, Edinburgh and Lothians **T.** 0131 661 4445

Craignethan Castle, Lanark, Greater Glasgow **T.** 01555 860364

Crichton Castle, Nr Pathhead, Edinburgh and Lothians **T.** 01875 320017

Crossraguel Abbey, Nr Maybole, Greater Glasgow **T.** 01655 883113

Dallas Dhu Historic Distillery, Nr Forres, Grampian **T.** 01309 676548

Dirleton Castle and Gardens, Dirleton, East Lothian **T.** 01620 850330

Doune Castle, Doune **T.** 01786 841742

Dryburgh Abbey, Nr Melrose, Borders **T.** 01835 822381

Duff House, Banff, Grampian **T.** 01261 818181

Dumbarton Castle, Dumbarton, Greater Glasgow **T.** 01389 732167

Dunblane Cathedral, Dunblane **T.** 01786 823 388

Dundonald Castle, Dundonald, Greater Glasgow **T.** 01563 851489

Dundrennan Abbey, Nr Kirkcudbright, Dumfries and Galloway **T.** 01557 500262

Dunfermline Abbey and Palace, Dunfermline, Fife **T.** 01383 739026

Dunstaffnage Castle, Nr Oban, Argyll **T.** 01631 562465

Edinburgh Castle, Edinburgh and Lothians **T.** 0131 225 9846

Edzell Castle and Garden, Edzell, Angus **T**. 01356 648631

Elcho Castle, Nr Bridge of Earn, Perthshire **T**. 01738 639998

Elgin Cathedral, Elgin, Highlands **T**. 01343 547171

Fort George, Nr Ardersier village, Highlands **T**. 01667 460232

Glasgow Cathedral, Glasgow **T**. 0141 552 6891

Glenluce Abbey, Nr Glenluce, Dumfries and Galloway **T**. 01581 300541

Hackness Martello Tower and Battery, Hoy, Orkney **T**. 01856 701727

Hermitage Castle, Nr Newcastleton, Borders **T**. 01387 376222

Huntingtower Castle, Nr Perth, Perthshire **T**. 01738 627231

Huntly Castle, Huntly, Grampian **T**. 01466 793191

Inchcolm Abbey, Firth of Forth, Fife **T**. 01383 823332

Inchmahome Priory, Lake of Menteith, Central **T**. 01877 385294

Iona Abbey and Nunnery, Island of Iona, Argyll **T**. 01681 700512

Jarlshof Prehistoric and Norse Settlement, Sumburgh Head, Shetland **T**. 01950 460112

Jedburgh Abbey and Visitor Centre, Jedburgh, Borders **T**. 01835 863925

Kildrummy Castle, Nr Alford, Grampian **T**. 01975 571331

Kinnaird Head Castle, Lighthouse and Museum, Fraserburgh, Grampian **T**. 01346 511022

Kisimul Castle, Isle of Barra, Western Isles **T**. 01871 810313

Linlithgow Palace, Linlithgow, West Lothian **T**. 01506 842896

Loch Leven Castle, Lochleven, Perthshire **T**. 01577 862670

MacLellan's Castle, Kirkcudbright, Dumfries and Galloway **T**. 01557 331856

Maeshowe Chambered Cairn, Nr Kirkwall, Orkney **T**. 01856 761606

Meigle Sculptured Stone Museum, Meigle, Angus **T**. 01828 640612

Melrose Abbey, Melrose, Borders **T**. 01896 822562

New Abbey Corn Mill, New Abbey, Dumfries and Galloway **T**. 01387 850260

Newark Castle, Port Glasgow, Greater Glasgow **T**. 01475 741858

Rothesay Castle, Rothesay, Isle of Bute **T**. 01700 502691

St Andrews Castle, St Andrews, Fife **T**. 01334 477196

St Andrews Cathedral, St Andrews, Fife **T**. 01334 472563

St Serf's Church and Dupplin Cross, Dunning, Perthshire **T**. 01764 684497

St Vigeans Sculptured Stones, Nr Arbroath, Angus **T**. 01241 878756

Seton Collegiate Church, Nr Cockenzie, East Lothian **T**. 01875 813334

Skara Brae and Skaill House, Nr Kirkwall, Orkney **T**. 01856 841815

Smailholm Tower, Near Smailholm, Borders **T**. 01573 460365

Spynie Palace, Nr Elgin, Grampian **T**. 01343 546358

Stanley Mills, North of Perth **T**. 01738 828268

Stirling Castle, Stirling, Central **T**. 01786 450000

Sweetheart Abbey, New Abbey, Dumfries and Galloway **T**. 01387 850397

Tantallon Castle, Nr North Berwick, East Lothian **T**. 01620 892727

Threave Castle, Nr Castle Douglas, Dumfries and Galloway **T**. 07711 223101

Tolquhon Castle, Nr Aberdeen, Grampian **T**. 01651 851286

Urquhart Castle, Drumnadrochit, Highlands **T**. 01456 450551

HISTORIC SCOTLAND
Longmore House, Salisbury Place, Edinburgh EH9 1SH
T. 0131 668 8999
E. hs.members@scotland.gsi.gov.uk
W. www.historic-scotland.gov.uk

Caerphilly Castle

CADW

English Heritage members can gain **half-price** admission to Cadw attractions during the first year of membership and **free** entry in subsequent years.

Beaumaris Castle, Anglesey LL58 8AP **T.** 01248 810361

Blaenavon Ironworks, Nr Pontypool, Torfaen NP4 9RN **T.** 01495 792615

Caerleon Roman Fortress, Caerleon, Newport NP18 1AE **T.** 01633 422518

Caernarfon Castle, Caernarfon, Gwynedd LL55 2AY **T.** 01286 677617

Caerphilly Castle, Caerphilly CF83 1JD **T.** 029 2088 3143

Carreg Cennen Castle, Nr Trapp, Carmarthenshire SA19 6TS **T.** 01558 822291

Castell Coch, Cardiff CF15 7JS **T.** 029 2081 0101

Chepstow Castle, Chepstow, Monmouthshire NP16 5EY **T.** 01291 624065

Cilgerran Castle, Nr Cardigan, Pembrokeshire SA43 2SF **T.** 01239 621339

Conwy Castle, Conwy LL32 8AY **T.** 01492 592358

Criccieth Castle, Criccieth, Gwynedd LL52 ODP **T.** 01766 522227

Denbigh Castle, Denbigh LL16 3NB **T.** 01745 813385

Dolwyddelan Castle, Dolwyddelan, Gwynedd LL25 0JD **T.** 01690 750366

Harlech Castle, Harlech, Gwynedd LL46 2YH **T.** 01766 780552

Kidwelly Castle, Kidwelly, Carmarthenshire SA17 5BQ **T.** 01554 890104

Lamphey Bishop's Palace, Lamphey, Pembroke SA71 5NT **T.** 01646 672224

Laugharne Castle, Laugharne, Carmarthenshire SA33 4SA **T.** 01994 427906

Margam Stones Museum, Margam, Port Talbot **T.** 01639 871184

Oxwich Castle, Oxwich, Swansea SA3 1ND **T.** 01792 390359

Plas Mawr, Conwy LL32 8DE **T.** 01492 580167

Raglan Castle, Raglan, Monmouthshire NP15 2BT **T.** 01291 690228

Rhuddlan Castle, Rhuddlan, Denbighshire LL18 5AD **T.** 01745 590777

Rug Chapel and Llangar Church, Corwen, Denbighshire LL21 9BT **T.** 01490 412025

St Davids Bishop's Palace, St Davids, Pembrokeshire SA62 6PE **T.** 01437 720517

Strata Florida Abbey, Pontrhydfendigaid, Ceredigion SY25 6ES **T.** 01974 831261

Tintern Abbey, Tintern, Monmouthshire NP16 6SE **T.** 01291 689251

Tretower Court and Castle, Tretower, Powys NP8 1RD **T.** 01874 730279

Valle Crucis Abbey, Nr Llangollen, Denbighshire LL20 8DD **T.** 01978 860326

Weobley Castle, Nr Llanrhidian, Swansea SA3 1HB **T.** 01792 390012

White Castle, Nr Abergavenny, Monmouthshire NP7 8UD **T.** 01600 780380

MANX NATIONAL HERITAGE

English Heritage members can gain **half-price** admission to Manx National Heritage attractions during the first year of membership and **free** entry in subsequent years.

Members must present a valid membership card on admission (Manx National Heritage permit free admission to the member only and children aged 4 years and under). Admission charges apply for special events. Travel connections between the Isle of Man's heritage sites are available through the Victorian Steam Railway, Manx Electric Railway, Horse Tram and Bus Vannin. **To book travel visit www.visitisleofman.com**

Rushen Abbey

Portcullis at Castle Rushen

Laxey Wheel

ISLE OF MAN

Castle Rushen – Castletown

The National Folk Museum – Cregneash

The Grove – Museum of Victorian Life – Ramsey

House of Manannan – Peel

Laxey Wheel and Mines Trail – Laxey

Manx Museum – Douglas

Nautical Museum – Castletown

Niarbyl Restaurant & Visitor Centre – Dalby

Old Grammar School – Castletown

Old House of Keys – Castletown

Peel Castle – Peel

Rushen Abbey & Abbey Restaurant – Ballasalla

The Sound Café and Visitor Centre – near Cregneash

MANX NATIONAL HERITAGE
Kingswood Grove, Douglas, Isle of Man IM1 3LY
T. 01624 648000
W. www.manxnational heritage.im

All images © Manx National Heritage

NEW ZEALAND HISTORIC PLACES TRUST

English Heritage members gain **free** admission to New Zealand Historic Places Trust attractions from the first year of membership.

New Zealand's built heritage may be considered young in world terms, but many of the properties cared for by the New Zealand Historic Places Trust (NZHPT) are physical reminders of the birth and development of this South Pacific nation and its enduring connection to Great Britain.

1 Old St Paul's (see opposite) **2** Alberton **3** Fyffe House **4** Kerikeri Mission Station **5** Totara Estate

English Heritage members have free standard entry to the 48 properties the NZHPT cares for nationwide – from the Kerikeri Mission Station in Northland, dating from 1821-22 and New Zealand's oldest standing building, to Hayes Engineering Works in the gold mining region of Central Otago. Please understand that charges may apply for special events and exhibitions.

There are a range of heritage properties and sites to visit where you can learn about the people and places that make New Zealand what it is today. These include impressive homesteads, centres of industry and innovation, battle sites and so much more.

AMONG THEM ARE:

1 Old St Paul's in Wellington – where stunning stained glass windows help illuminate the glorious native timber interior of this 19th century Gothic Revival church, a home away from home for US servicemen during World War Two.

2 Alberton and Highwic in Auckland – impressive dwellings that were home to two prominent businessmen and their families in colonial New Zealand.

3 Fyffe House in Kaikoura – where a whale of a time is guaranteed, the property built as part of the early whaling industry and partly on whale vertebrae foundations.

4 The Kerikeri Mission Station and Stone Store in Northland – the Mission Station is New Zealand's oldest standing building, built in 1821-22, while the nearby Stone Store is one of the country's most photographed buildings.

5 Totara Estate in South Canterbury – British dinner tables have featured our finest cuts of meat over many years, and Totara Estate is where New Zealand's billion dollar frozen meat industry began.

More information on heritage sites to visit can be found on the NZHPT's website www.historicplaces.org.nz. Our staff look forward to welcoming you.

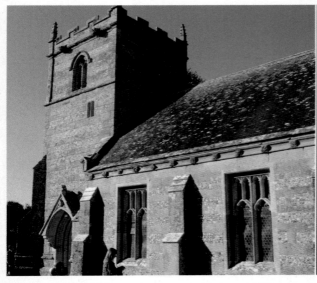

Left to right: Long Crichel, Dorset, where we repaired the tower in 2012 and Strachan glass at Brownshill (photos by Matthew Saunders).

THE FRIENDS OF FRIENDLESS CHURCHES

The Friends own redundant but beautiful places of worship that would otherwise have been demolished or left to ruin.

In the last two years we have taken a record number of new churches into care. One of them, the small Catholic chapel at Brownshill Glos contains the striking glass, by Douglas Strachan, shown top right. We have just finished a major conservation campaign at the chapel of St John the Baptist, at Matlock Bath, Derbs by Guy Dawber, helped by a very generous EH grant.

We are a small, voluntary organisation that works in partnership, sharing an office and staff with the Ancient Monuments Society, a statutory consultee on listed building consent in England and Wales.

We warmly welcome visitors to our churches, but do not claim sophistication in terms of parking, toilets, attendants or shops, and access may require approach to a key-holder. Our churches are places for quiet study and contemplation, preserved for posterity as beautiful historic buildings.

FRIENDS
OF
FRIENDLESS
CHURCHES

St Ann's Vestry Hall, 2 Church Entry, London EC4V 5HB
T. 020 7236 3934 E. office@friendsoffriendlesschurches.org.uk
W. www.friendsoffriendlesschurches.org.uk Registered charity no: 1113097

Left to right: Walpole Old Chapel, Nr Halesworth, Suffolk; Wallasey Memorial Unitarian Church, Liscard Village, Wallasey, Merseyside; and Petre Chapel, Thorndon Park, near Brentwood, Essex.

HISTORIC CHAPELS TRUST

An Important Story of Dissent and Faith.

The Historic Chapels Trust rescues non-Anglican places of worship in England that are no longer in use by their congregations. We aim to hand them onto future generations in good condition, as the physical record of religious life and a vital strand of our history.

Since 1993 we have rescued a remarkable collection of Non-conformist chapels, meeting houses and Catholic churches. Together, they are the evidence of a remarkable story of dissent from the Established Church and of self-determination and autonomy by people of faith, courage and social vision.

VISIT OUR CHAPELS AND CHURCHES

All our sites are Listed Grade II* or Grade I. Some are important for their architecture, some as rare survivals, some for their history, some for what the architectural historian John Summerson described as 'endearing simplicity'. All of them are worth visiting.

To visit our chapels and churches please arrange a time with our local keyholders at the site first. Details of how to find the buildings and our keyholders are on our website.

EVENTS IN OUR CHAPELS

Many of our chapels can be hired for concerts or other events. Some provide interesting venues for marriages or commemorative events. If you are interested in using one of our buildings look for details on our website.

Historic Chapels Trust gratefully acknowledges financial support from English Heritage.

St George's German Lutheran Church, 55 Alie Street, London E1 8EB
T. 020 7481 0533 E. chapels@hct.org.uk W. www.hct.org.uk
UK Registered charity No 1017321

ABOUT ENGLISH HERITAGE

PLANNING YOUR VISIT

We want you to enjoy every moment of your visit, and so please read the following section carefully. Each property listing will contain symbols to help you assess its suitability for your visiting party. We hope you will find all the information you will need to plan your perfect day, but if you have any questions please do not hesitate to call us on **0870 333 1181**.

ADMISSIONS

Admission charges apply to non-members, and prices are given in this handbook as follows: Adult; Concession (senior citizens, jobseekers and students with relevant ID); Child (age 5-15, under 5s go free). Where available, Family tickets normally admit two adults and three children (may vary at properties not managed by us).

For groups of 11 or more visitors paying together, discounts of 15% (10% at Stonehenge) are available. We recommend that groups book in advance. Call 0870 333 1181 for a copy of our Group Visits Guide.

If you are a visitor from overseas and are planning to visit a number of properties, an **Overseas Visitors Pass** (OVP) may make financial sense. As well as other benefits, this allows unlimited free access to all English Heritage properties marked with the OVP symbol over a 9 or 16 day period. Call 0870 333 1181 or visit **www.english-heritage.org.uk/ovp**

CAR PARKING

There is free parking at most of our properties. In cases where parking charges apply, you will often be reimbursed on admission (exceptions apply. See individual property listings). Any revenue raised from car parking will be re-invested back into our properties. Disabled parking is available at many of our sites.

CATERING AND PICNICS

Many of our properties offer delicious home-made food and drink. Visitors are welcome to picnic in the grounds of most of our properties.

DOGS

Dogs on leads usually are welcome but please see individual property listings. No restrictions on assistance dogs.

EDUCATIONAL VISITS

There is nothing more inspiring or educational than visiting an English Heritage property. We believe that experiencing the local historic environment should be central to the national curriculum of every school in England. We actively encourage groups for this purpose, offering free self-led educational visits to over 400 historic sites in England, supporting the national curriculum across a range of subjects and all key stages. We also provide a wide

range of free online teaching resources, and downloadable hazard information sheets for each of our sites. Book your school visit now and let us help bring the past to life **www.english-heritage.org.uk/education**

FAMILIES AND CHILDREN

Many of our properties are fascinating for children. We put on special exhibitions catering to children's needs, and at well over 50 properties we offer free activity sheets, back-packs, book boxes and Very Big Books. Our interactive Discovery Centres will keep younger visitors absorbed for hours. Please note that you will be responsible for the safety and supervision of your children at all times at our sites, so please ensure a sensible ratio of adults to children.

GUIDES AND TOURS

Guidebooks and audio tours help bring sites to life at more and more of our properties. We also provide audio-guides for children and people with learning difficulties, as well as in different languages. Specialist tours are available at certain sites for pre-booked groups of 11 or more. Many of our properties have dedicated guidebooks – including 50 or so in the 'Red Guide' series with their distinctive red spines. Written by leading experts, these feature a tour of the site together with a more in-depth history of the people who lived and worked there. Packed with plans, reconstruction drawings, eyewitness accounts and beautiful photography, they make essential reading as well as brilliant souvenirs of your visit. Short histories and descriptions of our free sites are also available online.

PHOTOGRAPHY

Taking pictures is not permitted in some properties, due to the sensitive nature of some materials. Non-commercial photography is welcome in the gardens and grounds of all our sites.

SAFETY AND SMOKING

Due to their historic nature, some of our sites have potentially hazardous features – please pay attention to all safety notices on site. If you have any doubts, our staff can always advise on safety issues. Please wear suitable footwear to avoid accidents, and do not climb on walls or monuments. In areas of woodland deer pasture there may be a slight risk of ticks, so keep vulnerable parts of your body covered and/or use insect repellent. Note that smoking is not permitted inside any of our properties.

TRAVEL AND TRANSPORT

Where possible in the property listings, we have provided public transport information which has kindly been supplied by the Confederation of Passenger Transport (**cpt-uk.org**). These details were correct at time of going to press. For cycle routes, call 0845 113 0065 or visit sustrans.org.uk. OS LandRanger/ Explorer map references have also been supplied for each property. A free Sat Nav download of our properties is available at **www. english-heritage.org.uk/ satnav**

ACCESS

We want as many people as possible to enjoy a day out with English Heritage. The handbook listings indicate areas of properties accessible to disabled visitors and visitors with babies and younger children – with the use of the 🚻 symbol. Remember that if you are disabled your carer is always admitted free, and many of our sites have parking spaces for the disabled.

For more detailed information, our free *Access Guide* offers an up-to-date and honest assessment about which properties and gardens are most suited to families and disabled people. There's information about parking and drop-off points, and about properties that have special features such as scented gardens or tactile objects for those with impaired sight.

For your free copy, call 0870 333 1181, minicom 0800 015 0516, or email customers@english-heritage.org.uk. You can also download it from our website.

ENGLISH HERITAGE IS UNIQUE

We are the government's statutory adviser on the historic environment, but we are also a members' organisation. This means our funding comes in part from the Department for Culture, Media & Sport (DCMS) and partly from memberships, donations and fundraising. Increasingly, we depend on you, our members, not just financially but in our work to care for the historic environment. Our remit is broad. We advise on what should be protected; we offer grants; provide training, education and information; we maintain the national archive and, crucially, we look after more than 400 sites – all of which are free to visit for all our members and their families.

We are a non-profit organisation, so every penny of your membership goes towards maintaining the properties in our care. We are overseen by a Commission of up to 17 Commissioners appointed by the Secretary of State. Day to day management is delegated to our Chief Executive, Dr Simon Thurley, supported by an Executive Board comprising the Executive Directors of English Heritage's four operational groups.

HERITAGE GIVES US A SENSE OF BELONGING

The built environment has shaped our history and touches all of us – every day. We are convinced that our lives would be so much poorer if we allowed our heritage to ebb away on a tide of indifference. From stately homes to princely castles and from industrial buildings to modest terraced houses, shops and offices, our heritage belongs to us all, and we all have a responsibility to preserve and care for it for future generations to enjoy. We also know that England's historic environment is paramount to our tourist industry, contributing hugely to the country's prosperity.

DESIGNATION

Where possible we want to see historic buildings come to life, rather than being preserved as museum pieces. We also wish to ensure that any changes to buildings are in keeping with their historic roots. To this end, we work with local authorities on designating listed buildings. Most listed buildings date from before 1840 but we also designate some later buildings. There are three grades of listing: Grade I, Grade II* and Grade II.

We also designate monuments and landscapes, and help local authorities in establishing Conservation Areas. For more information on listing, visit **www.english-heritage.org.uk/listing**

Battlefields are important sources of archaeological and historic interest, and over 40 are on our Register of Historic Battlefields. We also oversee a similar Register of Parks and Gardens. Visit **www.english-heritage.org.uk/ conservation**

OUR PARTNERSHIP WITH MEMBERS

We are determined to work closely with our members, and firmly believe we should join together to protect our nation's heritage. Please contact us on 0870 333 1182 or **members@english-heritage.org.uk** at any time if you have any comments or need our assistance. We endeavour to answer calls within 15 seconds, emails and letters within 5 working days, and will always protect your personal information.

INTERPRETATION

How we show our properties and the information we provide to visitors is essential. We use the latest technology to enhance your visit, but we do not want our properties only to be discovered through the prism of multi-media presentations. A large number of our sites now have audio guides and our new web resource, Portico, provides more comprehensive and scholarly information on properties curated by English Heritage. And our guidebooks, written by experts in their field, are renowned for their motivating content and illustration.

VOLUNTEERING

We welcome volunteers who are keen to share their passion and interest in the historic environment with others. Activities include room stewarding, gardening, curatorial cleaning and assisting with our education programme at selected properties. Find out more about this rewarding work by visiting **www.english-heritage.org.uk/volunteering**

OUR WIDER WORK

Supporting the heritage sector sits at the heart of everything we do, and our broad remit encompasses a range of initiatives connected to this.

We administer the **blue plaques** scheme in London. To find out more, visit **www.english-heritage.org.uk/blueplaques**

English Heritage gives **grants** to individuals, local authorities and voluntary organisations to help conserve and enhance England's historic environment. These are targeted where there is greatest risk of loss of historic significance as identified in our Heritage at Risk Register. We also advise the Heritage Lottery Fund. To find out more, visit **www.english-heritage.org.uk/grants**

We are the national archaeology service for England and we implement the statutory protection of England's 19,750 Scheduled Monuments. Visit **www.english-heritage.org.uk/archaeology**. We are also responsible for all **English maritime archaeological** sites up to 12 nautical miles off-shore. The seas and shores around England contain an immense wealth of important shipwreck sites – some of which are protected as they help contribute significantly to our understanding of the past. English Heritage administers a licensing scheme which enables free access to these sites for divers to enjoy and investigate. Designated Wrecks range from Bronze Age cargoes to early submarines. We advise the government on installations and extraction works at sea, which potentially can damage maritime archaeology.

Our **Research and Training** programmes increase understanding of the historic environment and help us guide its management

in an informed and sustainable way. The pressures on capacity and skills are intense. We are working to address skills shortages within the traditional crafts and built heritage sector, to ensure there is a continuing source of craftspeople to care for England's half a million listed buildings.

As part of our **statutory remit**, we advise local authorities and owners on proposals to change historic sites, ensuring the impact on historic significance is managed constructively. To find out more, visit **www.english-heritage.org.uk/your-property/planning-advice**

Another key responsibility is to develop robust **policies** to protect and promote the historic environment. We publish the evidence to support these policies annually as Heritage Counts (**www.heritagecounts.org.uk**). We also work closely with **UNESCO**, advising on the designation and management of World Heritage Sites in England.

ENGLISH HERITAGE ARCHIVES

Our archives, formerly part of the National Monuments Record (NMR), hold more than 12 million photographs, drawings and reports covering England's archaeology, architecture, social and local history.

Visit us online, at **www.english-heritage.org.uk/archive** to see:

- **1 million** descriptions of historical photographs and documents
- **90,000** historic photographs of England from the 1850s to the present day
- thousands of historic **aerial photos** from 1919 onwards

If you share our passion for England's historic environment and want to help us make the past part of our future, view our current vacancies or register for our job alerts at **www.english-heritage.org.uk/jobs**

Or contact us at:
Archive Services, The Engine House, Fire Fly Avenue, Swindon SN2 2EH
Tel: 01793 414600 Fax: 01793 414606
Email: **archives@english-heritage.org.uk**

THANK YOU FOR YOUR SUPPORT

I Kenwood House

Over the last year, English Heritage donors, members and volunteers have made a significant difference to the work we do. The government funding English Heritage receives only goes some way towards the ongoing conservation of the properties in our care. In order to undertake our most significant projects – those which help us to tell England's story and make it more accessible to everybody – we rely on donations, gifts in wills and the support of volunteers.

Last year over 90 percent of donations made to English Heritage and the English Heritage Foundation, the charity which supports our properties and collections, went towards the conservation and interpretation of the sites that we preserve for you. The remaining funds were used to generate further donations.

The generosity of donors means that this year we will be able to open the new **Stonehenge** visitor centre (3), providing significantly improved understanding of one of England's most recognisable but little understood landmarks. We are also well on our way to raising the funds needed for the restoration of the Grade I listed **Kenwood House** (1). With your support we will be able to ensure Kenwood's future and introduce it to a new generation of visitors. Thanks to our donors, we have also been able to undertake smaller but equally important projects, including

improved interpretation at **Wroxeter Roman Villa** (2) and the conservation of the **Royal Artillery Monument** (4). Without donations these projects simply would not happen.

Please consider making a donation today and help to preserve the story of England.

To make a donation or find out more about the difference you can make, please contact the Fundraising Team at foundation@english-heritage.org.uk; visit **www.english-heritage.org.uk/supportus**; or call Customer Services on 0870 333 1181

The English Heritage Foundation is a registered charity, no. 1140351

ENGLISH HERITAGE

EVENTS THAT BRING HISTORY TO LIFE

From family fun days and fighting knights to spectacular battle displays and exclusive members' events, you'll find something for everyone to enjoy in our events calendar. In fact, we have the largest historical events programme in Europe, so you'll have hundreds of activities to choose from throughout the year.

HISTORY LIVE!

An action-packed weekend for the whole family to enjoy. Our showpiece event will return this year with a brand new name. Bringing the story of England to life, History Live! spans 2,000 years of history and features over 50 shows each day. Kelmarsh Hall, Northamptonshire, 20-21 July.

BIG SPECTACULAR EVENTS

If you enjoy huge historical re-enactments, then our 'tour de force' events could be just for you. St George's Day Festival, Wrest Park, 20-21 April; World War II Weekend, Dover Castle, 25-27 May.

CASTLE SLEEPOVERS

A unique and special experience for children and adults alike! After enjoying a warming drink and enchanting supper, take part in games and activities before bedding down for the night in one of our castles. Check your members' magazine or our website for details.

PERFORMING ARTS

We've got a great variety of music and theatre events throughout the year – both indoors and out.

EXCLUSIVE MEMBERS' EVENTS

Go behind the scenes, learn a new skill and discover the secrets concealed by some of the most intriguing properties in England. We hold over 100 events throughout the year, which are available exclusively to members. See the members' magazine for details.

SIGN UP FOR EVENTS UPDATES

Get regular updates of news and events direct to your inbox. Simply visit www.english-heritage.org.uk/newsletter to register. Alternatively, keep up to date with our events programme at www.english-heritage.org.uk/events or check the latest copy of your members' magazine.

STAY WITH US

Comfort. Atmosphere. A unique setting. Value for money. Then, add in direct access to some of the finest historic properties in Britain and you end up with a compelling argument for staying at an English Heritage holiday cottage.

English Heritage offers 16 such cottages, available for rent at any time of the year. All have been given a stylish, contemporary 5-star makeover, all are equipped with the latest mod-cons and all are situated within, or with access to, the grounds of an English Heritage site. Choose from castles, abbeys and stately homes; when the crowds disperse and the car park is empty, you are left on your own to explore, allowing your imagination to wander where it pleases.

STAY WITH US, EAT WITH US, SHOP WITH US, EXPLORE WITH US.

Not only do you have exclusive access to the property where you are staying: during your stay we will also give you free entry to all other English Heritage properties, discounts at our shops and cafés and complimentary tickets to most English Heritage events.

Choose between 13th-century towers and four-bedroom family homes, private gardens and roof terraces, beaches and woodland walks. Pick from three, four or seven night stays. Prices from £522 per week.

Book now. Make history on your holiday.

SOUTH EAST
BATTLE ABBEY South Lodge

CARISBROOKE CASTLE
The Bowling Green Apartment

DOVER CASTLE
The Sergeant Major's House and Peverell's Tower

OSBORNE Pavilion Cottage

WALMER CASTLE
The Garden Cottage and The Greenhouse Apartment

EAST
AUDLEY END HOUSE Cambridge Lodge

HARDWICK OLD HALL East Lodge

KIRBY HALL Peacock Cottage

SOUTH WEST
PENDENNIS CASTLE
The Custodian's House and Callie's Cottage

ST MAWES CASTLE Fort House

WEST
WITLEY COURT Pool House Cottage

YORKSHIRE
MOUNT GRACE PRIORY Prior's Lodge

RIEVAULX ABBEY Refectory Cottage

For a brochure or to make a booking www.english-heritage.org.uk/holidaycottages or call 0870 333 1187

BOOKS & GIFTS

When you've whetted your appetite for information looking around our properties, make sure you visit our shop on site, where you'll find a huge range of fascinating books and unique gifts.

Scan & click

KENWOOD

ENGLISH HERITAGE

STRAWBERRY
WINE

Inspired by the wines traditionally made from hedgerow fruits and flowers

MADE FOR ENGLISH HERITAGE BY
LYME BAY WINERY

75CL   MADE IN ENGLAND   11% VOL

ENGLISH HERITAGE

WASSAIL

full bodied fruity beer underlying happiness

Elizabethan
GUNPOWDER
MUSTARD

ENGLISH HERITAGE

Finest handmade
RED ONION
MARMALADE
ENGLISH PRESERVE

SOUTH WEST

Bristol
Cornwall
Devon
Dorset
Gloucestershire
Isles of Scilly
Somerset
Wiltshire

⊞ English Heritage Sites
▲ Associated Attractions
⋔ The Churches Conservation Trust

Isles of Scilly

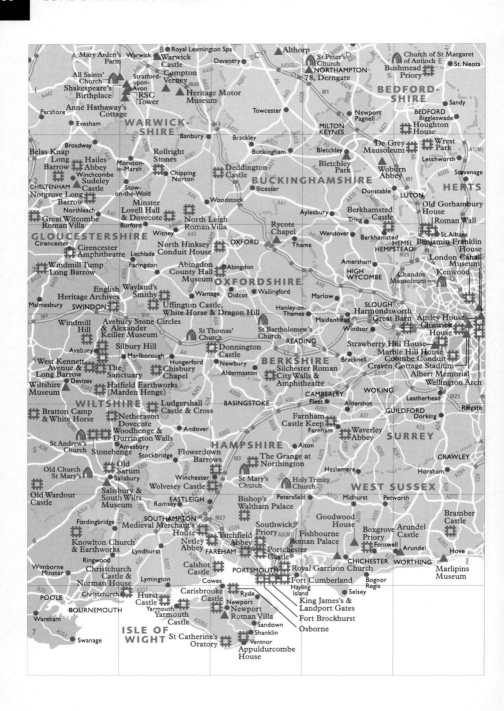

A Mary Arden's Farm
Royal Leamington Spa
Warwick
Warwick Castle
Daventry
Althorp
St Peter's Church
NORTHAMPTON
78, Derngate
Bushmead Priory
Church of St Margaret of Antioch
St Neots

All Saints' Church
Stratford-upon-Avon
Compton Verney
A4500
M1

Shakespeare's Birthplace
RSC Tower
M40
Heritage Motor Museum
BEDFORD-SHIRE
Sandy

Pershore
Anne Hathaway's Cottage
Towcester
Newport Pagnell
BEDFORD
Biggleswade

Evesham
WARWICK-SHIRE
MILTON KEYNES
Houghton House

Banbury
Brackley
A422
Bletchley
De Grey Mausoleum
Wrest Park
A1(M)

Broadway
Buckingham
A413
Letchworth

Belas Knap
Long Barrow
Rollright Stones
A361
Bletchley Park
Woburn Abbey
Stevenage

Hailes Abbey
Moreton-in-Marsh
Chipping Norton
Deddington Castle
BUCKINGHAMSHIRE
Dunstable
LUTON
HERTS

Winchcombe
Sudeley Castle
Stow-on-the-Wold
Bicester
Aylesbury
Berkhamsted Castle
Old Gorhambury House

CHELTENHAM
Notgrove Long Barrow
Woodstock
Tring
Roman Wall

Northleach
Minster Lovell Hall & Dovecote
North Leigh Roman Villa
Rycote Chapel
Wendover
Berkhamsted
St. Albans
Benjamin Franklin House

Great Witcombe Roman Villa
Burford
Witney
A40
OXFORD
Thame
HEMEL HEMPSTEAD
London Canal Museum

GLOUCESTERSHIRE
Cirencester
North Hinksey Conduit House
Chandos Mausoleum
Kenwood

Cirencester Amphitheatre
Lechlade
Abingdon County Hall Museum
Abingdon
AMERSHAM
HIGH WYCOMBE

Windmill Tump Long Barrow
Faringdon
OXFORDSHIRE
Wallingford
Marlow

Malmesbury
English Heritage Archives
Wayland's Smithy
Wantage
Didcot
Henley-on-Thames
SLOUGH
Harmondsworth
Great Barn
Apsley House
Chiswick House

SWINDON
Uffington Castle, White Horse & Dragon Hill
Maidenhead
Strawberry Hill House
Marble Hill House

Windmill Hill
Avebury Stone Circles & Alexander Keiller Museum
St Thomas' Church
St Bartholomew's Church
READING
Windsor
Craven Cottage Stadium
Coombe Conduit
Albert Memorial
Wellington Arch

Avebury
Silbury Hill
Marlborough
Donnington Castle
Bracknell
Leatherhead
M25

West Kennett Avenue & Long Barrow
The Sanctuary
Hungerford
Chisbury Chapel
Newbury
Aldermaston
BERKSHIRE
Silchester Roman City Walls & Amphitheatre
WOKING
Reigate

Wiltshire Museum
Devizes
Hatfield Earthworks (Marden Henge)
CAMBERLEY
Fleet
Aldershot
GUILDFORD
Dorking

Bratton Camp & White Horse
Ludgershall Castle & Cross
BASINGSTOKE
A30
A31
SURREY

Netheravon Dovecote
Andover
Farnham Castle Keep
Farnham
Waverley Abbey

WILTSHIRE
Woodhenge & Durrington Walls
Amesbury
HAMPSHIRE
Alton
Haslemere
CRAWLEY

St Andrew's Church
Stonehenge
Stockbridge
Flowerdown Barrows
M3
The Grange at Northington
Horsham

Old Sarum
Old Church St Mary's
Salisbury
Winchester
St Mary's Church
Holy Trinity Church
WEST SUSSEX

Old Wardour Castle
Salisbury & South Wilts Museum
Wolvesey Castle
Bishop's Waltham Palace
Petersfield
Midhurst
Petworth

Fordingbridge
Romsey
EASTLEIGH
Southwick Priory
Goodwood House
Bramber Castle

SOUTHAMPTON
Medieval Merchant's House
Titchfield Abbey
Fishbourne Roman Palace
Boxgrove Priory
Arundel Castle

Knowlton Church & Earthworks
Netley Abbey
Portchester Castle
Fontwell
Arundel
Hove

Wimborne Minster
Ringwood
Lyndhurst
FAREHAM
CHICHESTER
WORTHING

Christchurch Castle & Norman House
Calshot Castle
PORTSMOUTH
Royal Garrison Church
Marlipins Museum

POOLE
Christchurch
Lymington
Cowes
Fort Cumberland
Hayling Island
Bognor Regis
Selsey

Wareham
BOURNEMOUTH
Hurst Castle
Carisbrooke Castle
Ryde
King James's & Landport Gates

Swanage
Yarmouth Castle
Yarmouth
Newport
Newport Roman Villa
Sandown
Fort Brockhurst

ISLE OF WIGHT
St Catherine's Oratory
Shanklin
Ventnor
Osborne

Appuldurcombe House

LONDON AND SOUTH EAST

Berkshire
Buckinghamshire
East Sussex
Hampshire
Isle of Wight
Kent
Oxfordshire
Surrey
West Sussex

English Heritage Sites
Associated Attractions
The Churches Conservation Trust

Created by Arka Cartographics Ltd. for English Heritage. © 10/12

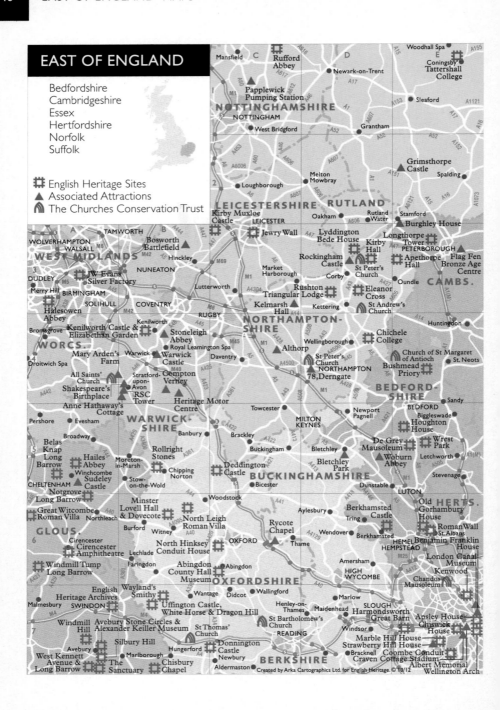

EAST OF ENGLAND

Bedfordshire
Cambridgeshire
Essex
Hertfordshire
Norfolk
Suffolk

English Heritage Sites
▲ Associated Attractions
⋔ The Churches Conservation Trust

Mansfield • C • Rufford Abbey • D • Woodhall Spa
Papplewick Pumping Station • Newark-on-Trent • Coningsby Tattershall College
NOTTINGHAMSHIRE • A17 • Sleaford
NOTTINGHAM • West Bridgford • Grantham
Melton Mowbray • Grimsthorpe Castle • Spalding
Loughborough
LEICESTERSHIRE RUTLAND • Stamford • Burghley House
Kirby Muxloe Castle • LEICESTER • Oakham • Rutland Water
Jewry Wall • Lyddington Bede House • Longthorpe Tower • PETERBOROUGH
TAMWORTH • B • Bosworth Battlefield • Kirby Hall • Apethorpe Hall • Flag Fen Bronze Age Centre
WOLVERHAMPTON • WALSALL • Hinckley • Rockingham Castle • St Peter's Church
WEST MIDLANDS • Market Harborough • Corby • Oundle • CAMBS.
NUNEATON • Rushton Triangular Lodge • Eleanor Cross
DUDLEY • JW Evans Silver Factory • Lutterworth • Kelmarsh Hall • Kettering • St Andrew's Church
Merry Hill • BIRMINGHAM • Rugby • NORTHAMPTON-SHIRE • Huntingdon
SOLIHULL • COVENTRY • Chichele College
Halesowen Abbey • Kenilworth • Althorp • Wellingborough
Bromsgrove • Kenilworth Castle & Elizabethan Garden • Stoneleigh Abbey • St Peter's Church • Church of St Margaret of Antioch • St Neots
WORCS. • Royal Leamington Spa • NORTHAMPTON • Bushmead Priory
Droitwich Spa • Mary Arden's Farm • Warwick • Warwick Castle • Daventry • 78, Derngate • BEDFORD-SHIRE
All Saints' Church • Stratford-upon-Avon • Compton Verney • Sandy
Shakespeare's Birthplace • RSC Tower • Heritage Motor Centre • Towcester • Newport Pagnell • BEDFORD • Biggleswade
Anne Hathaway's Cottage • MILTON KEYNES • Houghton House
Pershore • Evesham • WARWICK-SHIRE • De Grey Mausoleum • Wrest Park
Belas Knap • Broadway • Banbury • Brackley • Bletchley • Woburn Abbey • Letchworth
Long Barrow • Hailes Abbey • Moreton-in-Marsh • Rollright Stones • Buckingham • Bletchley Park • Stevenage
Winchcombe Sudeley Castle • Chipping Norton • Deddington Castle • BUCKINGHAMSHIRE • Dunstable • LUTON
CHELTENHAM • Stow-on-the-Wold • Bicester • Old HERTS
Notgrove Long Barrow • Minster Lovell Hall & Dovecote • Woodstock • Gorhambury House
Great Witcombe Roman Villa • Northleach • North Leigh Roman Villa • Aylesbury • Berkhamsted Castle • Tring • St Albans • Roman Wall
GLOUS. • Burford • Witney • Rycote Chapel • Wendover • Berkhamsted • HEMEL HEMPSTEAD • Benjamin Franklin House
Cirencester • North Hinksey Conduit House • OXFORD • Thame • London Canal Museum
Cirencester Amphitheatre • Lechlade • Amersham • HIGH WYCOMBE • Kenwood
Windmill Tump Long Barrow • Faringdon • Abingdon County Hall Museum • Abingdon • Chandos Mausoleum
English Heritage Archives • Wayland's Smithy • Wantage • Didcot • Wallingford • Marlow
Malmesbury • SWINDON • Uffington Castle, White Horse & Dragon Hill • Henley-on-Thames • Maidenhead • SLOUGH • Apsley House
Windmill Hill • Avebury Stone Circles & Alexander Keiller Museum • St Thomas' Church • Harmondsworth Great Barn • Chiswick House
Silbury Hill • READING • Windsor • Marble Hill House • Strawberry Hill House
West Kennett Avenue & Long Barrow • Avebury • Marlborough • Hungerford • Donnington Castle • Newbury • Bracknell • Coombe Conduit • Craven Cottage Stadium • Albert Memorial
The Sanctuary • Chisbury Chapel • BERKSHIRE • Aldermaston • St Bartholomew's Church • Wellington Arch

Created by Arka Cartographics Ltd. for English Heritage. © 10/12

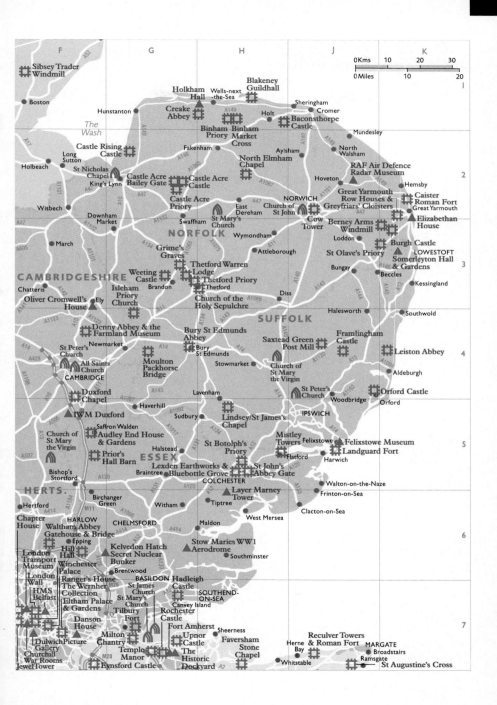

F | G | H | J | K

0Kms 10 20 30
0Miles 10 20

I

Sibsey Trader Windmill

Boston

Hunstanton

The Wash

Holkham Hall
Wells-next-the-Sea
Blakeney Guildhall
Sheringham
Holt
Cromer
Creake Abbey
Baconsthorpe Castle
Mundesley

Castle Rising
Long Sutton
Fakenham
Binham Priory
Binham Market Cross
Aylsham
North Walsham

Holbeach
St Nicholas Chapel
King's Lynn
Castle Acre Bailey Gate
Castle Acre Castle
North Elmham Chapel
Hoveton
RAF Air Defence Radar Museum
Hemsby

Wisbech
Downham Market
Castle Acre Priory
East Dereham
Church of St John
NORWICH
Great Yarmouth Row Houses & Greyfriars' Cloisters
Caister Roman Fort
Great Yarmouth

March
Swaffham
St Mary's Church
Wymondham
Cow Tower
Berney Arms Windmill
Elizabethan House

NORFOLK
Attleborough
Loddon
Burgh Castle

Grime's Graves
St Olave's Priory
LOWESTOFT
Somerleyton Hall & Gardens

CAMBRIDGESHIRE
Weeting Castle
Thetford Warren Lodge
Bungay
Beccles
Kessingland

Chatteris
Isleham Priory Church
Brandon
Thetford Priory
Thetford
Diss
Halesworth
Southwold

Oliver Cromwell's House
Ely
Church of the Holy Sepulchre

Denny Abbey & the Farmland Museum
Bury St Edmunds Abbey
SUFFOLK

Newmarket
Bury St Edmunds
Saxtead Green Post Mill
Framlingham Castle
Leiston Abbey

St Peter's Church
All Saints Church
CAMBRIDGE
Moulton Packhorse Bridge
Stowmarket
Church of St Mary the Virgin
Aldeburgh

Duxford Chapel
Lavenham
St Peter's Church
Woodbridge
Orford Castle
Orford

IWM Duxford
Haverhill
Sudbury
Lindsey/St James's Chapel
IPSWICH

Saffron Walden
Audley End House & Gardens
Church of St Mary the Virgin
Halstead
St Botolph's Priory
Mistley Towers
Felixstowe
Felixstowe Museum
Landguard Fort

Prior's Hall Barn
Lexden Earthworks & Bluebottle Grove
St John's Abbey Gate
Flatford
Harwich

Bishop's Stortford
ESSEX
Braintree
COLCHESTER
Layer Marney Tower
Walton-on-the-Naze

HERTS.
Birchanger Green
Witham
Tiptree
West Mersea
Frinton-on-Sea
Clacton-on-Sea

Hertford
Chapter House
HARLOW
Waltham Abbey Gatehouse & Bridge
CHELMSFORD
Maldon
Stow Maries WW1 Aerodrome
Southminster

London Transport Museum
Hill Hall
Epping
Kelvedon Hatch Secret Nuclear Bunker

London Wall
Winchester Palace
Brentwood
BASILDON
Hadleigh Castle

HMS Belfast
Ranger's House
The Wernher Collection
St James Church
St Mary's Church
SOUTHEND-ON-SEA

Eltham Palace & Gardens
Tilbury Fort
Canvey Island
Rochester Castle

Danson House
Milton Chantry
Fort Amherst
Upnor Castle
Sheerness
Faversham
Reculver Towers & Roman Fort
MARGATE

Dulwich Picture Gallery
Temple Manor
The Historic Dockyard
Stone Chapel
Herne Bay
Broadstairs
Ramsgate

Churchill War Rooms
Jewel Tower
Eynsford Castle
Whitstable
St Augustine's Cross

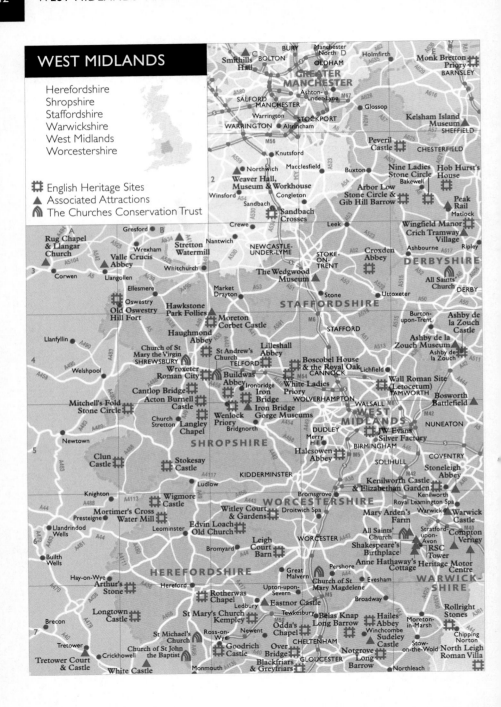

WEST MIDLANDS

Herefordshire
Shropshire
Staffordshire
Warwickshire
West Midlands
Worcestershire

English Heritage Sites
Associated Attractions
The Churches Conservation Trust

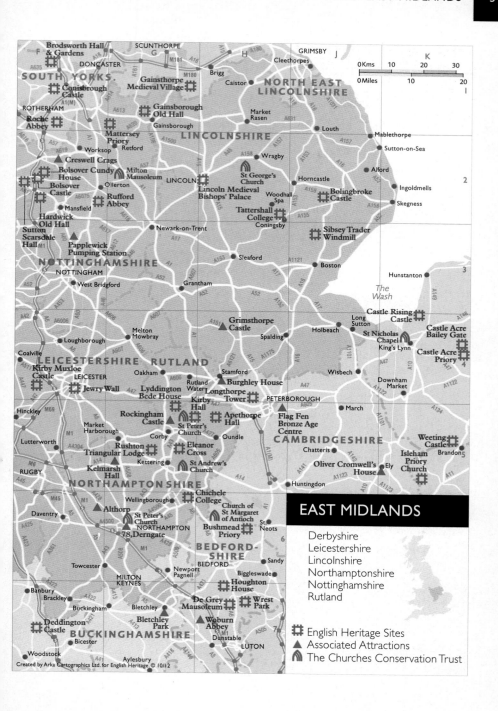

Brodsworth Hall & Gardens
SCUNTHORPE
GRIMSBY
Cleethorpes
DONCASTER
Brigg
Caistor
NORTH EAST LINCOLNSHIRE
0 Kms 10 20 30
0 Miles 10 20

SOUTH YORKS.
Gainsthorpe Medieval Village
Conisbrough Castle
ROTHERHAM
Gainsborough Old Hall
Market Rasen
Louth
Mablethorpe
Roche Abbey
Gainsborough
LINCOLNSHIRE
Sutton-on-Sea
Mattersey Priory
Worksop
Retford
Wragby
Horncastle
Alford
Ingoldmells
Creswell Crags
Bolsover Cundy House
Milton Mausoleum
LINCOLN
St George's Church
Bolingbroke Castle
Skegness
Bolsover Castle
Ollerton
Rufford Abbey
Lincoln Medieval Bishops' Palace
Woodhall Spa
Hardwick Old Hall
Mansfield
Tattershall College
Sutton Scarsdale Hall
Newark-on-Trent
Coningsby
Sibsey Trader Windmill
Papplewick Pumping Station
NOTTINGHAMSHIRE
Sleaford
Boston
NOTTINGHAM
West Bridgford
Grantham
Hunstanton
The Wash
Castle Rising Castle
Long Sutton
Castle Acre Bailey Gate
Grimsthorpe Castle
Holbeach
St Nicholas Chapel
Melton Mowbray
Spalding
King's Lynn
Castle Acre Priory
Loughborough
Coalville
LEICESTERSHIRE RUTLAND
Wisbech
Downham Market
Kirby Muxloe Castle
Oakham
Stamford
LEICESTER
Rutland Water
Burghley House
Jewry Wall
Lyddington Bede House
Longthorpe Tower
PETERBOROUGH
March
Hinckley
Kirby Hall
Rockingham Castle
Apethorpe Hall
Flag Fen Bronze Age Centre
CAMBRIDGESHIRE
Weeting Castle
Market Harborough
St Peter's Church
Oundle
Brandon
Lutterworth
Corby
Rushton Triangular Lodge
Eleanor Cross
Chatteris
Isleham Priory Church
RUGBY
Kelmarsh Hall
Kettering
St Andrew's Church
Oliver Cromwell's House
Ely
NORTHAMPTONSHIRE
Chichele College
Huntingdon
Wellingborough
Daventry
Althorp
Church of St Margaret of Antioch
St Peter's Church
NORTHAMPTON
78, Derngate
Bushmead Priory
St Neots
BEDFORD-SHIRE
Towcester
Newport Pagnell
BEDFORD
Sandy
Biggleswade
MILTON KEYNES
Houghton House
Banbury
Brackley
De Grey Mausoleum
Wrest Park
Buckingham
Bletchley
Deddington Castle
Bletchley Park
Woburn Abbey
Dunstable
BUCKINGHAMSHIRE
Bicester
LUTON
Woodstock
Aylesbury
Created by Arka Cartographics Ltd. for English Heritage. © 10/12

EAST MIDLANDS

Derbyshire
Leicestershire
Lincolnshire
Northamptonshire
Nottinghamshire
Rutland

English Heritage Sites
Associated Attractions
The Churches Conservation Trust

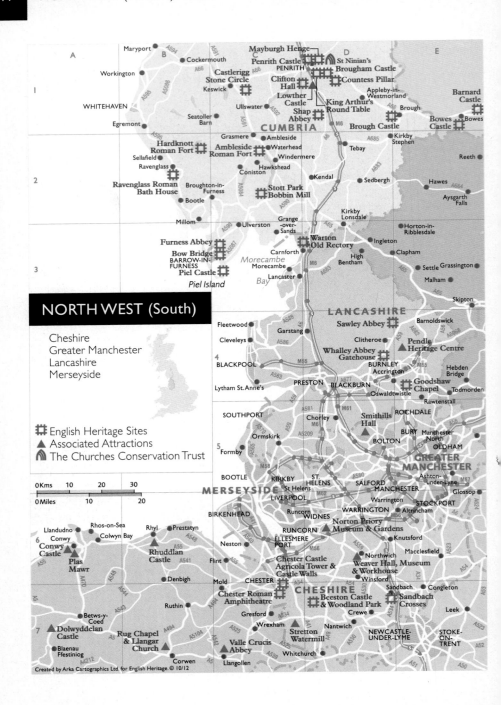

NORTH WEST (South)

Cheshire
Greater Manchester
Lancashire
Merseyside

⊞ English Heritage Sites
▲ Associated Attractions
⋔ The Churches Conservation Trust

| 0 Kms | 10 | 20 | 30 |
| 0 Miles | 10 | 20 |

Maryport
Cockermouth
Workington
Mayburgh Henge
Penrith Castle
St Ninian's
PENRITH
Brougham Castle
Castlerigg Stone Circle
Clifton Hall
Countess Pillar
Keswick
WHITEHAVEN
Ullswater
Appleby-in-Westmorland
Lowther Castle
King Arthur's Round Table
Brough
Barnard Castle
Seatoller Barn
Shap Abbey
Bowes Castle
Bowes
Egremont
CUMBRIA
M6
Brough Castle
Grasmere
Ambleside
Kirkby Stephen
Reeth
Hardknott Roman Fort
Ambleside Roman Fort
Waterhead
Tebay
Sellafield
Windermere
Ravenglass
Hawkshead
Kendal
Sedbergh
Hawes
Ravenglass Roman Bath House
Broughton-in-Furness
Coniston
Stott Park Bobbin Mill
Kirkby Lonsdale
Aysgarth Falls
Bootle
Millom
Ulverston
Grange-over-Sands
Warton Old Rectory
Horton-in-Ribblesdale
Furness Abbey
Ingleton
Clapham
Bow Bridge
Carnforth
High Bentham
Settle
Grassington
BARROW-IN-FURNESS
Morecambe
Piel Castle
Morecambe Bay
Lancaster
M6
Malham
Piel Island
Skipton
LANCASHIRE
Fleetwood
Sawley Abbey
Barnoldswick
Cleveleys
Garstang
Clitheroe
Pendle Heritage Centre
BLACKPOOL
Whalley Abbey Gatehouse
BURNLEY
Hebden Bridge
PRESTON
BLACKBURN
Accrington
Lytham St. Anne's
Goodshaw Chapel
Todmorden
Oswaldtwistle
Rawtenstall
SOUTHPORT
Chorley
Smithills Hall
ROCHDALE
Ormskirk
BURY
Manchester North
BOLTON
OLDHAM
Formby
GREATER MANCHESTER
BOOTLE
KIRKBY
ST. HELENS
SALFORD
MANCHESTER
Ashton-under-Lyne
MERSEYSIDE
St Helens
LIVERPOOL
Warrington
STOCKPORT
Glossop
BIRKENHEAD
Runcorn
WIDNES
WARRINGTON
Altrincham
Norton Priory Museum & Gardens
Llandudno
Rhos-on-Sea
Rhyl
Prestatyn
RUNCORN
Knutsford
Conwy
Colwyn Bay
ELLESMERE PORT
Conwy Castle
Neston
Northwich
Macclesfield
Plas Mawr
Rhuddlan Castle
Flint
Weaver Hall, Museum & Workhouse
Winsford
Denbigh
Mold
CHESTER
Chester Castle Agricola Tower & Castle Walls
Sandbach
Congleton
Chester Roman Amphitheatre
CHESHIRE
Sandbach Crosses
Ruthin
Beeston Castle & Woodland Park
Leek
Gresford
Crewe
Dolwyddelan Castle
Betws-y-Coed
Wrexham
Stretton Watermill
Nantwich
NEWCASTLE-UNDER-LYME
STOKE-ON-TRENT
Rug Chapel & Llangar Church
Valle Crucis Abbey
Blaenau Ffestiniog
Whitchurch
Corwen
Llangollen

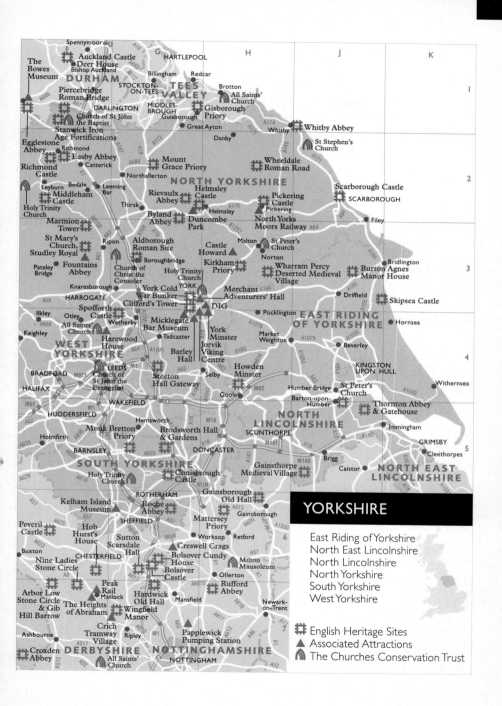

Spennymoor
F
Auckland Castle
G
HARTLEPOOL
H
J
K
The
Deer House
Bowes
Bishop Auckland
Museum
Billingham
Redcar
Brotton
DURHAM
STOCKTON-
TEES
All Saints'
ON-TEES
VALLEY
Church
I
Piercebridge
MIDDLES-
Gisborough
Roman Bridge
BROUGH
Priory
DARLINGTON
Guisborough
Church of St John
Great Ayton
the Baptist
Stanwick Iron
Danby
Whitby
Whitby Abbey
Age Fortifications
St Stephen's
Egglestone
Church
Abbey
Richmond
Easby Abbey
Catterick
NORTH YORKSHIRE
Richmond
Northallerton
Castle
2
Leyburn
Bedale
Leeming
Mount
Wheeldale
Middleham
Bar
Grace Priory
Roman Road
Castle
Thirsk
Scarborough Castle
Holy Trinity
Rievaulx
Helmsley
Pickering
SCARBOROUGH
Church
Abbey
Castle
Castle
Marmion
Byland
Helmsley
Pickering
Tower
Abbey
Duncombe
North Yorks
Filey
St Mary's
Park
Moors Railway
Church,
Ripon
Aldborough
Malton
St Peter's
Studley Royal
Roman Site
Castle
Church
Pateley
Fountains
Boroughbridge
Howard
Norton
Bridlington
Bridge
Abbey
Church of
Kirkham
Wharram Percy
Burton Agnes
Christ the
Holy Trinity
Priory
Deserted Medieval
Manor House
Knaresborough
Consoler
Church
Village
HARROGATE
York Cold
YORK
Merchant
Driffield
War Bunker
Adventurers' Hall
Skipsea Castle
Spofforth
Clifford's Tower
DIG
Ilkley
Otley
Castle
Pocklington
EAST RIDING
Hornsea
Keighley
All Saints'
Wetherby
Micklegate
York
OF YORKSHIRE
Church
Harewood
Bar Museum
Minster
Market
House
Tadcaster
Jorvik
Weighton
Beverley
WEST
LEEDS
Barley
Viking
YORKSHIRE
Church of
Hall
Centre
KINGSTON
BRADFORD
St John the
Steeton
Howden
UPON HULL
Evangelist
Hall Gateway
Selby
Minster
Withernsea
HALIFAX
Goole
Humber Bridge
St Peter's
WAKEFIELD
Church
Barton-upon-
HUDDERSFIELD
Humber
Hemsworth
NORTH
Thornton Abbey
Holmfirth
Monk Bretton
Brodsworth Hall
LINCOLNSHIRE
& Gatehouse
Priory
& Gardens
SCUNTHORPE
Immingham
BARNSLEY
DONCASTER
GRIMSBY
SOUTH YORKSHIRE
Brigg
Cleethorpes
Holy Trinity
Conisbrough
Gainsthorpe
Caistor
NORTH EAST
Church
Castle
Medieval Village
LINCOLNSHIRE
Gainsborough
ROTHERHAM
Old Hall
Kelham Island
Roche
Museum
Abbey
Gainsborough
Peveril
SHEFFIELD
Mattersey
Castle
Hob
Priory
Hurst's
Worksop
Retford
Buxton
House
Sutton
Creswell Crags
Milton
Nine Ladies
CHESTERFIELD
Scarsdale
Bolsover Cundy
Mausoleum
Stone Circle
Hall
House
Ollerton
Bolsover
Peak
Rail
Castle
Rufford
Arbor Low
Matlock
Hardwick
Mansfield
Abbey
Stone Circle
The Heights
Old Hall
Newark-
& Gib
of Abraham
Wingfield
on-Trent
Hill Barrow
Manor
Crich
Ashbourne
Tramway
Papplewick
Croxden
Village
Ripley
Pumping Station
Abbey
DERBYSHIRE
NOTTINGHAMSHIRE
All Saints'
NOTTINGHAM
Church

YORKSHIRE

East Riding of Yorkshire
North East Lincolnshire
North Lincolnshire
North Yorkshire
South Yorkshire
West Yorkshire

⌗ English Heritage Sites
▲ Associated Attractions
⋔ The Churches Conservation Trust

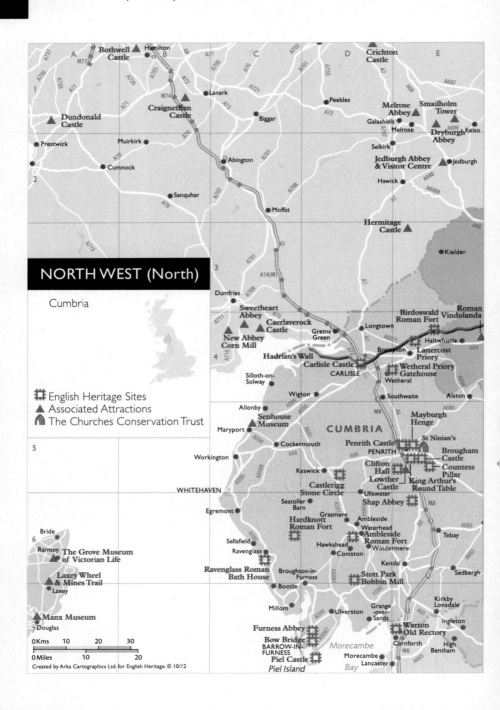

NORTH WEST (North)

Cumbria

English Heritage Sites
▲ Associated Attractions
♠ The Churches Conservation Trust

Bothwell Castle
Hamilton
M77
Craignethan Castle
M74
Lanark
Dundonald Castle
Prestwick
Muirkirk
Cumnock
Sanquhar
Abington
Biggar
Peebles
Melrose Abbey
Smailholm Tower
Galashiels
Melrose
Dryburgh Abbey
Kelso
Selkirk
Jedburgh Abbey & Visitor Centre
Jedburgh
Hawick
Moffat
Hermitage Castle
Kielder
Crichton Castle
Dumfries
Sweetheart Abbey
Caerlaverock Castle
New Abbey Corn Mill
Hadrian's Wall
Gretna Green
Longtown
Birdoswald Roman Fort
Roman Vindolanda
Haltwhistle
Brampton
Lanercost Priory
Carlisle Castle
CARLISLE
Wetheral Priory Gatehouse
Wetheral
Silloth-on-Solway
Wigton
Southwaite
Alston
Allonby
Senhouse Museum
Maryport
Cockermouth
CUMBRIA
Mayburgh Henge
St Ninian's
Penrith Castle
PENRITH
Brougham Castle
Countess Pillar
Workington
Keswick
Clifton Hall
Lowther Castle
King Arthur's Round Table
Castlerigg Stone Circle
Ullswater
Shap Abbey
WHITEHAVEN
Seatoller Barn
Grasmere
Ambleside
Egremont
Hardknott Roman Fort
Waterhead
Ambleside Roman Fort
Windermere
Tebay
Sellafield
Hawkshead
Coniston
Ravenglass
Kendal
Sedbergh
Ravenglass Roman Bath House
Broughton-in-Furness
Stott Park Bobbin Mill
Bootle
Millom
Ulverston
Grange-over-Sands
Kirkby Lonsdale
Ingleton
Bride
Ramsey
The Grove Museum of Victorian Life
Laxey Wheel & Mines Trail
Laxey
Manx Museum
Douglas
Furness Abbey
Bow Bridge
BARROW-IN-FURNESS
Piel Castle
Piel Island
Warton Old Rectory
Carnforth
High Bentham
Morecambe
Lancaster
Morecambe Bay

0 Kms 10   20   30
0 Miles   10   20

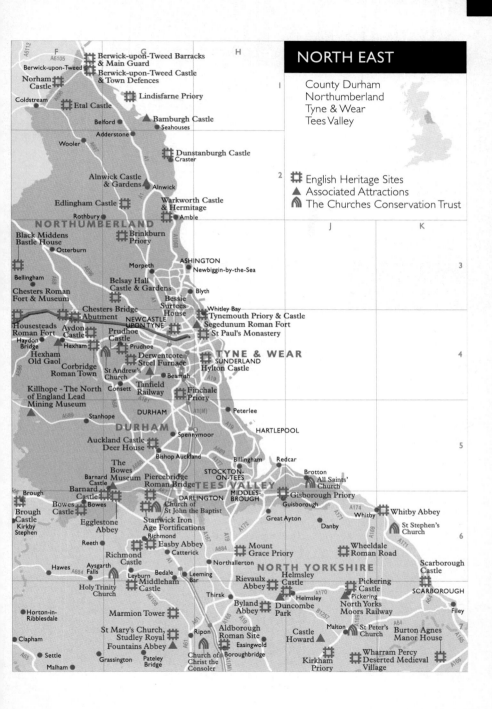

NORTH EAST

County Durham
Northumberland
Tyne & Wear
Tees Valley

⊞ English Heritage Sites
▲ Associated Attractions
🏛 The Churches Conservation Trust

A6112

F
Berwick-upon-Tweed Barracks
& Main Guard
Berwick-upon-Tweed
A6105
Berwick-upon-Tweed Castle
& Town Defences
Norham
Castle
Coldstream
Lindisfarne Priory
Etal Castle
Belford
Bamburgh Castle
Seahouses
Adderstone
Wooler
Dunstanburgh Castle
Craster
Alnwick Castle
& Gardens
Alnwick
Edlingham Castle
Warkworth Castle
& Hermitage
Rothbury
Amble
NORTHUMBERLAND
Brinkburn
Priory
Black Middens
Bastle House
Otterburn
Morpeth
ASHINGTON
Newbiggin-by-the-Sea
Bellingham
Belsay Hall
Castle & Gardens
Blyth
Chesters Roman
Fort & Museum
Bessie
Surtees
House
Whitley Bay
Chesters Bridge
Abutment
NEWCASTLE
UPON TYNE
Tynemouth Priory & Castle
Housesteads
Roman Fort
Aydon
Castle
Prudhoe
Castle
Segedunum Roman Fort
St Paul's Monastery
Haydon
Bridge
Hexham
Prudhoe
Hexham
Old Gaol
Corbridge
Roman Town
St Andrew's
Church
Derwentcote
Steel Furnace
Beamish
TYNE & WEAR
SUNDERLAND
Hylton Castle
Killhope - The North
of England Lead
Mining Museum
Consett
Tanfield
Railway
Finchale
Priory
Stanhope
DURHAM
Peterlee
DURHAM
Spennymoor
HARTLEPOOL
Auckland Castle
Deer House
Bishop Auckland
Billingham
Redcar
The
Bowes
Museum
Barnard
Castle
Piercebridge
Roman Bridge
STOCKTON-
ON-TEES
Brotton
All Saints'
Church
Brough
Barnard
Castle
MIDDLES-
BROUGH
Gisborough Priory
Brough
Castle
Bowes
Bowes
Castle
DARLINGTON
Church of
St John the Baptist
Guisborough
Whitby
Whitby Abbey
Kirkby
Stephen
Egglestone
Abbey
Stanwick Iron
Age Fortifications
Great Ayton
Danby
St Stephen's
Church
Reeth
Easby Abbey
Richmond
Catterick
Mount
Grace Priory
Wheeldale
Roman Road
Hawes
Richmond
Castle
Northallerton
NORTH YORKSHIRE
Scarborough
Castle
Aysgarth
Falls
Leyburn
Bedale
Leeming
Bar
Rievaulx
Abbey
Helmsley
Castle
Pickering
Castle
SCARBOROUGH
Holy Trinity
Church
Middleham
Castle
Thirsk
Helmsley
North Yorks
Moors Railway
Filey
Horton-in-
Ribblesdale
Marmion Tower
Byland
Abbey
Duncombe
Park
Malton
St Peter's
Church
Burton Agnes
Manor House
Clapham
St Mary's Church,
Studley Royal
Fountains Abbey
Ripon
Aldborough
Roman Site
Easingwold
Castle
Howard
Settle
Grassington
Pateley
Bridge
Church of
Christ the
Consoler
Boroughbridge
Kirkham
Priory
Wharram Percy
Deserted Medieval
Village
Malham

CELEBRATE WITH US

☒ PROPERTIES FOR HIRE

Properties available for hire are marked with a ☒ throughout the handbook. Those also licensed for civil ceremonies are marked with a ▲.

Eltham Palace

LONDON
▲ **Eltham Palace**
020 8294 2577

Kenwood
020 7973 3416

▲ **Marble Hill House**
020 7973 3416

▲ **Ranger's House**
020 8294 2577

Wellington Arch
020 7973 3416

SOUTH EAST
Osborne
Isle of Wight 01983 203055

EAST
▲ **Bolsover Castle**
Derbyshire 01246 856456

▲ **Wrest Park**
Bedfordshire 01525 863704

SOUTH WEST
▲ **Old Wardour Castle**
Wiltshire 01305 820868

▲ **Pendennis Castle**
Cornwall 01326 310106

▲ **Portland Castle**
Dorset 01305 820868

▲ **St Mawes Castle**
Cornwall 01326 310106

WEST
▲ **Kenilworth Castle and Elizabethan Garden**
Warwickshire 01926 857 482

For more information on exclusive hire, please contact the Hospitality Managers on the property telephone numbers above, or visit **www.english-heritage.org. uk/hospitality**

Wellington Arch

Wrest Park

Bolsover Castle

Details of OS LandRanger and Explorer map references are provided for easy location of each property, with specific map numbers (LandRanger; Explorer) followed by the grid reference.

NB. All maps in this handbook are created using Ordnance Survey mapping. Unless otherwise credited, they are © Crown Copyright and database right 2012. All rights reserved. Ordnance Survey Licence number 100019088.

English Heritage Handbook 2013/14

For English Heritage:
Luke Whitcomb, Johanna Lovesey, Kathryn Steele-Childe, Tersia Boorer, Charles Kightly.

Design and Publishing:
Ledgard Jepson Ltd.

For Ledgard Jepson Ltd:
David Exley, Bev Turbitt, Andrea Rollinson.

Print: Pindar plc.

Transport Information:
John Burch, CPT.

Images:
All images in this handbook are © English Heritage unless otherwise stated.

All CCT images are © CCT unless otherwise stated.